Attack on Starvation

other recent AVI books on foods

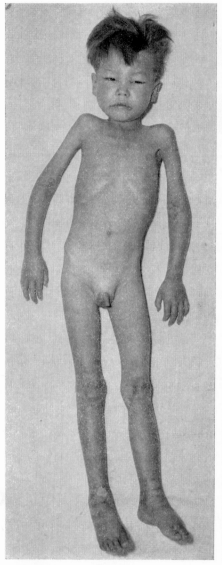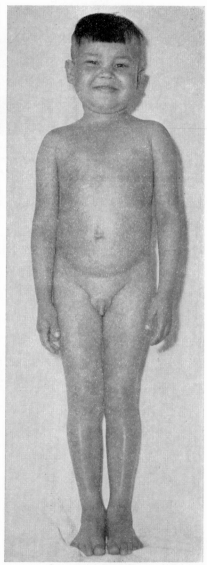

ADEQUATE AMOUNTS OF COMPLETE PROTEINS ARE NEEDED FOR PROPER GROWTH

Same child: at left, with protein deficiency disease
at right, nourished to health with good food.

Attack on
STARVATION

by NORMAN W. DESROSIER, Ph.D.

*Professor of Food Technology, Purdue University,
Lafayette, Indiana. Formerly Director, Radiation
Preservation Division, Quartermaster Food and
Container Institute for the Armed Forces,
Chicago, Illinois*

WESTPORT, CONNECTICUT

THE AVI PUBLISHING COMPANY, INC.

1961

Printed in the United States of America

BY MACK PRINTING COMPANY, EASTON, PENNSYLVANIA

Preface

Each of us has no doubt experienced the effects of starvation to some degree sometime during his lifetime. With the expanding human population on earth, the degree and the frequency of occurrence of starvation will also increase. The question we must ask is, "Can we do anything constructive about the situation?" The answer must be, "Yes." Yet, the situation will not correct itself in a way we will accept if we ignore the problems we face. Conscious action is required.

As a start it would be useful to explore the nature of the problems which face us before we seek their solutions. It would be important to know what good food is, how food influences man, and what a man needs to consume to achieve good health. With this background we might then seek to learn how our food producing systems developed and what influences these have had and are having on us.

Acceptable solutions can be found by recognizing our difficulties, locating and defining them, forming a number of tentative ideas concerning possible solutions, reviewing experiments and observations that are available (which would be useful in accepting or rejecting ideas) and making conclusions. We might then consider applying these conclusions for our mutual benefit.

To help in this pursuit, information is streaming from research laboratories studying plant and animal physiology, human physiology and nutrition, space medicine and biology, and the peaceful uses of atomic energy. Some of these will have their influences on food production and distribution, which, in turn, can influence human health and living. For example, one of the goals of space flight research is to learn how to supply men with air to breathe, water to drink, and food to eat in order to permit the exploration of other planets. Presently the essential components of workable systems appear to be available. So, perhaps it might also be possible to resolve the problem of how to feed the 3.0 billion people on earth by employing some of the information already available.

The job is formidable. We need more than three and a half trillion pounds of good food a year just to feed the present human population. Something near half this amount is available with present practices.

We can postulate how to control the future numbers of children born into this world but this does nothing to solve or ease the present situation concerning inadequate food supplies and food consumption habits of those already alive. The situation is tragic because present knowledge appears adequate to resolve present difficulties.

It is exciting to contemplate what life on earth would be like if most of us enjoyed good health. The achievement of this goal is worthy of our best efforts. The achievement of this goal would go a long way in influencing another pressing problem on earth—the population explosion. It is well established that the rate of population growth is related in general to the standard of living of people. It is now recognized, too, that the highest fertility levels in a population are generally found in intermittently starving people.

It is not sufficient to hope that starvation will eliminate itself as a human problem. We must be willing to do something about the situation, and not only as individuals, but as nations and groups of nations. As is so often the case, those people with the greatest needs are least able to help themselves.

Yet, in a way, we are all human biologists since we are members of the human race on earth and we need not be uneasy with our shortcomings. Ideally, a human biologist would be a physiologist, geneticist, anthropologist, historian, psychologist, sociologist, economist and demographer all in one, and much else besides. He must also be a reasonable person.

Since no one can be all of these things, what is written herein is a product of a combination of knowledge and ignorance, as well as the product of a great deal of careful and anxious thought.

Unfortunately, the maps available showing the world harvests of wheat, corn and hogs are already a decade old. As of this date, these are the most recent available of this type from the U. S. Department of Agriculture or the United Nations. Since the purpose of these maps is to convey an over-all impression of the distribution of these crops, rather than to recite absolute numbers of units produced per country, it is felt that the inconclusion of these maps improves the presentation of the concepts being developed. More recent information shows that the relative positions indicated in these maps are still essentially correct.

Obviously the ideas contained in this book were generated by a host of people from the various disciplines and I have questioned my professional colleagues without mercy. Among the many I have turned to for advice, for factual material or for review of the manuscript or all three, have been —Professor Ronald Tukey, Professor Jules Janick, Professor Durward Allen, Professor Vernon Ruttan, Professor Gladys Vail, and Professor Nathan Kent Ellis. In addition, I am indebted to Professor Helen Clark and Mr. Gordon Wilhite for their assistance with several chapters.

And, I would like to give a special note of appreciation to Dr. Donald K. Tressler for his guidance and suggestions concerning this manuscript, his encouragement in its preparation, and for his grasp and sympathy for what I have tried to do.

To all the above, and to all those from whom I have drawn information so liberally, I am most humbly obliged. However, mistakes of fact or errors of judgment are mine alone.

The opportunity for great service rests on governments, foundations, the food industries, scientists of the various disciplines, and those individuals with knowledge and organizational talents to evolve the complex and interwinding programs which this problem requires for adequate solution.

The challenge is of immense proportions.

NORMAN W. DESROSIER
West Lafayette, Indiana

April 15, 1961

Contents

Illustrations

PART I

Man and Food

CHAPTER 1

Introduction

All men have requirements for food, oxygen, and water and there can be no compromise with these essentials without losing some of the desirable characteristics of human life. In fact, lack of food alone can limit the growth, the development, the vigor, and the accomplishments of men.

Poor health results when man does not consume his nutrient needs; this condition can occur because of a lack of good food to eat, because of defects in eating practices, or both. Since both are widespread, it is not surprising to find that the World Health Organization reports that most people do not experience good health throughout their lives.

Fortunately, the situation is not at all one which finds the human organism so overwhelmingly inadequate and, because of this, there can be cautious optimism that the starvation prevalent among men can be conquered.

Eating Habits Critical

Human beings can make decisions and one decision made every day (when a choice is available) is what to eat. All people have food preferences and these are found to vary in the different areas of the world. These preferences are learned, and, for the most part, conform to available food supplies.

1

Local eating habits are more or less successful solutions evolved to cope with the problem of human nutrition. Once gained, these habits are perpetuated by being handed down from one generation to the next. Eventually, what is eaten is considered "best."

Yet we must ask how solidly founded these food preferences really are. Are these preferences designed to nourish people or are these preferences merely compromises between what the human organism requires to flourish and what is available?

Furthermore, in recent years, man's eating habits have been under attack and the situation is becoming even more complicated. At the present time, men are bombarded with propaganda through advertising media which can confuse the issues due to exaggerated claims. Man is plagued with notices to eat no fat, to eat fat, to eat no sugar, to eat sugar, to eat no meat, and to eat only meat. He is urged to swallow several capsules of vitamins a day, gorge sunflower seeds, wheat germ, yeast and iron, gulp a glass of black strap molasses, a quart of milk, five glasses of water, and even generous amounts of vinegar. He is even urged to take a capsule to suppress his natural hunger drive!

Fortunately, there is available more than half a million years of experience concerning man, food, and eating habits. This storehouse of knowledge should reveal possible solutions to man's food problems. To be certain, all needed information is not available, but certainly sufficient is now known to form the basis for intelligent evaluations, hence action.

What is Good Food?

From a biological sense there are recognized to be a number of chemical compounds which are essential for optimum human growth and development; the frequency of consumption of these compounds is also found to be important.

From a cultural sense, the forms in which these compounds are consumed are significant. Successful diets also solve the problem of monotony as it is directly related to morale, enjoyment of life, and the individual's ability to help himself and to contribute to his society.

The solution to feeding people resolves itself into furnishing the nutrients they require (biological aspect) and in forms they will accept (cultural aspect).

Good food, then, can be defined as that which meets the biological and cultural requirements of men. A minimum adequate human food supply must meet at least the biological requirements of men.

Starvation would not exist if diets contained at least the nutrient needs of men. This is not the case found. But, it could be a goal! Serious problems usually develop when a man must choose between inadequate foods.

Five Major Problems

To launch an attack on starvation, it is necessary to identify the problem areas. There are at least five. First, there is the problem of producing the food men require to eat (problems in agriculture). Second, the nutrients do no good until consumed (problems in education and economics). Third, foods are an avenue for the spread of diseases and parasites which can stagnate an eager life or inflict an early death (problems in public health). Fourth, between harvest and consumption, foods can spoil and become unfit for human diets, which can frustrate the entire effort (problems in food storage and distribution). Fifth, continued expansion of human numbers on earth at present rates will limit the effectiveness of all efforts to combat starvation.

Current Limiting Factors

Visit the countries of the world. First view the lands from the air, then develop an over-all impression of the general richness of the soils, the extent of this resource, and the density of human populations. Then observe the state of health of the people who live in the various areas. Several conclusions concerning the adequacy of present practices become obvious.

One, the state of well being of people living on various continents is directly related to the condition of their soils. Two, current practices are not supplying most people with their needs for good foods. Three, the chances of this situation changing by itself in the near future are slim.

Attempts to rejuvenate the degraded soils of the world in the past 8,000 years have been less than successful. The best of present efforts would require decades or even centuries and even at that would hold no promise of being able to cope with the problem even if successful. The gains that are being made are unable to keep abreast of even the biological demands of the populations in most countries. This is particularly the case in those areas on earth where civiliza- tions have existed for long periods of time.

History reveals what eventually happens to even newly populated lands. The good earth disappears and with it goes the good life of its inhabitants.

On the other hand, just two hundred years ago, the United States was an agricultural nation. In this short period of time a revolution has occurred; men have been freed for other pursuits by the employ- ment of mechanical devices and an ever-expanding agricultural tech- nology. A century and a half ago, one man on the farm supplied his family with food and a little more. Twenty-five years ago one man on the farm could supply eight or nine others with food. Currently one man on the farm, with good soil, the latest technology, and the capital resources required to exploit this soil's food producing ca- pabilities, can supply more than twenty-five others with food.

Now this technology is available to mankind throughout the world. An important question then exists. Why is the success a rather local affair? One answer is that good agricultural land on earth is limited. Another is that capital resources are limited. Another answer might be that present practices are inadequate in spite of the great ad- vances that have been made. Present practices are not supplying the world's food needs, no matter what the explanation (United Nations 1960).

**Need for Evolution in Methods of
Food Production and Consumption**

It would appear that some supplementary methods of generating foods are required to overcome present dilemmas, and this is the theme of this book.

To explore the possibilities available, it is useful to gain a back- ground into what probably can and cannot be done. To address ourselves to this task we need information on man's biological re- quirements for food to define the problem we are trying to solve; we need information on his cultural requirements for food; we need in- formation on what food is, how it is presently generated, and the limits of present systems; and with this information, we might be able to find solutions. Once we accept the idea that agriculture must evolve, several directions for evolution become obvious.

Purpose of Book

Toward this end, this book attempts to explore our food needs, to show what men hae done, and what might be done to supply these needs, and to illustrate some of the problems which do not appear at present to have been adequately resolved. Included are some possible solutions.

CHAPTER 2

Diets and Deeds

INTRODUCTION

Aside from the moral responsibility, a society has a practical reason for launching a concerted attack on human starvation. A fruitful society must have healthy members and good health cannot be achieved without good food.

The deeds of men are recognized to be the result of a collusion of heredity and environment interacting with culture. For practical reasons, men are known by what they do; what they might have done is not known. Toward this end, it is important to know what portion of the people have the mental equipment to be classified as normal (genetic factor) and what portion of the individual's abilities are ordinarily developed (cultural factor).

There are obviously variations in the world. Cultures vary, people vary, and diets vary. What are the effects of diets on people, and of people on cultures? Since there is no genetic basis to explain the differences of cultures or races, diets must have a profound effect on both people and cultures.

The abilities of a person to think and act are critical to his existence. The inability to think critically can limit man's effectiveness, yet thinking is not widely considered to be a biological process. But, thinking must be considered a biological process, and it is readily influenced by diet, disease, and climate, as well as by exposure to educational and cultural factors. It is, therefore, of some significance to explore the effects of diet on human behavior.

EFFECTS OF INVOLUNTARY STARVATION

There is voluminous literature on the effects of brief but severe food restrictions on men, found characteristically to have plagued explorers, sailors, soldiers, and world travelers. Furthermore, during World War II, when whole populations were faced with famine or near-famine in concentration camps and in besieged cities, submarginal human nutrition was widespread. As a result of studies of each situation some of the effects of starvation are known.

During prolonged semi-starvation there is a loss of strength, an increase in muscular pains, followed by a reduction of body movements, then a reduction in the efficiency of speech, and the retardation of all mental processes. Physical exertions of any magnitude lead to rapid exhaustion and the person may pass into coma. While there is a general increase in sensory thresholds, pain sensitivity itself decreases. There is a lowered blood pressure and a slower pulse (Keys *et al.* 1950).

The behavior of people in advanced semi-starvation is characterized by sluggish intellectual processes, decreased abilities to concentrate, and dramatic incapacities for sustained mental effort. There are reports of a lowering of all higher interests and feelings of man. The victim develops a tendency to daydream; he becomes restless and irritable. Some become sullen and obstinate and develop an alarming lack of tact (Benedict 1919; Huntington 1945).

Voluntary Experiments on Healthy Men

Experiments conducted at the end of World War II revealed important findings with normal, young, healthy men who voluntarily lost one-fourth of their pre-experimental body weight (Keys *et al.* 1950).

The sensory functions of these men were remarkably resistant. Visual thresholds remained unaltered. The acuity of hearing increased. In this study, measured intellectual performances did not change drastically, although the men complained about an inability to concentrate and a difficulty in maintaining a trend or a span of thought.

There was a sharp decline in the spontaneous mental effort and achievement which only gradually returned to a normal condition after the men were renourished to good health. Men who were cheerful at the beginning of an experiment became quarrelsome and sullen. Whenever specific nutrients are withheld, for example, vitamins, dramatic repercussions can occur, for example, night blindness.

In other studies, observations were made on a volunteer group of college students who reduced their food intake until their weights had dropped 10 per cent. Then they maintained this reduced level for three months, eating enough to maintain this weight, but not as much as they wanted.

Results of tests undertaken by this group were perhaps more dramatic than even those given above. For example, in this group of students, there was a distinct decrease in ability to trace drawings, to discriminate musical pitch, to cancel numbers, and to perform addition. There was also a decrease in their sensitivity to electrical stimulation, in speed of movement of hand and eye, in strength of grip, in ability to maintain a low pulse rate under exertion, and in the capacity for improvement at clerical tasks with practice.

Some capacities such as memory, power of eyesight, and ability to find the right path in a maze were *not* affected, nor were the reactions to words, numbers and objects seen.

It can be concluded from the above that diet is a major limiting factor in the level of efficiency attained by man.

Demand for Mental Achievements in the Past

The widespread demand for mental achievement by man is relatively new. We have made or created this situation by ourselves from the kinds of mass cultures and civilizations we have permitted to evolve.

European societies of 500 years ago, for example, were rural and agricultural, with no great complexity of technologies and no particularly great demand for literacy occurred except for a few chosen members of a society. Today, a highly industrialized society demands that virtually all members attend school, be literate, and attain rather complex technical skills as prerequisites to becoming economically independent.

In the 1400's in Europe (and in the technologically undeveloped societies of the present) virtually all of the moderately subnormal people in terms of mental capacities were not particularly noticeable. Actually, such people were usually capable of taking care of themselves and of performing productive roles, such as tilling the soil, performing the work of a herdsman, or becoming practitioners of trades and crafts of a simple nature.

Subnormal people, who are presently in special schools and institutions or who are not in such isolation but who play a non-productive role in the family unit, were not noted by a society as being a special challenge 500 years ago. Most of them could have learned adequately, if rather slowly, to chop a tree, to drive a nail, to shoe a horse, sew a seam, or bake bread. Yet, many villages had village fools and the communities accepted and cared for them.

Mental Levels of Populations

It is useful to have some measure of the prevalence of mental subnormality in a large population of people. Estimates which have been made indicate that from one to nine per cent of a population (depending upon the age, the group studied, and the nation surveyed) are diagnosed as mentally subnormal. In the United States it is estimated that between three and four per cent of the population falls into this group. But, even in this group, three-fourths are only mildly subnormal, one-fifth are moderately subnormal, and only one-twentieth are severely subnormal (Trachtman, 1959).

In accordance with present concepts of biological variations, we should find that at the opposite end of this grouping of people on the basis of mental ability, some people should have extremely acute mental abilities and perhaps occur in about the same relative incidence as the subnormal, from one to nine per cent of a large population.

Individual variations between people in their food requirements due to specific metabolic disorders has also been a fruitful area of research. It appears that progress in this area has been made and further progress can be made with even the mentally subnormal person, who has special biochemical demands. The individual and variable food needs of people will be discussed in subsequent chapters.

Are There Several Levels of Nutritional Adequacy?

If we think in terms of minimum food needs, we define the smallest amount of nutrients which will support "normal" performance and prevent body disorders. The general concern in evolving good eating practices is how to attain good health, satisfy hunger, and reap the reward of the pleasure of eating good food.

The optimum requirement for food is the amount needed for optimum health and performance. The question then arises, "Are there two levels of adequacy?"

The distinction between minimum and optimum is a result of an inaccuracy in measurement techniques. When we consume less than a "minimum" some detectable "abnormality" occurs. If improvements can be obtained by consuming above a "minimum" level, then obviously the minimum is too low.

If the optimum level of nutrient intake yields maximum human performance, levels above the optimum yield no improvement.

It must be that minimum and optimum nutrient requirements for a person are identical if we could measure nutrient needs with accuracy (Williams 1959).

SIGNIFICANCE OF GOOD FOOD TO NATIONS

Semi-starved people rarely accomplish very much. Furthermore they are most sensitive to the invasion of disease organisms.

From the standpoint of civilization and history, Huntington (1945) considers the important aspects of diet as follows:

"The quest for food has probably been the most potent of all forces in making people work and in encouraging inventions. Next, agriculture, which is the main method of obtaining food, has been of paramount importance in the early development and growth of the civilized mode of life. Diet, through its effect on health and vigor, is one of the main factors in determining human efficiency and thus has a great effect upon a national character and national progress. This proposition finds general acceptance but the part played by diet in determining national character is not sufficiently emphasized."

Huntington made observations relative to the effects of prolonged hot, humid weather and the consequent effects on people and nations. Moist heat permits the rapid destruction of the fertility of soils and the heavy rains which fall, leach away the soil minerals almost as fast as they become soluble, hence are not available to nourish plant growth. Under these conditions in India, neither the milk nor the flesh of animals is as nutritious as counterparts in cooler climates. Analysis of milk from this area indicates a third less in vitamin C, for instance, than milk from cows in Northern America. There is some evidence that the Hindu reverence for cattle reaches its greatest force and is most strictly applied in regions where cattle are of relatively low value as food. Huntington concludes, that if Hinduism could be established in a region such as England, which has favorable conditions for cattle growth, the religious prohibition of the use of beef would probably be modified.

Apparently almost any belief or custom can be introduced into a population in almost any part of the world, but the degree to which it is accepted and the length of time that it persists are greatly influenced by the adaptation of the belief or custom to the physical environment.

Stagnation of Nations?

It is not known for certain what all the specific results are from semi-starvation when prolonged throughout a lifetime, which is the experience of more than a billion people in the world today. On the basis of available evidence it is thought that the stagnation of large cultures of men can be explained partly on the basis of diet (Huntington 1945).

Interaction of Man and Food

We have attitudes about foods; we like some foods and dislike others. Our likes and dislikes are significant because these influence our eating patterns. When we have a choice we choose what we want to eat. Together, we exert a control over what foods become available in quantity. Foods which no one desires are unimportant in diets.

A second important interaction is the impact the food we eat has on us. We have seen that the existence of men at semi-starvation nutritional levels can have marked influences on their abilities. Under such conditions, large numbers of people may become characterized or grouped as being dull. The true potential of each is not manifested.

It appears then that there is an interaction of man on food supplies, and of food supplies on man in terms of human achievement.

WHAT FOODS TO EAT

There are many proponents for diets composed of all animal or all plant foods. Information on both sides of this argument is voluminous.

The Stefanssonian Way

One school of thought is that the best diet man can undertake is composed of lean meat and fat—"living from the fat of the land." Stefansson (1937, 1956) has written that tooth decay is only one of the several important losses in health suffered by substituting grains for meat, although the substitution has enabled man to dwell in large cities and have a "high" standard of living. He has written extensively on his personal experiences since the 1900's, of human experiences on an 80 per cent fat—20 per cent lean meat diet, which forms one of the challenging discussions of food and man. Many agree with him that his concepts are controversial.

Russell-Sage Experiment

It would appear that each generation demands that men repeat many experiences of the preceding generation. In 1926 the United States was passing through a phase of nutritional consciousness during which many were trying to prove that meat was harmful to eat. There were reports that meat was supposed to cause high blood pressure, kidney diseases, hardening of the arteries, arthritis, and related ailments. In addition, there were a host of vague prejudices of religious, humanitarian, or aesthetic origin, and from the subconscious, it is thought that the ancient idea was returning that anything man enjoyed was bad for him. All of these forces seemed to operate against consuming liberal portions of meat in meals. It required a great deal of effort on the part of many people before the intelligent citizen was able to consume as much lean meat and as much fatty meat as he wanted without fear. A number of critical studies have been made on men living solely on meat and animal products. The data accumulated from these experiences and concurrent laboratory experiments are noteworthy.

The most dramatic part of the study was the suprisingly undramatic nature of the findings (Stefansson 1956).

Experiments with High Protein-High Animal Fat Diets

A number of experiments have been undertaken recently with high protein-high fat diets in the United States. The DuPont diet was principally one in which men consumed a high meat and fat diet, mainly of animal fats from beef sirloin. The Holiday diet, very similar to the DuPont diet, was composed of generous portions of meat and fat, but with additions of green salads, fruits, and token amounts of potato. Stefansson reports these to be modified Stone Age diets.

Results indicate than an improved state of mind as well as improved vigor was achieved by participants in these tests (Stefansson 1956).

Since there is evidence of loss of vigor and alterations in the state of mind due to starvation, it is reasonable to suggest that, with optimum nutrition, man should have an improved state of mind and improved vigor, and indeed these are found.

High Vegetable Fat Diets

What about vegetable fats in high fat-high protein diets? Investigations on the usefulness of vegetable fats in nutrition have been undertaken, for example, the one at Denton (Texas) State College for Women. Girls at this college were for the most part in their late teens and were asked to volunteer to live for an extended period of time on one of three variations of essentially the "basic seven" diet. The variations were in the amount of calories to be eaten in terms of fat; there were low, medium and moderately high fat diets.

The subjects varied as might be expected: Some were tall, some were short, some were troubled with complexion difficulties, and in sum total the group was considered "average."

Results of studies with the three diets involving the various fat levels showed that weight status was more easily retained, the skin condition was superior and fatigue resistance was better on the highest of the three fat levels, which contained 35 per cent of the total calories eaten. Margarine was one of the components of the total fat in the diet, and gains were equal to those with animal fats in the DuPont experiments (Stefansson 1956).

Controversy Over Diets and Heart Diseases

The American Medical Association (1961) reports that there is no evidence that restricted intakes of fats improve the health of people.

While it is not the intent to dwell on this subject, it might be fitting to summarize the issue by quoting from Stefansson (1958).

He wrote, "except that presumably I should have been dead of heart failure long ago, I might have been frightened to death by the recent proclamations in the press. Instead, I felt rather annoyed thinking of the Russell-Sage battle of 1928 (results of which were noted above) and that it might have to be fought over again. The attack on meat in the diet 50 years ago had been launched by men as prominent in their day as the viewers with alarm are today. In the 1920's and before, people attacked meat because of the lean element it contained—animal protein. Now they are attacking meat because of its fat element. Probably the great authorities of today are as wrong, I guess, as the great were then—everyone now seems to praise animal protein, which was so feared then. Very likely, within another 20 years, everyone will become dithyrambic once more about animal fats. It seems to me to be a good bet."

Plant Diets vs. Animal Diets

The best that perhaps can be said at present is that groups of men have consumed exclusively animal product diets or exclusively plant product diets and members of both groups have had good health. However, evidence indicates a less complicated dietary pattern in the animal product diets which are supplemented with succulent fruits and vegetables (which also enhance the pleasure of eating).

The food needs of man from a biological sense is the subject of Chapter 4. Suffice it to say here that man requires high quality proteins and fats. Man must eat fat to obtain the three essential fatty acids for good health. He requires fat to give his diets satiety value, that full, satisfied feeling which comes only from fat in good food. Man can gorge himself on a fat free diet and still remain hungry, although bloated. In addition, fats alone are the carriers of the important group of fat soluble vitamins. The other vitamins are found only in the watery portion of foods. Man needs all of both groups.

Although foods perform many roles, from a biological sense there have now been isolated a large number of essential nutrients for man. There are more than 50 such nutrients. For good health, man must eat the foods which supply these nutrients and he can find them in either plants or animals.

FOOD PREFERENCES AND HUMAN TEMPERAMENT

It is quite clear at this point that diets are important for good health and can influence human deeds. Further, the essential nutrients required for good health obviously can be obtained from all plant sources or all animal sources.

With these points in mind, it would be useful to know if what a man freely chooses to eat has any significance in terms of man the social being. There is a common notion among people that the meat eaters have ruled the world. Is there any evidence from scientific research with people that could yield information on this point? While the evidence is fragmentary, some answers are becoming available.

Military Tests

It is recognized from a practical standpoint that the food available to a soldier is directly related to his morale and this is related to his execution of assigned duties. It is not surprising, then, to find food research organizations in the military establishments of various countries. Napoleon recognized the need when he said, "An army travels on its stomach."

Because one of the largest purchasers of food in the world is the Quartermaster Corps of the United States Army, it is of considerable importance that it understands not only the food requirements of men but also food preferences. Furthermore, considering the large number of subjects available for study (more than 12 million men in World War II, for example), many opportunities exist to explore the relation of man and food. Recent studies have been reported on the relationship between man's temperament and his food preferences.

Food Aversions Related to Neurotic Tendencies

A number of investigations have shown a high relationship between the aversion a man may have for certain foods and his anxiety and neurotic tendencies (Peryam et al. 1958). One of the studies undertaken was to determine if there is a relationship between the likes and dislikes for food and the temperament traits of people who could be described as being normal and well-adjusted. The term food preferences is used here in the specific sense of expressing a rating for foods.

Test Procedures.—One study included 100 men who had volunteered to participate in a program to evaluate just this point (Schutz and Kamen 1957). These men were observed for a one month period, three meals a day. They were allowed to take any amount of or to reject partially or entirely any item of food served. Records were kept of the amount taken and the amount eaten. The meals served contained regular Army menu items. Approximately 150 different foods were offered in this study. At the end of the second and fourth week, food preference investigations were made. Psychological tests of temperament were administered to each of the subjects during the four weeks.

Fifty-four foods were selected from the menu as representative of the main types of foods served. Each item was rated on a nine-point scale ranging from "like extremely" to "dislike extremely."

The relation between the ratings given during the first and second, and third and fourth weeks were found to be very significant. These men were reported to be stable in terms of their ratings of foods.

The correlation between the values obtained in this study and the mass feeding of men indicated that the food preferences for the present study were typical of those of the army population as a whole (Peryam *et al.* 1958).

Temperament Tests.—The temperament evaluation schedule, developed by Thurstone, consists of a questionnaire with 140 items which appraises seven areas or traits of humans who can be classed as well-adjusted, normal people. The traits covered are: active, vigorous, impulsive, dominant, stable, sociable, and reflective.

An active trait finds a man working and moving rapidly. He is restless when inactive, hurried in speaking, walking, writing, driving, and working.

A vigorous man uses the large muscle groups and has great expenditures of energy. He participates in sports, outdoor occupations, and manual work.

The impulsive person decides quickly on actions or changes, is happy-go-lucky, carefree, relatively a daredevil, and enjoys competition.

A dominant person thinks of himself as a leader, enjoys public speaking, tries to persuade others, organizes social activities, and usually takes the initiative.

A stable trait in a man finds him cheerful, with an even disposition, able to remain calm in crisis, and able to concentrate despite distractions.

A sociable trait finds a person enjoying the company of others; he is sympathetic, cooperative, receptive, and agreeable to others.

A reflective trait refers to the person's preference for theoretical problems rather than practical problems; he desires to plan rather than to execute. He tends to be quiet, likes to work alone, and enjoys work requiring accuracy and detail.

The items in the Thurstone Temperament Evaluation Schedule deal with the everyday attitudes and behavior of people. It is not considered particularly unusual or abnormal if the respondent answers "yes," "no," or "cannot decide," to an item. Statistical studies show many significant correlations between the traits. Therefore, they cannot be considered completely independent.

Studies were undertaken to relate each of the temperament traits listed above with the food preferences of the men tested.

Data was also developed on the number of times each man rejected an item of food offered to him at the serving line during the test period (four weeks). In addition, four types of meats, vegetables, starches, desserts, and salads were selected from the 150 items of food offered in the food preference studies as representative of the five major types of foods people eat. Each respondent's average rating for each food type was obtained and correlated with his personality score.

Temperament Traits vs. Ratings for Foods.—The traits "dominant" and "sociable" were found to be statistically related to the preference for foods, considered as a whole. Those men having high scores on these traits expressed greater liking for foods in general than those having low scores.

Preference for *meats* was most highly related to the temperament traits. Those men having high preferences were characterized by being more *dominant, more stable,* and *more sociable* than those who rated meats low.

Only one trait was significantly related to the high preference for vegetables; those who liked vegetables tended to be very reflective. On the other hand, soldiers who rated starches high were less reflective than the "low" raters. High dominance was descriptive of those who rated desserts high. Sociability was positively related to preferences for salads (Schutz and Kamen 1957).

Temperament Traits vs. Food Actually Eaten.—Do temperament traits influence what food a man eats? Analysis of the data from these studies shows that high scores on two traits, active and impulsive, were positively related to the frequency of refusal to accept foods from a serving line. These two correlations were consistently high for each of the four weeks of the test. It was noted that these two traits did not predict ratings very well, while those traits that were related to ratings were not effective in predicting the number of rejections by a man at the serving line. Thus, some traits are associated with rating behavior, and others with food consumption. Nevertheless, traits that were significantly correlated with a favorable attitude toward food describe individuals who were outgoing rather than withdrawn.

Two other areas of interest were studied. First, the amount of calories taken, the amount of food left, and diet composition were found not to be significantly related to any of the seven traits studied. Contrary to the commonly accepted stereotype, there was no evidence that heavier people differ from the lighter ones on any of these traits or on the liking for food.

Second, another trait, apart from any specifically defined by a group of items, can be inferred from the response of people to the temperament schedule—this is the tendency to avoid giving a definite answer: a "noncommital" factor. The number of times each respondent gave a "cannot decide" answer in the temperament tests was correlated with the number of times he rated foods "neither like nor dislike" (the neutral category on the food rating scale used). Those who refused to commit themselves on one type of study also tended to refuse expressing liking or disliking on another.

Important in Survival

At the United States Air Force Survival Training School, airmen who accept the major item in a survival ration, which is a low-preference dried-meat bar, have a higher score on tests measuring leadership, adaptability, socialized aggressiveness, social adjustment, and motivation for achievement—all traits characterizing outgoing individuals (Peryam et al. 1958).

Stress Changes Preferences

It is also to be recognized that changes in food preferences result from changes in environmental conditions of eating, such as stress. The prediction on the basis of personality measurements of the susceptibility to changes in behavior toward food, as well as patterns of eating, would be of obvious practical importance to men in many situations in civilian and military pursuits.

SUMMARY OF TEST RESULTS

The significant feature of these studies was that those men who were allowed to eat in freedom of a well balanced diet for 30 days demonstrated significant relationships between the foods that they would eat and their personality traits measured by the Thurstone Temperament Schedule.

The same trait did not predict preference for each of the five food groups equally well. Preferences for meat, vegetables, and starches can be predicted from the personality scores better than those for salads and desserts.

Traits that are most highly correlated with preference were not necessarily those most closely related to acceptance. From the evidence available, it appears that there is a relationship between the food likes and dislikes of a man and his personality traits, which appear to be manifestations of man as a social being (Peryam 1958; Schutz and Kamen 1957).

Obviously, all meat eaters are not leaders. However, the fact that leaders evidence high preferences for many foods has meaning. These men appear highly adaptable.

Starvation Exacts a Penalty from Man and Society

The food a man eats influences human deeds, and since everyone eats, everyone experiences knowingly or not the impact of diet on human endeavor.

Well-fed people tend to be more vigorous than the poorly fed. Furthermore, in the long run, diet has a profound effect upon mental activity. Well-fed people are alert, adaptable, and demonstrate creativity to a much greater degree than do their poorly fed brethren.

The essential nutrients for human nutrition can be obtained from all plant sources or all animal sources. However, there are clearly less complicated dietary patterns with less opportunity for error when generous amounts of animal products are consumed.

We recognize we are creatures of habit, and these habits have their origin in the past. These habits control to a large part what we do today. What we eat today controls what we will eat tomorrow. Any change must necessarily be slow moving.

Without a definite program of instruction in eating, a child is apt to confine his food choices to favorite foods which may be inadequate. Children cannot project benefits of their eating habits into the future. They have no concern or appreciation for what the future will bring if they fail to eat certain foods. A willingness to eat and to choose foods in the quantities needed must evidently be established. Adequate eating habits, required for good health, must be learned. The emphasis and practice must also occur early to be effective.

There is conclusive evidence, both scientific and that resulting from practical experience, that the health and productivity of a man can be limited by the foods he eats. There is also clear evidence to indicate a relationship between a man's food likes and dislikes and his personality. Food preferences reflect some of the qualities of man as a social being as well. Repercussions of good nutrition, therefore, extended beyond good physical health.

Individuals All

On the basis of what has been presented so far, it would seem appropriate to explore next the individual variability of people, and what influence this might have on establishing the requirements for adequate food supplies for all people. If all men differ greatly perhaps it is impossible to develop a food supply system that would be useful to most people. This subject will be explored in this chapter.

The division between normal and abnormal is an arbitrary decision; a commonly used division is whether a large part (perhaps 95 per cent) of a population possesses the factor being studied.

The whole of the human race can be divided into two groups depending on the presence or absence of a particular characteristic which is measurable.

The vast majority possessing the characteristic would be considered normal, the minority not possessing the characteristic would be considered abnormal.

Each Different

Many factors or characteristics of people are not interrelated. When such is the case for one measurable factor we might find that 95 per cent of the population possesses the factor. But when we measure the occurrence of ten such factors, slightly more than half of a given population might contain all ten. If we measure 100 factors, less than one per cent of the population would have the 100.

The very fact that each of us has a vast number of characteristics which are measurable makes it quite clear that each of us is a deviate from the norm in some respect.

Each with Distinctive Health Difficulties

Williams (1956) has stated that there is a strong probability that the variations which exist between people are closely related to the fact that practically every person born into this world sooner or later gets into some distinctive health difficulty of one kind or another. Furthermore, the number of kinds of such difficulties is very large.

21

Biochemical Variations Distinctive

Studies of the composition of blood of a group of normal, healthy young men revealed values for blood constituents which vary by as much as a factor of two. Taste threshold values for these people varied from individual to individual over a twenty-fold range.

Each individual exhibits a distinctive pattern. Williams reports that the whole problem of human health and welfare is vastly different if a population, instead of being composed mostly of individuals with normal attributes or characteristics, is made up of individuals all of whom possess unusual attributes.

Such individuals might deviate from the normal range for one or more important characteristics.

What Is a Normal Population?

Williams elaborates on this concept by postulating two groups of men. Group I would be composed of men of average height, average weight, average foot size, average amount of hair on their heads, average tendencies to gain weight, average tendencies to consume alcohol, average sex urge, average types of lenses in their eyes—being neither farsighted or nearsighted, about average emotional reaction, about average digestive tracts, and with average teeth. Group II men might yield similar average values and be average or nearly average in many respects, but some men in Group II would be very tall or very short, have long or short feet, highly overweight or underweight, some would be completely bald, some would be alcoholics, some would have extreme sex urges, some would be nearsighted or farsighted, some have fits of anger and depression, some would suffer from digestive upsets, and some would have very bad teeth. If a population were composed of the first type, Group I, the problem of finding even a bed adequate in size to sleep in would not exist. Finding shoes to fit or problems of mental health, baldness, alcoholism, sex aberrations, nearsightedness, farsightedness, indigestion, and dental troubles would be practically non-existent. But within Group II above, all of these specific problems could exist in an acute form.

Williams (1956) reports that in comparison with these two imaginary populations, real populations on earth are composed in nature more like group II than I.

Any consideration of a human population to be like the first group fails to recognize problems which probably can be resolved. On the other hand, if those in Group II are rather typical of a human population, everyone is considered to be a deviate from the norm.

Nature of Human Characters

It is a fact that what we inherit from our forebearers is a range of capacities to respond to a range of environments. The characteristics of an organism are the result of an interaction of heredity and environment.

Impact of Food

The availability of food and the nature of the food available can limit the chemical reactions that can take place in an organism. It is well established that every enzyme and every enzyme system in our bodies arises from inheritance. The ability of an organism to carry out any chemical reaction required in its metabolism is an inherited quality, but chemical reactions can not occur without the components of a reaction.

Impact of Heredity

It is recognized that we are huge gene pools. We currently accept the one gene-one enzyme relationship. When we consider the large assortment of genes possessed by each of us, indeed we *must* all be individual.

Because of the complexity of the nature of inheritance, children of the same parents usually will appear more like the parents than other unrelated individuals, yet there will be a difference between the child and its parents. No two human beings possess exactly the same gene combinations, when considered in total. No two human beings possess the same fingerprints. Strikingly, even with identical twins, metabolism will not be identical in every respect.

We recognize that genetics really determines the potential that each of us carries, provided that the food necessary is available, in suitable form, and we exist in a suitable environment.

Principle of Genetic Gradients

Whenever an extreme genetic character appears in an individual, it should be taken as an indication that less extreme and graduated genetic characters of the same sort exist in other individuals (Williams 1956).

For example, if one studied the size of the adrenal glands in a group of rats and found one individual with a gland one-fifth the average size, the principle then would lead us to suspect that this was merely an extreme case and that other rats could be found which would have adrenal glands of various sizes intermediate between a minimum and a maximum under the environmental conditions being considered. In another case, if an individual child is found to have a low content of an enzyme in his blood, it can be assumed that probably other children would be found to have graded amounts intermediate between the observed low value and some maximum value. If one human, for genetic reasons, has an extremely low thyroid activity, others should be found with extremely high activity because of genetic reasons. The principle of genetic gradients would suggest that intermediate activity should be found to exist in any given large group of people.

The whole biological world has perhaps more degrees of complexity than we are able to conceive. This seems to be contrary to what we would like to hear, because we like to think that situations or things are simpler than they actually are. Furthermore, sometimes it is difficult to accept a series of facts which are applicable to human beings. Since genetical, hence biological, variability exists, it may then be useful to generalize about people.

Anatomical Variations

The anatomy of people varies; there are observed variations in all the structures of the human body. From the data available, the human structure varies substantially from one individual to another.

Biochemical Variations

On the basis of available information, each individual tends to maintain a distinctive pattern in the composition of his blood. Saliva is highly individualistic. The constituents of gastric juice vary substantially in concentration from individual to individual.

Mineral constituents of the blood may vary from person to person by as much as threefold. The chemical composition of hair varies for some constituents by a factor of at least two.

There is no doubt that with human females the ability to produce milk is controlled by genetical factors. It might be expected that milk, if produced, would vary in composition between individual women. It is found that the vitamin A content of human milk may vary by a factor of two, thiamin content by a factor of four, and vitamin C content a factor of ten. According to Williams, a variation from twofold to fifteenfold in vitamin content is found in the composition of human milks.

Variable Food Needs of People

It is well established that most of the components of an individual human vary when compared to those of other individuals. It must, therefore, follow that the nutrient requirements of individuals vary from individual to individual.

Variable Enzyme Efficiencies in People

Enzymes are those biochemical entities synthesized by living organisms under the guidance of the genetical components of living cells.

Each individual human has a distinctive pattern of enzymes. While the enzymes present perhaps generally do not differ between individuals, it appears from the evidence available that enzyme efficiency in normal human beings varies by a factor of two or three.

Metabolism Similar But Specifically Different

When two individuals with similar heights, weights, and metabolisms are studied it is not unusual to find that their over-all metabolic patterns are substantially the same. But the factor of importance is that *in specifics the metabolism of each of the two individuals may be different.* Even though some specific reactions may vary by as much as tenfold, the end results appear to be two rather equal individuals from a physical standpoint. They arrived at such a condition for different reasons.

Distinctive Hormonal Activity

A wide variability is also found in the function of hormones in various individuals. It has been found that "normal" people have "average" hormonal activities and "abnormal" individuals depart significantly from these averages.

Each individual, "normal" or not, appears to have a distinctive hormone pattern which is based upon the specific glands and balances which exist between the various hormones within each individual. The distinctiveness of these patterns involves differences in single hormones, which vary. It appears that the hormone activity in people may vary as much as tenfold. Hormone activity in different people is "as variable as the houses in which human beings live."

Variable Responses to Drugs

We vary substantially in our responses to drugs. It is almost impossible to find a useful drug which will act with complete uniformity for all people. In order to have the response uniform, the individuality which we all possess would have to be eliminated. Yet, some drugs are found which are effective for many people. For example, penicillin is useful in combatting certain infections for a large majority of the population. A small portion of the population, however, is extremely sensitive to this antibiotic, as is expected.

Variations in Growth of Body Structures

It has been found that muscles and fat layers and the cartilage in newborn children are distinctive for each individual and different for the two sexes. Furthermore, children tend to follow one of about ten channels of growth or patterns of growth. If they stray from the channel in which their physique places them early in life, something is apparently going wrong, indicating either infection or malnutrition. Williams suggests that the normal child of a certain age concept (that a child should attain a certain height, and a certain weight) is not particularly defensible with present day information. It appears that two children of the same age who have the same over-all dimensions may possess entirely different genetical potentialities for growth and development.

Variations in Body Temperature

Variations are found in the temperature of human bodies. Temperature measurements further indicate the existance of individuality of people.

Sensitivity to Pain

Sensitivity to pain is variable in people. Some people lack all sensitivity to the usual pains from burning, scraping or bruising. Individuals can be found with sensitivities ranging from practically insensitive up to ultra-sensitive.

Variations in Ability to Taste and Smell

One of the striking experiments or demonstrations that can be undertaken with a group of people is their ability to taste phenylthiocarbamide (PTC). Most people will either find PTC objectionably bitter or completely tasteless. A small group, however, will assign various tastes to the material, ranging from sweet to salty.

Probably as many people are tasteblind as are colorblind and the factor is genetically controlled.

The sense of smell is very variable in a group of people and this sense is also a genetically controlled factor.

Wisdom of the Body

Considering our individual requirements for specific nutrients to support human growth and development, it is to be anticipated that large variations between individuals will be encountered. Such is in fact found to be the case.

A wisdom of the body apparently exists which can be described as the wisdom to eat. Apparently this wisdom is fundamental in a general way. On a long range basis we eat because we are hungry, we select what we like to eat, and stop when we feel we have had enough. It is remarkable that most people strike a general balance in this regard!

What significance self-selection of food has in meeting individual requirements is not known. A part of one's individual needs are apparently met through the process of self-selection.

Danger of Inferior Foods

Striking reports are available on small children who were given a free choice of good (wholesome) food. Results indicate that children will each choose slightly different foods but all will somehow thrive to some degree (Williams 1956).

A baby can evidently get along reasonably well on a large variety of wholesome foods. However, when the choice available includes inferior foods, (i.e., pure sugar) it appears that the wisdom of self-selection breaks down.

Does the Choice Matter?

If a diet which is deficient, or is made deficient, is available to a large number of people, they apparently have no wisdom to guide them away from deficiencies. They starve themselves. There is therefore great danger in being tolerant to making available food of inferior quality to a population. The wisdom of self-selection of food breaks down

Each with Individual Food Needs

It has become clear that each of us has a distinctive pattern of nutritional requirements. We vary by several folds from one another in specific needs. We may each be suffering from important deficiencies, which may not be identifiable by present techniques.

Food a Limiting Factor Which Can Be Controlled

Williams summarizes the significance of our individual variations as follows: If, in the embryonic stage, a particular fertilized egg has needs for chemical building blocks which it does not have available, then it either dies or its organs and functions fail to develop adequately.

During childhood, if an individual has nutritional needs which are not fully satisfied, then his metabolism is altered accordingly. He becomes an easy prey for disease organisms, and his growth becomes retarded or distorted.

If, during adulthood, the individual, through ignorance or deception, fails to meet his particular nutritional needs, then he becomes deficient. He is then more susceptible to diseases and fails to resist them successfully.

As an individual ages, some of his organs and tissues fail earlier than others. This may be in accordance with their genetical hence predetermined and limited nature.

But organs and tissues have peculiar individual characteristics or weaknesses. These weaknesses may involve unusual and very high nutrient requirements for specific substances which may not be provided adequately by the environment in which the organ or the tissue resides.

Unless we know of our distinctive nutritional requirements (which are imposed on each of us by our genetical inheritance, hence beyond our control) we may be unable to meet these needs by chance or random feeding practices. *It would appear that the only solution available to us is to consume first a broad basic diet, then attempt to increase individual nutrients contained therein and establish the point of maximum response for each.* Such techniques would not fit into "health mill" programs. Health mill programs have not been successful, so their loss would not be significant anyway.

Unrealized Levels of Human Performance

Two ideas appear quite clearly. First of all, we must be wary of inferior food products. These lead us to errors in wisdom.

Second, that level of performance at which each of us is individually capable of attaining (if we consumed the optimum amount of specific nutrients required for our individual and peculiar needs) is unknown. Some human beings no doubt achieve this level, but for most of us it is basically an unrealized level of human performance.

CHAPTER 4

Our Food Needs

Since no two people are identical, it is important to explore each individual's food needs. How can men establish their individual food needs and are these compatible with existing food supplies? This chapter deals with the food needs of man.

Hunger is one of our strongest drives and we do not need a bell to remind us to eat. We have a physiological signal. Our blood usually contains about one-tenth per cent sugar and draws on the body to maintain this sugar level. A large portion of the sugar obtained from a meal is stored in the liver and slowly released on demand. When the blood sugar falls, we begin to feel sluggish, and the muscular contractions of an empty stomach tells us we must eat. We can eat sugar to boost our blood sugar level temporarily but a stomach must be at least partially filled and coated, even thinly, with fat to overcome hunger.

In addition to the physiological aspects, there is a mental response to hunger which stimulates the flow of saliva.

Food Characteristics

Our interest in food is basic to our existence. Food is an absolute need, our energy source. Food should contain the building blocks we need to grow and to repair tissues. Food should contain the nutrients we need to regulate our body systems (see Table 1).

Our life process can be seen as a constant use of energy and a constant exchange of materials. While occasionally our own tissues can yield some nutrients to meet a temporary shortage, we can not do so long. We need food, and there must be a balance between the food we eat and our nutrient needs if we are to achieve a feeling of well being.

Components of Foods

Plants and animals as a group contain sugars, proteins, fats, minerals and water. Eaten as food, starch and sugars are either burned, stored as fat, or stored as glycogen (animal starch). Protein is broken down into amino acids which are used to build and repair

TABLE 1

RECOMMENDED DAILY DIETARY ALLOWANCES[1,2]   (Allowances are intended for persons normally active in a temperate climate)

Designed for the maintenance of good nutrition of healthy persons in the U.S.A.

Group	Age (Years)	Weight Kg. (Lbs.)	Height Cm. (In.)	Calories	Protein (Gm.)	Calcium (Gm.)	Iron (Mg.)	Vitamin A (I.U.)	Thiamin (Mg.)	Riboflavin (Mg.)	Niacin[3] (Mg. Equiv.)	Asc. Acid (Mg.)	Vitamin D (I.U.)
Men	25	70 (154)	175 (69)	3,200[4]	70	0.8	10	5,000	1.6	1.8	21	75	....
	45	70 (154)	175 (69)	3,000	70	0.8	10	5,000	1.5	1.8	20	75	....
	65	70 (154)	175 (69)	2,550	70	0.8	10	5,000	1.3	1.8	18	75	....
Women	25	58 (128)	163 (64)	2,300	58	0.8	12	5,000	1.2	1.5	17	70	....
	45	58 (128)	163 (64)	2,200	58	0.8	12	5,000	1.1	1.5	17	70	....
	65	58 (128)	163 (64)	1,800	58	0.8	12	5,000	1.0	1.5	17	70	....
	Pregnant (second half)			+300	+20	1.5	15	6,000	1.3	2.0	+3	100	400
	Lactating (850 ml. daily)			+1,000	+40	2.0	15	8,000	1.7	2.5	+2	150	400
Infants[5]	0–1/12[5]												
	2/12–6/12	6 (13)	60 (24)	Kg. ×120	See Footnote	0.6	5	1,500	0.4	0.5	6	30	400
	7/12–12/12	9 (20)	70 (28)	Kg. ×100		0.8	7	1,500	0.5	0.8	7	30	400
Children	1–3	12 (27)	87 (34)	1,300	40	1.0	7	2,000	0.7	1.0	8	35	400
	4–6	18 (40)	109 (43)	1,700	50	1.0	8	2,500	0.9	1.3	11	50	400
	7–9	27 (60)	129 (51)	2,100	60	1.0	10	3,500	1.1	1.5	14	60	400
Boys	10–12	36 (79)	144 (57)	2,500	70	1.2	12	4,500	1.3	1.8	17	75	400
	13–15	49 (108)	163 (64)	3,100	85	1.4	15	5,000	1.6	2.1	21	90	400
	16–19	63 (139)	175 (69)	3,600	100	1.4	15	5,000	1.8	2.5	25	100	400
Girls	13–15	49 (108)	160 (63)	2,600	80	1.3	15	5,000	1.3	2.1	17	80	400
	16–19	54 (120)	162 (64)	2,400	75	1.3	15	5,000	1.2	1.9	16	80	400

[1] Food and Nutrition Board, National Research Council (1958).

[2] The allowance levels are intended to cover individual variations among most normal persons as they live in the United States under usual environmental stresses. The recommended allowances can be attained with a variety of common foods, providing other nutrients for which human requirements have been less well defined. See text for more detailed discussion of allowances and of nutrients not tabulated.

[3] Niacin equivalents include the preformed vitamin and the precursor, tryptophan; 60 mg. tryptophan equals 1 mg. niacin.

[4] Caloric allowances apply to individuals usually engaged in moderate physical activity. For office workers or others in sedentary occupations they are excessive. Adjustments must be made for variations in body size, age, physical activity, and environmental temperature.

[5] The Board recognizes that human milk is the natural food for infants and feels that breast feeding is the best and desired procedure for meeting nutrient requirements in the first months of life. Breast feeding is particularly indicated during the first month when infants show handicaps in homeostasis due to different rates of maturation of digestive, excretory, and endocrine functions. Recommendations as listed pertain to nutrient intake as afforded by cow's milk formulas and supplementary foods given the infant when breast feeding is terminated. Allowances are not given for protein during infancy.

body tissues, burned for energy, changed into sugar, or contribute to the production of fat. Fat is broken down in digestion, passed into the body, recombined into fat, changed into important body chemicals and burned for energy or stored as fat in tissues. All these substances (sugar, protein, and fat) may be used from any food source as fuel by our bodies.

Energy Value of Foods

The unit of energy value of foods is the calorie, a unit of heat. While the human body does not operate on the basis of heat in the sense of being an engine, nevertheless, heat is the product of body work.

The Calorie

A calorie is a unit of measure of the energy value of our foods, and is the large calorie. One calorie is the amount of heat we need to put into one pound (one pint) of water to raise the temperature $3.96°F$. In the metric system, it is the amount of heat to increase the temperature of one kilogram (2.2 lbs.) of water one degree Centigrade.

Calorie Value of Foods

When we burn sugar, fat, and protein, a portion of the energy obtained initially through photosynthesis is released. It is found that if we burn a gram, about one-fourth of a spoonful ($1/454$ lb.) of sugar in our bodies, we obtain four calories. If we eat one pound of sugar we obtain four times 454 or 1,816 calories per pound. From a gram of fat we obtain nine calories or 4,036 per pound. If we eat a gram of protein, we obtain four calories, or 1,816 per pound. To review, sugar and starches yield four calories per gram, fat yields nine, and protein yields four. Convenient charts are available in books relating the calorie content of food in terms of an average serving of an edible portion, or 100 gm., or one-fourth pound portions.

Energy Value of Foods in Calories

To find what a food has in energy value for us, we must know the carbohydrate (sugar or starch), fat, and protein content of the food. With this information, it is easy to establish the caloric value of the food. If we had 100 gm. of milk (approximately three ounces), and the milk contained 5.0 per cent carbohydrates, 4 per cent fat, and 4 per cent protein (the remainder water with traces of vitamins and minerals), then we could estimate the caloric value of milk. In 100 gm. we would have 5 gm. of carbohydrates or 20 (5 × 4) calories, 4 gm. of fat or 36 (4 × 9) calories, and 4 gm. of protein or 16 (4 × 4) calories. This four per cent butterfat milk would then contain 72 calories per 100 gm., or about 150 calories per six-ounce glass. Skim milk contains practically no fat (hence practically no fat soluble vitamins!) and has less calories (110) per glass. The number of calories in milk is largely dependent on its butterfat content, which varies.

The caloric value of foods is useful to us.

Estimating Food Needs

We can estimate the average expenditure of energy per hour under many conditions of muscular activity we may undertake. Thus it is possible to evaluate our food needs, then determine in a general way our food needs. Table 2 may be useful for this determination.

It is possible with this table to estimate the food we need for various activities. For example, if we work eight hours, sleep eight hours, and the other eight hours we spend inactively, what would we require daily in food?

| | Energy Used by | | | |
| | 170 Lb. Man | | 120 Lb. Woman | |
Activity	Hard Work	Easy Work	Hard Work	Easy Work
Sleep for eight hours	580	580	380	380
Spend 2 hours at light exercise	370	370	220	220
Work 8 hours	4,240	1,500	2,750	880
Spend 6 hours eating, sitting, reading, relaxing	660	660	430	430
Total calories required per day	5,850	3,110	3,780	1,910

Very few of us indeed usually do very severe physical labor. It is also apparent from the table the burden excess weight inflicts on our caloric needs. Some of the food requirements in calories for several occupations for the 170 lb. man would be:

Activity of	Calories per day
teacher or office worker	2,600
machinist or draftsman	2,800
mason or carpenter	3,500
ditch digger or lumberjack	5,600
combat soldier	6,000

For the 120 lb. woman, some of her occupations might require:

Activity of	Calories per day
housewife—no children	1,900
clerk	1,900
stenographer	2,000
teacher	2,200
housewife with one child	2,200
housewife with two children	2,600
light factory work	2,600
heavy factory work	3,000
housewife with four children	?

These must be recognized as generalities. It is not possible to establish food needs for a person in such a crude manner. He or she must evaluate his or her own activity, to establish food needs.

The energy required to function in our daily living may be evaluated and equated then with our food needs. There must be a balance between the food we need and the food we eat. If we take too little, the body itself will try to supply the nutrients. We therefore suffer. If we consume more than we require, we will store the excess in body fat and lose vigor. The mainspring in a watch must be wound to power the gears to keep time properly. Food is the human mainspring required to power life. The most noticeable

TABLE 2

CALORIE NEEDS PER HOUR[1] FOR BODY WEIGHT IN POUNDS (MAN OR WOMAN)

Activity	100	120	140	160	180	200	220	240	260
Sleeping	43	52	60	69	78	86	95	103	112
Awake, lying still	50	60	70	80	90	100	110	120	130
Sitting at rest	65	78	91	104	117	130	142	156	169
Reading aloud	69	83	97	110	124	138	152	166	178
Standing relaxed	69	83	97	110	124	138	152	166	178
Sewing	72	86	101	115	130	144	158	172	186
Standing at attention	74	89	103	118	133	148	163	178	193
Dressing	77	93	108	123	138	154	169	184	199
Singing	79	94	110	126	142	158	174	190	206
Typing	91	109	127	146	164	182	200	218	236
Ironing	93	112	130	149	168	186	205	224	252
Sweeping	109	131	153	174	196	218	240	262	284
Light exercises	110	132	154	176	198	220	242	264	286
Walking slowly	130	156	182	208	234	260	286	312	338
Active exercise	188	226	263	301	340	376	415	452	488
Walking fast	195	234	273	312	352	390	429	468	507
Walking downstairs	236	283	331	378	425	472	518	567	614
Running	307	369	430	492	553	614	675	737	800
Hard work	312	375	437	500	562	624	686	748	812
Very hard exercise	390	468	546	625	702	780	858	936	1,000
Walking upstairs	718	868	1,000	1,150	1,290	1,436	1,578	1,726	1,868

[1] Adapted from Sherman (1952).

effect of insufficient food is pronounced lethargy. In addition, and as previously discussed, mental activities are altered when food intake is out of balance with our needs. It shows in children in school, administrators in business, housewives in homes, professors in universities, kings on their thrones, and clowns in a circus. It matters not if we are princes or paupers; food powers each of our lives and it does it by the identical process.

Basal Metabolism

The living substance of life is protoplasm, which is peculiar in itself and has no counterpart in the world we know. Just existing, protoplasm is constantly being used and rebuilt. The dual process of waste and repair during the life of a living entity is termed its metabolism. A term is used which describes this energy requirement when completely at rest, not thinking, but awake. Our energy need under this circumstance is called our basal metabolism. The basal metabolism is then the measure of the process of waste and repair and growth of our bodies. The activities of life add to this basic requirement of our body. This basal metabolism varies with people, sex, and age, and is measured in terms of calories required per 24 hours.

Estimating Basal Metabolism

The work involved in just keeping ourselves alive is recognized as a continuing expenditure of energy. It is related to the surface area of the body, which is related to our height and weight. A method of calculating the basal metabolism for men and women is available.

Adult Males

Energy required per day = 130 + 6 times weight in pounds
+ 12 times height in inches
— 7 times age in years

Adult Females

Energy required per day = 660 + 4 times weight in pounds
+ 5 times height in inches
— 5 times age in years

The calories required per day for a man or a woman at rest may be obtained from the above. If you are a man six feet two, weight 190 pounds, and are 35 years old, the following calculations will give you your calculated basal metabolic requirements in calories.

$$\begin{aligned} \text{Basal metabolism} &= 130 + 6 \times 190 + 12 \times 74 - 7 \times 35 \\ &= 130 + 1{,}140 + 888 - 245 \\ &= 2{,}150 - 245 \\ &= 1{,}913 \text{ calories per day} \end{aligned}$$

Usefulness of Metabolic Studies

One method of determining whether the gears that make people function are meshing properly is by measurement of a subject's basal requirement.

If our basal metabolism is found to be over or under the normal rate some body process is not functioning properly. This is related to glandular (thyroid) activity. Another use of basal metabolism is to determine our food requirements. For our 35 year old, six feet two inch, 190-lb. man, a food intake of slightly over 1,900 calories is required each day just to maintain the body. The calories needed to do his work must be added to this figure. If this fellow consumed 1,500 calories per day, he would draw on his body tissues to supply the remainder. He would not remain at 190 lbs. long.

Overeating and Overweight

Unless we are ill, the body normally functions in a predictable fashion. The weight of our body is directly a function of the amount of food we eat, and our activity. Overweight is a result of overeating.

Surplus food in our diet whether carbohydrate, fat, or protein, tends to accumulate as fat. If we are fat, we have eaten too much in accordance with our activity. Some people tend to fatten more easily than others; this problem can extend beyond satisfying hunger when disturbances in hormone gland functioning are involved.

Control of Body Weight

Our basal metabolism can be increased by the administration of drugs but this is dangerous and should not be permitted except under strict direction of one with knowledge and experience in the use of appropriate medicinals.

The main essential to the control of body weight is the exercise of the intelligence. The solution to the problem of weight control involves not the question of whether food is fattening or not. The solution is found in asking ourselves what does this food yield in calories, how good a source of protein is it, and are the necessary vitamins and minerals present? Mitchell (1959) suggests "no calories without vitamins!" There is usually room for us to reduce our caloric intake among foods that are not important sources of vitamins and minerals; these are the foods which should be reduced in amount from our diets.

Weight Reduction Programs

Weight reduction programs should not involve "crash" plans but should be methodical, continuing reduction in calories without sacrificing essential nutrients—reduction in carbohydrates and fat, and not in protein, vitamins and minerals. The caloric value of the food should be reduced, but the vitamin and mineral intake should not be. They are necessary, and we cannot draw endlessly from our own tissues for their supply.

Eliminating 500 calories per day from our diet will mean a burning of almost a pound of body fat a week if our diet is adequate in other respects. This energy will be drawn from our fatty tissues with a reduction in body weight. If overweight we would be rewarded by reducing to an improved state of well being and vigor.

Satisfying Diets

A man of 170 lbs. and moderately active requires some 3,000 calories per day. A women of average size, 120 lbs, needs perhaps 2,500. About 25 per cent of this food value should come from fat to give the diet some satisfaction value. In Europe during World War II, the people were receiving adequate calories but the diet was low in fat. As a result, they were always hungry. Eating fat coats the walls of our stomachs, and this gives us that comfortable feeling. Fat is essential in the diet. In addition to decreasing the bulk necessary to eat to obtain energy, fat improves the flavor of foods, improves reproduction ability, lactation, food utilization and the physical health as well. Normal skin health requires the essential fatty materials found in the fats we eat. A minimum amount of fat is needed to insulate the body against heat loss and cushion internal organs. Nothing need be said of excessive fat.

Generalized food needs

The average man needs at least 70 gm. (one-sixth of a pound) of pure protein. Remember that lean beef has only about 20 per cent protein! Our average woman needs 60 grams of protein as a minimum. We need a suitable supply of water, amounting to three and a half quarts a day. Some foods contain 60–90 per cent water and we obtain some of the necessary water in our foods. It is not necessary that we drink three and a half quarts of water a day; our foods should yield this with a modest supplement from a drinking fountain. This is naturally dependent upon the activity we undertake and the climate in which we operate. We require, as mature adults, at least a quart of liquid water a day, and obtain much of it in wet foods usually. It is interesting to note that we are not able to differentiate the thirst for salt from the thirst for water. The animals can (salt licks for cows), but we have lost this ability. We need, under normal conditions, about five grams of table salt a day (one teaspoonful). We obtain this by salting our food and obtain some naturally in our foods.

Mineral Requirements

Of the nutrients which are essential to human nutrition, fourteen are the following mineral elements: calcium, chlorine, cobalt, copper, fluorine, iodine, iron, magnesium, manganese, phosphorus, sodium, and sulfur. Minerals occur in foods in organic and inorganic compounds. The major inorganic compounds are the carbonates, chlorides, sulfates, and phosphates of sodium, calcium, potassium, and magnesium. The average man requires approximately 0.8 gm. of calcium, 0.012 gm. of iron, and 0.0002 gm. of iodine per day.

We may not obtain sufficient iodine from our foods in certain areas, so salt is fortified with iodine to prevent goiter formation.

Vitamin Requirements

In addition, we require vitamins. The name rises from what was thought to be the need we have for certain vital chemical compounds—amines (vital-amines = vitamins). It was found later that these chemical vital-amines were not all amines.

The easiest method of demonstrating the role of vitamins for us is to observe the consequences of a diet lacking a vitamin. If vitamin C (ascorbic acid) is omitted from a diet (sailors on long voyages away from port) and the food is adequate otherwise, some of the chemical reactions that normally take place do not. For instance, if we remove a gear from our watch, we cannot expect it to keep time. Our body without the help of vitamin C shows certain conditions we now recognize as scurvy. There is an analogy between mortar placed between concrete blocks in building a wall and the role of vitamin C in the building of healthy tissue layers in our body. The mortar binds the concrete blocks together. Vitamin C is essential to us, enabling us to cement the cells that make up our tissues in a firm, rigid structure. Without vitamin C, for instance, our teeth loosen our mouth tissues become cracked and inflamed. We develop a condition known as scurvy. On voyages at sea, without fresh foods or sources of vitamin C, English sailors learned that if they ate limes, scurvy would not develop. Limes are a good source of vitamin C. It is no accident that English sailors are called "Limeys." Other early travelers learned interestingly that a germinating seed prevents scurvy, while a seed that has not germinated helps very little.

Disorders from Lack of Vitamins.—If any one of our vitamins is omitted, our body does not function properly. The lack of a vitamin, sooner or later, results in a nutritional disease (avitaminosis) which is characteristic for the vitamin in question. Each vitamin is specific. If uncomplicated and not allowed to become too severe, the nutritional disorder can be cured by administering the vitamin; however, if we are lacking in a vitamin, we have very low resistance to disease; we succumb to attacks of disease-causing organisms we ordinarily might resist.

Classes of Vitamins.—Vitamins are divided into two groups—fat soluble and water soluble. Some of the older vitamin factors have been shown to be complexes rather than single entities.

When the vitamins were discovered, they were called factor A. Then another was found and called B. The next was called C. The next D, and then E was discovered. It was later realized that what was called vitamin B was really made up of two, one destroyed by heat (thiamin) and another destroyed by light (riboflavin). So, these were called vitamin B_1 and B_2 respectively. Later it was found that if the vitamin mixture were heated and exposed to light, more vitamins remained. These were grouped under the term B-complex. It now has been shown that there are more than a dozen factors in the B-complex.

Each vitamin is different and each is necessary for us. We can obtain these vitamins from our food. A balanced diet of natural foods generally provides the vitamin requirements of man. Certain requirements of vitamins for man have been reasonably established. For an average man, these are: 5,000 International units of vitamin A, 1.5 milligrams of vitamin B_1 (thiamin), 1.8 milligrams of vitamin B_2 (riboflavin), 20 milligrams of vitamin PP (Pelegra Preventative or nicotinic acid), and 75 milligrams of vitamin C (ascorbic acid). The adult male requires little vitamin D, unless confined indoors. Women in pregnancy and lactation and children require vitamin D. The requirements of man for other vitamins have not been clearly established, but a well balanced diet furnishes such factors so far as is known.

Nutrition in Pregnancy

A pregnant woman requires added nutrients. She needs some 20 per cent more calories and 50 per cent more protein in the latter half of pregnancy, along with a one-third increase in the vitamins and minerals. (She needs about twice as much calcium.)

Child Nutrient Demands

Children require special attention in their food needs. While less than a year old they require 45 calories per pound of body weight per day. They need about 1.6 gm. of protein per pound of body weight per day. They need, as a minimum, half the adult vitamin requirement, except for vitamin D. Now a child needs a balance in the mineral elements and vitamin D to form bone. The calcium and phosphorus in bone must be supplied in a ratio of two to one. Vitamin D must be present in adequate amounts for maximum bone development. Milk contains the proper balance in these nutrients, but little vitamin D. Vitamin D is added as an enrichment to processed milk for the benefit of growing children.

From One to Four Years of Age

Children between one and four years of age with moderate activity and of average weight need some 1,200 calories per day, 40 gm. of protein, and approximately one half the vitamin requirement of the adult. The child needs about 20 per cent more calcium than his parents.

From Four to Six

Children between 4 and 6 years of age need one-fourth more of everything over what they received earlier (1600 calories, 50 gm. of protein, etc.). Children between 7 and 9 years of age need about one-fourth more than the preceding age group (2,100 calories, 60 gm. of protein, etc.).

To grow in height a young body must have a balance in nutrients it requires to form new bone, new muscle, and new tissue. If a child is growing normally it must be obtaining a fair diet. On the other hand it is possible to have weight for age but not height. Adding weight to a child at the sacrifice of height is an index of an inadequate diet. After World War II, Mitchell (1948) studied many children in Western Europe, evaluating the nutritional condition of children in war-torn areas. Weight records appeared adequate but the children were shorter for their ages than predicted from the normal growth curves for these countries. Height for age is an index of adequate nutrition in children. "Weight for age" without height may mean poor nutrition or physiological abnormalities.

From Ten to Twelve

Children between 10 and 12 years of age need one fourth more than the earlier group. Their calorie intake will be about 2,500 calories, and they need approximately the other requirements of adults, except that they still require vitamin D.

Children Over Twelve

Children over twelve differ in their food needs now on the basis of sex. Girls from 13 to 15 need 10 per cent more nutrients than the twelve-year olds. Boys between 13 and 15 need the food requirements of an adult man (3200 calories, 85 gm. of protein, vitamin D, etc.). Boys between 16 and 20 eat as though they had been working at hard labor on a farm. They need 3,600 calories, 100 gm. of protein, vitamin D and the other nutrients of an average adult male.

The above food requirements are averages only. Growing boys may eat over 4,000 calories.

RECOMMENDED DIETARY ALLOWANCES

The above requirements of man are those recommended by the Food and Nutrition Board, National Research Council, Washington,

D. C. An important publication is available from the Council. It is entitled "Recommended Daily Dietary Allowances" and is available for distribution. It is an important statement on the subject of adequate diet in terms of good health and vigor.

It is important that we recognize that the well balanced diet furnishes the above nutrients . . . the minimum recommended requirements. They represent the lowest level which could yield healthy adults!

ALL NUTRIENTS AT ALL MEALS

Today it is realized that we require a continuous supply and a balance of sugars, fats, proteins, vitamins, minerals, and water in a sustaining diet. These we may obtain from a variety of sources. If we had only one choice, we should choose a fresh animal, and consume most of it. An equally sustaining diet can be eked from all-plant sources, providing we know which to choose. There is no one plant which is sustaining to man. A diet restricted to corn or potatoes, or rice alone results in malnutrition and death. The best diet we know consists of carefully selected combinations of plant and animal tissues to yield optimum nutrition and a feeling of well being. Without this balance we lose that elusive state we call "good health."

There have been other interesting studies conducted with mice that bear noting. If fed half the essential amino acids at one eating and the other half at a later feeding, the mice starve. A well balanced food program is the only solution. Everything in order, and in balance. Animal and fish and poultry flesh foods have all ten essential amino acids. Corn lacks two. A diet of corn then is not sustaining alone. Corn and fish together, or meat and beans, yield the ten. Rice and fish are consumed together for the same reason.

Danger of Self Experimentation

During our history, geographical and economic circumstances have created ample opportunities to study food and health. On the other hand, deliberate studies have been undertaken. Stiebeling (1959) tells of a physician, William Stark, in the 1700's. At the age of 29 and reportedly a healthy, vigorous man, he set out to establish the effect of diet on health. He ate carefully weighed amounts of bread and water and, in his scheme, was to add the various food items of his ordinary diet, one at a time. He fell ill and in a few months died. In light of present knowledge, he probably died of severe vitamin deficiencies. There are countless instances of self-experimentation of this nature, some with more fortunate results, especially where the starting food was animal flesh rather than grain.

Usefulness of Animal Products in Diets

The difficulty of a diet composed largely of plant food is that the nutrient balance may be suboptimum. This was demonstrated in a classical experiment by Sherman at Columbia University.

Small animals are commonly used in nutrition research. Their life span is short, their metabolism is much like our own, and can be interpreted in terms of ours, providing that the factor being measured is significant to both man and the animal. We have then an excellent nutrition research tool.

Sherman (1946) grew more than 80 generations of rats under controlled conditions. The animals were divided into two groups. The first received what is considered an adequate diet predominantly of plant origin. The other consumed a diet made more generous with animal protein than vegetable protein, with additional vitamins, and with added milk. The first group was considered by all tests to have grown and reproduced normally. The animals receiving the second diet made distinct gains over the other (normal) group in health, had an earlier maturity, lived longer, had greater success than normal in rearing their young, and had an increased vigor over the life span.

The Organization

By the time we reach 70 years of age we may have eaten about 1,000 times our body weight in food. Our body viewed as an enzyme apparatus is certainly influenced by the foods we feed it.

It is noteworthy too that even the calcium in our bones is changed in a period of half a dozen years. At one time it was thought that once formed, bones remained in constant composition. Using radioactive calcium it has been shown that there is a constant exchange of calcium in our bones, and that, in a period of 6 to 8 years, our bodies change completely, even the atoms. We need to pay careful attention to our diets, throughout life. If we like, perhaps we can think of our body in terms of a university. Nothing remains constant–the students, the faculty or the buildings–the only thing that remains is the organization! So, too, with our bodies. Life is the only thing constant in this organization. The vitality of this organization is a reflection of the food we eat.

SUMMARY OF FOOD NEEDS

The amount of food we need depends upon the individual and his activity. We vary in general in the amounts of food we must eat, but not in the kinds of nutrients we require under usual circumstances. Greater food need must be met by a proportional increase in all factors and nutrients.

An ordinary diet may be composed of several foods which contain many carbohydrates, proteins and fats. Carbohydrates, proteins, and fats may be used in our bodies as fuel from any suitable food source. Therefore, our bodies are not restricted to the use of any one food. The entire potential of all our foods is available to support work in all parts of our bodies. Sugars, proteins, and fats are so intimately related in this service that we group them into one term and designate it "food." Since all three components can give us energy, we commonly use energy when referring to the value of foods.

The energy required to function in our daily living may be calculated. The energy values of our foods are established. It is clear that there must be a balance between the food we need and the food we eat. If we take too little, the body itself will try to supply the lacking nutrient(s). Thus we suffer. If we consume more than we require, we store the excess in body fat, and lose vigor.

Food is the mainspring we require to power our lives. The most noticeable effect of insufficient food is a pronounced lethargy. Both physical and mental activities are altered if food intake is out of balance with needs. Information is available with which each person can estimate with some precision his individual food needs. To the best of current knowledge most people are able to gain the reward of good health by consuming an adequate amount of good food.

Fountainhead of Foods

CHAPTER 5

Discovery and Spread of Agriculture

The food needs of man and the repercussions of starvation were discussed in Part I. Part II is designed to explore how man developed his present food supplies, what limits his present system has, and what might be done to expand it to meet his food needs.

This chapter is devoted to the discovery and spread of the knowledge of agriculture and the stages through which it has evolved.

DISCOVERY OF AGRICULTURE

The practice of agriculture is a key component of the Neolithic Revolution which occurred first in the prehistory of the Near East, again about 2,000 years ago in Tropical America, and has still to occur in certain sectors of the world.

Let us consider the Near East at that time. The earth's rain belts were shifting, and with the decreasing rainfall and drying of the highlands, men and their animals were driven to the water available in the valleys of the Tigris-Euphrates Rivers.

Excavations in the area indicate early settlements of modern men who had built grain storage silos. Considering the storage capacity of such silos and the grain that could be collected in the wild, it is believed that the only means of developing such quantities of grain would have been to plant it as a crop. In any event, wheat storage silos were built, filled, and used thousands of years ago in the Near East.

It is now possible to establish that time with some precision, using radioactive carbon dating techniques. An inevitable consequence of living on earth is to incorporate radioactive carbon into all living substances. The dating technique developed by Libby (1952) permitted calculation of the age of the grains uncovered in the above mentioned silos. It was thus learned that some of these grains were produced about 8,000 years ago, plus or minus a few hundred years. Hence, these grains turn out to be the oldest ever found on earth in quantities which would indicate that agriculture had been practiced at that time. Calculations from the Bible indicate that the Garden of Eden occurred about 6,000–8,000 years ago (Jensen 1953). Perhaps the Garden of Eden then refers to the discovery of agriculture.

Man above all can be ingenious and a remarkable feature is that this genius is not restricted to any one area on Earth. Many of man's fundamental problems were solved independently in different areas, at different times, and without known communications between the different peoples. For example, the boomerang was invented in Australia and the bow and arrow in Europe and Asia, pottery making in Europe and America, agriculture in the Near East and in America.

One of the early successful plant cultivations was the cereals which became increasingly important to man and animals. However, cereals alone are a dull diet for man and, to supply his other food needs, he developed the olive grove, the fruit orchard, and the vineyard and invented the required cultivation techniques whose origins are lost in prehistory. The products of such orchards still are important sources of energy, vitamins and minerals in diets, and improve the pleasure of eating.

While it took great foresight to grow cereals, the cultural arts needed to grow fruit orchards successfully are of a different magnitude. A few examples would include the pruning of fruit trees to control fruit production, the grafting and budding of improved varieties to limbs of other compatible fruit trees, the growing of grapes (and making of wine), and the hand pollination of the date palm when sex in plants was unknown. Another was the development of methods to intensively force the growth of vegetables. As a result, a technology developed in food production and irrigation, and these brought more people together—first in small groups, then in villages first small, then large.   Men needed to be concentrated to develop specialization.

Agriculture permitted a new way of life; with increasing food supplies, some people could be released from food production tasks to engage in other functions in communities.   Surplus commodities developed and simple food products were prepared and bartered.

By 4,000 B.C., with the growth of cities and accumulated knowledge of nature, the Urban Revolution began in the Near East.   This brought with it the centralization of power and with it sharp class and occupational distinctions.   Specialized and even leisure classes of people evolved.   Nutritionally, some groups were better fed than others, and this tended to amplify the differences between people.

Spread of Food and Agricultural Practices

Civilizations developed early in four areas on earth.   These were in Central Asia, the Mediterranean region, Southeastern Asia, and in tropical America.   In each of these regions, early attempts to cultivate plants were successful.   While these areas were the places where the useful plants were native, each region yielded plants which eventually became valuable to all mankind.

A part of the story of agriculture involves the selection of new species of plants, and improvements in culturing methods.   The solutions varied in different areas of the world: in Iraq it was wheat, in Egypt, wheat and barley, in India, rice and wheat, in China, rice, and, in America, corn and potatoes.   In each area, grains were first isolated from the wild, cultivated and sorted—one grain was better than another, relative to yielding food.

Agriculture in India

From the Near East the practice of agriculture spread east into India, where men took up the same food production patterns as the Tigris-Euphrates River valley inhabitants, except here they added humped cattle and chickens.   Rice and wheat were their staple cereals.   They wore cotton rather than woolen or flax clothing, built two-storied buildings, and huge grain storages.

Agriculture in China

Agriculture was under way in China 4,000 years ago in the valley of the Yellow River, where cattle breeding and cereal growing were practiced. Pigs, cattle, sheep, goats, chickens, ducks and water buffalo were raised. Rice was the staple cereal and silk was woven for clothing rather than cotton, wool, or linen.

Spread into Europe

From the beginning of farming, the Mediterranean populations reflected the wealth of their soils. For a time they prospered and grew in the Near East, with their new supplies of oats, wheat, barley, root crops, meat, milk, fruits, vegetables, oils, and spices. But, after about 2,000 years and exhausted soils, there was a migration of food producers up the Danube and along the Mediterranean Sea coast into Europe. Seeds and food animals were brought with the migrants.

A soil was tended so long as it gave reasonable harvests, and when productivity was lost, there was always new crop land available. Evidently there was something lost in a soil which was necessary for continued, satisfactory crop production.

Independent Discovery of Agriculture in the Americas

Indian artifacts found in South America are being reported in the 5,000–20,000 year old class. In Europe, archeological findings have gaps separating the Paleolithic (Old Stone Age) man from the Neolithic (Agricultural) man. In America the gap is also found.

The American Indian came from Asia by way of the Bering Straits during the close of the last glacial period, and became isolated from Asia during the warming trend which followed the last glacial advance. These migrant Asian hunters spread over most of North, Central, and South America. Their culture at that time was of the Stone Age.

As in Europe and Asia, where great cultures rose and fell, so too in America. At the time of Columbus there were perhaps one million natives in the now United States and less than 30 million people in North and South America.

The Inca Empire of South America has been compared with the Roman Empire as a civilization. The pre-Inca period lasted for 1,500 years, and the Inca Empire for another 13 generations, until the coming of the Spaniards. At its peak the empire covered 400,000 square miles.

The basis of the Inca Empire was intensive agriculture, and they had a land-use technology which has yet to be rivaled. Immense terraces and irrigation aqueducts were constructed and maintained. They had grain storages, and a surplus food problem. The Inca saved and perpetuated the food potential of the empire. A population greater than that in the area today used the same land and its water for nearly 2,000 years. The dominant long range Inca policy was maximum human use of land and water with total conservation. Babylonia, Greece, Rome, and, more recently, Spain destroyed their basic agricultural resources of soil and water through policies which exhausted the earth without maintaining soil fertility and productivity.

Different from the Inca civilization were those in Guatemala and Mexico—the Mayan and Aztec Indians. Mayan records extend to 2,400 years ago, and they had a many sided agriculture (and a writing system). The Mexico City seen by Cortez contained food markets, restaurants, and an elaborate Aztec culture. These civilizations, too, were upset by the Spanish Conquest.

Inca Agriculture

Indian corn, or maize, developed in prehistory in Central or South America and domesticated by the Indian, eventually had an impact on life on both American continents. It helped bring about the settling and populating of such empires as that of the Inca, which reached 12 million people. The word "corn" in Europe and in their literature refers to cereal grains as do the Biblical references. The development of corn by the Indians is thought to have been one of the most remarkable achievements in agriculture. Of all the grains, the origin of corn is the most completely elusive. The ancestor of corn has not been determined; corn has never been found growing in wild virgin areas on either continent, or any other place on Earth; corn is a completely domesticated plant, whose ancestry is lost.

In addition to corn, the prehistoric American Indian contributed to the world the potato, sweet potato, tomato, vanilla, turkey, peanuts, beans, squash, pumpkin, chocolate, rubber, quinine, cocaine, and tobacco. Other foods used by these Indians include pecans, brazil nuts, avocados, and maple sugar.

Of the three thousand species of plants known to the American Indian for food, fiber, medicines, beverages, and dyes, nearly half were used for food. Present day expeditions into the upper Amazon still discover new plants useful to man. The potato has influenced nutrition and history, ranking in importance with corn. When the potato became accepted in the Old World, substantial changes in food consumption patterns were made.

The peanut is native to South America and has found great industrial and commercial uses.

The banana is not native to the Americas but was introduced from the Far East, where it was cultivated as early as 2,000 B.C. The banana was introduced to the Western Hemisphere by missionaries 400 years ago. The plantain (a larger species than the banana) is the "potato" of the tropics. The banana and the potato are much alike nutritionally.

There was an absence of dairy cows in the Americas prior to the Spanish discovery, although the llama was milked by the Inca people. The North American Indian drank the milk of freshly killed female antelopes but did not practice animal husbandry except in domesticating the dog. The Aztecs bred several varieties of dog for food. Turkeys were their main domestic fowl, with some geese and ducks. At the time of Columbus, there were no horses or dairy cows in the New World.

PROBLEM OF MAINTAINING SOIL PRODUCTIVITY

From the beginning of agriculture to the present, one of man's problems has been to keep soil productive. Under low level cultivation of plants, a soil essentially never wears out or becomes seriously depleted. It is only under concentrated or intensive cultivation that a soil becomes unproductive.

If we plant a few seeds in a window box of fertile soil and obtain good plant growth, next year the window box will probably not be able to produce equal plants. The soil has lost a portion of its productive capacity.

If this soil structure were broken down and brought into good physical condition, then allowed to incubate, there would be a gradual release of nutrients, in a form available for plant growth, which would now almost equal that of the original soil.

Under low level cultivation, major losses in productivity are from physical factors and from leaching and erosion. The soil becomes compacted and does not favor plant growth, or a portion of the soil becomes washed away. The nutrients needed for plant growth are leached away in the water. These situations can occur in a flower box or in fields.

In addition to the above losses, plants take up nutrients from soils. If we weigh the plants we grow in a soil, dry them and determine the weight, then burn them and weigh the ash, we would have an index of what the plant took from the soil. The dried plant has perhaps 20 per cent of the weight of the live plant, the other 80 per cent being water. The ash may amount to two per cent of the live weight. This ash represents the direct depletion of mineral nutrients in the soil by the plants. The non-ash portion of the dried plant represents the products of photosynthesis.

The soil yielded the ash content to the plant, and may have yielded almost all of the mineral elements it had in a form available for plant growth. A very fertile soil has less than one per cent by weight of nutrients available for plant growth.

When man harvests crops, he harvests solubilized minerals from the soil as well. If these are not replaced, the soil eventually becomes deficient in one or more essential minerals for plant growth. Less crops are harvested; men grow hungry.

While solutions to the problems of soil productivity were slow in evolving, over an eight thousand year period a technology nevertheless evolved. It is now possible to see the stages through which agriculture has passed. An example of what has been learned is found in potato production where 1,000 bushels to the acre can be obtained under favorable circumstances.

STAGES IN DEVELOPMENT OF MODERN AGRICULTURE

Natural Husbandry Agriculture

With the discovery of agriculture man mainly scratched seeds into the ground and waited for the crop to grow.

He performed a minimum of assistance to the crop and obtained a meager yield—perhaps two or three times the amount of seed planted. This stage of development was called natural husbandry farming. In natural husbandry, nature was the sole provider of the soil's productive capacity and soils were abandoned when productivity dropped. This form of agriculture was practiced by early peoples and remains in modern times in areas with backward habits.

Naked-Fallow Agriculture

The plow used by early man was simply a scratching tool and similar in effect to a hoe. In addition to preparing the seed bed, this "plow" was used mainly to eliminate weeds. These scratching tools were perhaps comparable to present day cultivators which are sometimes still referred to as plows and hoes.

Much of the early difficulty in plant production was not so much the loss of nutrients from soils but weeds. This is evidenced by the next development in agriculture—the naked-fallow system, where the ground was prepared for planting but not seeded. Weed seeds were encouraged to germinate in an attempt to kill them out. Then cattle were grazed on the weeds and the growth and manure accumulations were then scratched into the soil.

The land responded some to this treatment and it was more than the mere resting of land. The Sabbatical Year was an ancient plan for "resting" land every seventh year.

Either one-half or one-third of a farm was left in naked-fallow, the latter yielding superior results. The gross return under this system was nearly twice that in natural husbandry. Naked-fallowing returned perhaps an average of 6 and 8 bushels of wheat per acre.

In Babylonia, 4,000 years ago, this form of agriculture was the chief method of providing a livelihood and yielded luxurious living for a few. Elaborate food storage methods were developed. Fruits were dried and some fish and meat were salted and dried.

Development of Agricultural Handbooks

Observations of plant and animal culturing methods were recorded as early as man learned how. By 700 B.C. agricultural handbooks of a sort were written, giving such information as how and when to plant, how the seed should be sown and irrigated, harvested, and stored.

Development of Greek World Agricultural Trade and Its Decline

By 500 B.C. "world" trade was underway for many agricultural products. This Greek commerce developed specialized farming, orchards, and vineyards; civilization flourished.

By 350 B.C. a local highly specialized agriculture had evolved in Greece. The products of the local regions were supplemented by food importations. With the decline of Athens and the Greek

Empire, food importations nearly ended, leaving a population dependent on specialized crops, creating food shortages in important items. What was available was inadequate to feed large numbers of people. Descendants still occupy this area, and many continue to consume the same types of diets that were enforced on the crumbling Greek Empire during its decline.

Development of Roman Agriculture and Its Decline

By the time of the Roman Empire, the production and preservation of many agricultural commodities were understood. Yet the poorer Romans were vegetarians, not by desire, but by position. Meat was expensive then, and now.

Roman trade involved every known food of the day and was also a "world" trade. Salted, pickled, and fresh fish, cured meats, fermented drinks, bakery products, condiments, fruits, and grains were items of commerce. Some 140,000,000 bushels of wheat were required annually for the 2,000,000 people of Rome. An estimated 50,000,000 bushels were imported! Cane sugar was even imported all the way from India.

Fish were kept live in ponds in Rome until eaten.

The nations touched by the Romans retained much of their technology. In addition, the Roman learned about the wearing of trousers, heating homes, using butter to replace olive oil, deep soil plowing, wooden barrels and the cultivation of new crops.

Food adulteration was a problem of which the Roman was also well aware. White clay was added to bread to increase its weight and deceive the buyer.

Legume Rotation Agriculture

At its peak, the naked-fallow system of farming, in certain areas of the Roman Empire, gave way to a legume rotation method of land improvement. The field that had been left unplanted in the naked-fallow method was planted either in part or in whole to legumes. The legumes include such plants as beans, peas, vetches, cow peas, chick peas, alfalfa, trefoil, and clover. Non-legumes include our cereal crops, grasses cut for greens, vegetables, fruit, and other plants.

An important point to consider is that the Greek Empire was built on trade for food produced in areas adjacent to rivers. These areas flooded, thereby increasing the fertility of the soils in the flooded areas. The Roman Empire was the beginning of basic foodstuff production away from river valleys, and this is the significance of the development of the legume rotation. The new Roman kind of agriculture did not rely solely on flooding to increase soil fertility.

Nitrogen is recognized now as a principal nutrient of plants, along with phosphorus, potassium and calcium. Legumes are plants that, in combination with bacteria, take nitrogen from the air and fix it in the soil in the form of nitrates which are usable by plants. Legumes can add nitrogen to soil; non-legumes consume nitrogen from soil. It is remarkable to find that the legume rotation was invented and practiced in selected parts of Italy and Greece, in the third century, A.D.

With the destruction of the Roman Empire in the Third Century, A.D., the civilized world, with its dependency for goods upon neighbors, became disrupted. The war invaders broke the political unity of the Roman Empire, precipitating the Dark Ages. With the fall of the Empire, the large agricultural holdings became the manors of Medieval Europe. Local famines developed due to the disappearance of food in world commerce, and severe nutritional deficiency diseases appeared. Only the stout peasantry of the North, which was not constantly oppressed, remained in reasonable health. The peasants of the north had grasslands and cattle, therefore had meat to eat.

Regression of Agriculture Following Fall of Rome

Agriculture returned to the naked-fallow system, and remained there for more than a thousand years. But the legume rotation was not lost to the world. The Church continued to practice the system in isolated areas of Spain, but the legume rotation did not come into widespread use again until the 17th Century, when it was introduced into England and the Low Lands by monks.

The legume rotation system of agriculture requires a high level of civilization to function. Every bit of vegetation must not be harvested if the fertility of a soil is to be improved or even maintained.

The legume rotation was successful, and following its rediscovery, it was widely used and helped nourish men after the Dark Ages.

Development of Grassland Agriculture

The next important stage in the development of food production practices is called grassland farming. This is an improvement over the legume rotation because all crops could be used either for food for animals or food for man. Land was alternately pastured and cropped. Large populations of animals could be cultured summer and winter. The soil was maintained and improved because legumes were a part of the new system, and all land was planted either to cereals or grasses, or legumes. Fruit and vegetable production could be substituted for cereals in one portion of the crop rotation. Grassland farming, as it is called, was operating in the 18th Century in Europe and America.

Scientific Crop Rotation

In the late 19th Century, new ideas were developed concerning the mineral nutrition of plants. With the turn of the 20th Century, two more improvements in food production evolved. These were systems of *scientific crop rotation* and *specialized intensive agriculture.*

In scientific crop rotation, crops were selected to bring about a series of desired results, one crop helping along the succeeding crop. For example, clover planted with wheat improves the soil (clover is a legume), improves the yield of the wheat crop, and after the wheat has been harvested, the land yields clover.

Carefully alternating crops improves the fertility of the soil, improves the ability of the soil to hold water, holds nutrients in the soil rather than allowing them to be washed away in rains, and reduces the incidence of weeds. This scientific rotation yields a maximum of food and a minimum loss in soil fertility and productive capacity. Supplemented with fertilizer, this land-use technology is in balance.

One of the famous crop rotations in England is clover, wheat, turnips, and barley. The most widespread rotation in the Corn Belt in the U. S. consists of clover (or other legumes), corn or soybeans, and wheat in a three-year rotation series. Peas, tomatoes, sweet corn, or any vegetable crop adapted to the region can be substituted for either corn or beans in this rotation.

Scientific crop rotation is the latest system or development in agriculture which can be called extensive farming.

Extensive farming is a condition where large areas of land are used to produce food with a small number of people. Intensive farming is a condition where plants are placed in rows and forced with fertilizer and water and labor to yield its greatest amount of crop.

In extensive farming the interest is in the volume of production of food per unit of labor. In intensive farming the interest is in the volume of production of food per unit of land.

Up to the scientific crop rotation system, agricultural history is a development of plant and animal cultivation. In natural husbandry, in the naked-fallow system, and in the legume rotation plants and animals met on the land. Animals were pastured on stubble remaining in the fields, and over harvested fields to recover grains left behind. In the grassland farming, plants then animals, alternately, used the soil. In the scientific crop rotation system, animals are removed from the fields, but their needs are carefully provided for. All these systems are extensive farming.

If the land is intensively farmed, enormous crop productions are possible, providing that the land-use technology is in balance. A balance of man, animals, plants, land, fertilizers, and water is required for greatest rewards. Furthermore, some land is best planted in grass for animal grazing; others are best adapted for timber production and/or water conservation.

Specialized Intensive Agriculture

In the latest and most productive farming system, animal and plant cultures are separated again. Land is used indefinitely for one purpose only. This specialization is in the form of one important crop, such as fresh vegetables, or fruit, or it may be a dairy farm, producing basically fluid milk or even corn alone. Specialization breaks agriculture into such things as horticulture, animal husbandry, poultry production, hog raising, milk production, and fiber production.

Specialization is the logical, ultimate development of agriculture. It requires a high level of civilization. Capital is required in large amounts for fertilizer, irrigation, farm machinery, seed, feed, and other necessities. Soil becomes increasingly more intensively worked, but enormous crop production is possible. Fertilizer type and its placement relative to the seed, soil pulverization, chemical weed control, cultivation, moisture control, and a host of considerations are necessary. As many as 1,000 bushels of potatoes per acre are harvested on peat soils in northern Indiana; 250 bushels of corn to the acre are possible there while the average in the country is less than 100 bushels. This is the potential of our modern agriculture.

Modern day agriculture is big business with heavy long and short term capital investments, technological improvements, mechanization, and decreasing man-hour requirements. The possibilities of intensive agriculture are tremendous, where these factors can be applied. However, the significance of this form of agriculture in providing the good food needs of all people must not be over-estimated.

SUMMARY

The civilization of modern man followed the discovery of how to produce food. Next, plants and animals were selected to fit human requirements and it was no doubt a paradise for a while. But, with the discovery of agriculture, a foundation for many more people was available; it was then inevitable that the number of people would increase, and it did. Then began the pressure of populations on food supplies which, with few exceptions, has yet to show signs of subsiding.

The plants and animals used for food and feed have been important from the beginning of civilization. Although each area on earth had its own native flora and fauna, eventually the important food sources were spread over the earth.

During the past 500 years, there have been many improvements in agricultural crops and practices, but modern man has not developed any major new food sources of any consequence. These activities have been essentially refinements of age old crops and systems. *This is a notable failure of present day man and no doubt has contributed to his present dilemma.*

Whereas men as nomads were mainly meat eaters, increasing population pressures on food supplies in civilized life forced large numbers of men to shift their diets to include the grains which were available. Then, they evolved cultural systems which eventually made the whole idea acceptable, and some of these ideas have been perpetuated ever since (i.e., living on boiled rice).

Measured by achievements, the greatest developments of men on Earth have been found in limited areas—in a band between the frozen tundra and the disease infested tropics. The Northern and

Southern Hemispheres apparently offered equal opportunities for advancement when agriculture was rewarding.

Whenever a dynamic civilization developed, foodstuffs were abundant; food storage from one harvest to the next, and food distribution from areas of surplus to areas of shortage played no small role in keeping and spreading civilization.

In prehistoric times it is estimated that more than 10,000 acres of land were available to yield the food needs of one man. As the qualities we term humanistic became dominant, man began to focus some of his talents on a steady food supply. Slowly he evolved a technology of food production which yielded increasing food supplies, and the land requirements to feed a person gradually dropped to 1,000, to 100, 10 and to one acre of land, providing the technology available were applied and the land were responsive to the treatments. But this change in the land requirement to feed one person was forced by the increasing human populations. Eventually population pressures on food supplies overran the ability of land in an area to yield more food and some of the people migrated. The pressure of populations on food supplies continues to this day, but now most of the good land has been settled. It is therefore of some significance to explore the nature of the world's land resources to see what is available and how far present technology could be extended.

Easing the pressure now might demand a different approach.

CHAPTER 6

The World's Agricultural Land Resources

What is the nature of, and what are the limits of, the world's land resources from the viewpoint of food production? This chapter attempts to answer these questions. Toward this end, the chapter is divided into three sections. The first deals with the nature of land, soils and soil productivity. The next section focuses on soils as the key to possibilities in food production. The third section deals with the unexploited land resources that could be used for food production.

LAND, SOILS, AND PRODUCTIVITY

The surface of this planet has an area of about 197 million square miles, of which slightly less than 30 per cent is occupied by land masses. The general distribution of this land in square miles is shown in Table 3.

The uses of land in a number of selected countries are shown in Table 4. There is obviously a wide range in the amount of arable land per person in various countries, and also a wide range in the productive capacities of the arable land available which such tabulations do not indicate.

Land means many things to many people. To the farmer it is the basis of a livelihood. To the city dweller it may be a space or place to build a house, or a recreation ground. To all of us it is that soil beneath our feet, which contributes in more than one way towards the satisfaction of human needs.

Two hundred generations of men have contributed all that is known about land and its ability to produce food. It is widely recognized at present that there is a need for the management of land resources in order to meet the food needs of mankind as well as satisfy other human needs in living. The uses of land should in all ways attempt to conserve and to improve it in order to meet the human needs of tomorrow.

Climate, surface characteristics and soil quality are major factors which influence the land's potential utility. Climate is a critical factor, because temperature and water supplies influence the uses to

59

TABLE 3

WORLD LAND AREA[1] (INCLUDES WATER SYSTEMS WITHIN CONTINENTAL LIMITS)

Western Hemisphere		16,000,000
North America	9,000,000	
South America	7,000,000	
Eastern Hemisphere		35,500,000
Europe	4,000,000	
Asia	16,000,000	
Africa	11,500,000	
Oceania	4,000,000	
Antarctica		5,000,000
Total		56,500,000

[1] From Jones (1941).

which land can be put. The uses and management of land profoundly influences the lives of men who occupy it.

Land resources are not inexhaustible, and sufficient land to satisfy the needs of all in terms of their varied desires for land usage is not available. It is important therefore that the land resource available be employed with care and skill, giving due consideration to the greatest amount of good which can be obtained from its adequate use and management.

Relative to food production to meet the needs of an ever growing population on earth, the component of all land surface of significance is soil. Soil is a continuous cover over the land surfaces of the earth, except for those steep slopes or rugged mountain peaks, or under perpetual snow and ice. Soil is related to the earth as the peel is related

TABLE 4

LAND USES IN SELECTED COUNTRIES[1]

Country	Arable Land[2]		Pasture and Woodland[3]		Forest Land		Other Land[4]	
	Per Cent	Acres per Capita	Per Cent	Acres per Capita	Per Cent	Acres per Capita	Per Cent	Acres per Capita
United States[4]..	23.0	2.68	36.0	4.22	23.0	2.68	18.0	2.11
British Isles ...	29.2	0.42	47.8	0.69	4.6	0.07	18.4	0.26
France	38.0	1.20	22.5	0.71	20.0	0.63	19.5	0.61
Germany ...	38.5	0.48	20.0	0.25	28.0	0.35	13.5	0.17
Japan.........	16.0	0.17	2.5	0.02	66.5	0.69	15.0	0.16
China.........	9.5	0.50	20.0	1.05	8.5	0.45	62.0	3.27
India	38.5	0.82	0.0	0.00	12.5	0.27	49.0	1.07
Canada	3.5	5.74	2.5	4.15	35.0	57.60	59.0	96.76
Soviet Union...	10.0	2.59	5.5	1.43	28.0	7.29	56.5	14.60

[1] From: Huberty and Flock (1959).
[2] Fit for tillage.
[3] Woodland usually grazed.
[4] Including urban, roads, railroads, waste, etc.
[5] Figures for United States do not include Alaska.

to the potato or an orange. The outer covering of the earth however, is far less uniform than these peels. Soils vary in quality and in quantity, and the differences found on earth are significant.

Land can obviously make a bigger contribution to the welfare of the human beings in the future than it has in the past, providing that we take advantage of the knowledge that is available and give care in the management of the resources available.

In reviewing the land resources of the world, primary emphasis will be given in this book to that land that can produce abundant plant materials and from which food and agriculture have or can evolve productively and usefully.

Because soil must have water available in it to be useful in agriculture, the value of land depends directly on the availability of water. The subject of the water resources of the world will be undertaken mainly in a subsequent chapter. The purpose of this chapter on the world's land resources is to explore land as the key to food production.

What Is Soil?

The land surface of this planet is almost entirely covered wth a fine loose material that has been formed by the breaking down of rocks. This material varies in thickness from a few inches to several hundred feet. Only a few feet of this surface layer has been acted upon by organisms. The surface layer in which the remains of animals and plants are found is called soil. Soils vary in quality, quantity and utility. Plants are adapted to and nourished by these soils.

Nutrient Needs of Plants From Soil

The amount of plant nutrients drawn from soil in the production of some major crops is shown in Table 5. Crops generally vary in the amounts of nutrients required for optimum growth but not in the kinds of nutrients required. In general the nutrient needs of plants are considerably smaller than might be supposed. At the most, plants contain a few per cent of minerals.

Building Soil in Nature

There are generally three classes of rock from which soils are made: (1) *igneous*—those rocks formed through the agency of heat (granite); (2) *sedimentary*—those rocks formed through the agency of water (limestones, sandstones and shales); (3) *metamorphic*—those rocks formed by the combined action of both these agencies and pressures (marble from limestone and slate from shale). There are many kinds of rocks included in these classes and each produces a distinct soil by decomposition. One rock can form different soils depending on where located, however.

When the decomposed rock remains in place it is called a residue and the soil formed is a residual soil. In swampy areas the partly decomposed mosses and grasses accumulate in quantities and soils will be formed largely from them. These would include *peaty swamp soils*. Soils formed in shallow sea water along the coasts are *Marsh soils* while those in fresh water are *swamp soils*.

TABLE 5

POUNDS OF ELEMENTS[1] IN 1000 POUNDS OF PLANT MATERIALS[2]

Materials	N	K	Ca	Mg	S	P	Ash
Corn	13.9	3.40	0.12	1.08	1.47	2.60	12.1
Oats	17.4	4.19	1.02	1.18	1.95	3.95	33.8
Wheat	16.5	5.20	0.50	1.30	1.98	3.73	16.4
Soybeans	63.1	19.13	2.10	2.23	4.06	5.92	50.6
Corn stover	8.8	17.18	4.72	0.86	1.74	0.95	65.2
Wheat straw	2.8	7.96	2.05	0.60	1.50	0.36	34.5
Clover hay	20.8	17.01	11.42	2.70	1.76	1.69	67.6
Bluegrass hay	14.6	12.90	3.08	2.20	3.07	2.22	48.2
Apples	0.4	1.18	0.04	0.05	0.06	0.09	2.7
Potatoes	3.3	2.72	0.05	0.58	0.25	0.47	6.7
Onions	2.6	1.83	0.33	0.17	0.76	0.41	5.5
Cabbage	1.9	1.73	0.41	0.15	0.63	0.18	5.0
Wheat bran	25.2	13.20	1.25	5.31	2.67	11.10	60.6
Cottonseed meal	57.4	16.56	2.66	5.48	4.90	13.52	69.8

[1] From Bear (1953).
[2] $K \times 1.2 = K_2O$; $Ca \times 1.4 = CaO$; $Mg \times 1.7 = MgO$; $S \times 2.5 = SO_3$; $P \times 2.3 = P_2O_5$.

The material formed in the breakdown of rocks may be carried to great distances from their place of origin, or the weathered and loosened particles may be carried downward from cliffs, for example, forming a soil slope.

Soils are also formed from sediment carried and deposited by water, and those deposited by glacial movements.

Rocks disintegrate slowly under the influence of climatic factors such as the sunlight, rain, freezing, and wind. Freezing and thawing, heating and cooling, and wetting and drying, all tend to weaken the structure of rock. There is also some interaction between water, air, and minerals in the rock. Such changes are important in weakening rock structures. Gradually they disintegrate and decay; the weathered material loosens and becomes a component of the soil. The parent material for soil is therefore disintegrated rock in one form or another. Regolith is the term applied to this component of the surface of the earth. The regolith may be moved by water, wind, and combinations of both.

The sequence of plant growth in the regolith can be as follows: The first invaders are lichens. Bacteria and fungi are also early invaders, followed by more complex plants. Small microscopic animals then become a part of the new biological community. These organisms rise and fall in numbers, grow and die, and the bodies which are left become a part of the soil's organic matter. Higher plant components also decay and add to the organic matter present in the surface layer. The organic matter component of the surface layers is usually present in greater quantities than is found in the deeper layers (U. S. Dept. Agr. 1957, 1958).

Kinds of Soil

The soils of the world fall into broad groupings. These are indicated generally in a map of the world in Figure 1. Each zone obviously has several or many sub-types of soil present, and the various soil groupings found around the world can be subdivided into thousands of types (U. S. Dept. Agr. 1958).

The six general types may be considered as follows. The first type consists of the mountains and similar country side where stony shallow soils are found, with large variations. The second is the tundra. The tundra regions due to the cold climate, have restricted biological activity. The regolith is permanently frozen at some depth below the surface. Yet, soils which have good drainage in the tundra may be as productive as those of the podzolic soils, which compose the third type. The podzolic soils are the important soils of the higher latitudes of the Northern Hemisphere and occur also in smaller areas in the southern half of the world. The soils of this group were formed under forest vegetation and humid temperate climates. These soils have been strongly weathered and leached through time. They are commonly acid, low in calcium content, and low in organic matter. Fertility is moderate to low. Moisture holding capacity is variable, depending on the soil depth and soil texture. These soils however are responsive to the management techniques of modern agriculture.

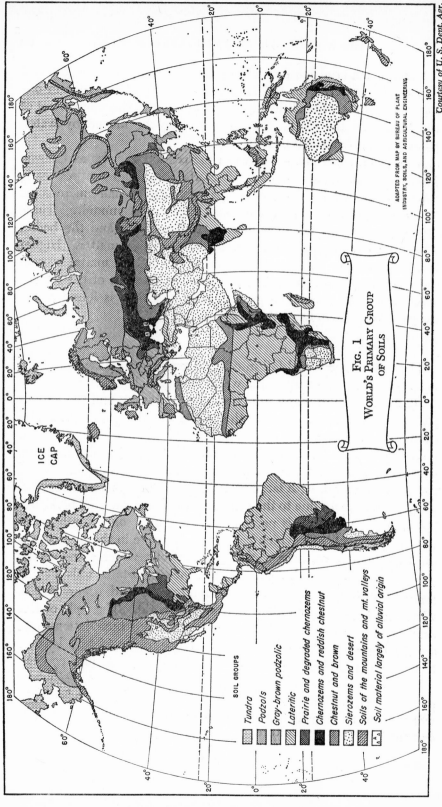

SOIL GROUPS

- Tundra
- Podzols
- Gray-brown podzolic
- Lateritic
- Prairie and degraded chernozems
- Chernozems and reddish chestnut
- Chestnut and brown
- Sierozems and desert
- Soils of the mountains and mt. valleys
- Soil material largely of alluvial origin

FIG. 1
WORLD'S PRIMARY GROUP
OF SOILS

ICE CAP

ADAPTED FROM MAP BY BUREAU OF PLANT
INDUSTRY, SOILS, AND AGRICULTURAL ENGINEERING

Laterite soils are the fourth type and are found to dominate the equatorial belts of Africa and South America, southeastern parts of Asia and North America, Northeastern Australia and the larger islands of the western Pacific Ocean. While the podzolic soils are generally brown, gray-brown and gray in color, soils of the laterite type are reddish brown, yellowish-brown, and reddish-yellow. These soils have been found to be formed under forest and vegetation conditions in tropical and sub-tropical, humid to fairly dry climates. These soils are not found in arid regions but are found in those which may be alternately wet and dry, due to local climatic conditions. The soils are strongly weathered and leached, usually to great depths. It is thought that these are the world's most weathered soils. The soil color comes from its large content of iron, aluminum and magnesium oxides. The mineral nutrients required for plant growth are normally low in supply. Water penetrates easily yet the soils are rather resistant to erosion, as roots easily penetrate and tend to hold the soil. In southern Brazil, roots of trees have been found to penetrate to sixty feet. The productivity of these soils is low unless combined with modern scientific agricultural practices.

Chernozemic soils are the fifth type and are formed under grassland vegetation conditions, in humid to semi-arid, and temperate to tropical climate. These are the soils found most extensively in the temperate zones, and also in some areas in the tropics. These soils are usually fertile and only slightly weathered. In temperate zones these soils are high in organic matter and nitrogen content. In tropical and sub-tropical areas this is not the case. These soils are less acid and higher in plant nutrients generally than the other four soils discussed above. The moisture holding capacities of this type are usually moderate to high, and they are the most fertile soils in the world, under natural conditions. About 90 per cent of the grains found in commerce are produced on such soil (i.e., the corn and the wheat producing zones). The management and working of chernozemic soils in tropical and sub-tropical areas is difficult. These soils are subject to shrinkage and swelling, and, when used without the technology of modern agriculture, their productivity is low.

Desert soils are the sixth type that have been formed; these support mixed grass and shrub vegetation in arid areas of the world when moisture is available. The deserts in Africa, Asia, Australia and the small ones from North and South America are of this type.

This soil is usually red or reddish-brown. In addition to the desert soils, the deserts of the world contain huge quantities of sand and rock land which lack agricultural possibilities.

Desert soils are usually leached, but due to the absence of moisture in these areas, the soil has not been weathered. Due to this limited water condition, plant growth has been limited, resulting in low organic matter contents in these soils, and the top soil may be quite shallow. These soils respond to agricultural management with good productivity, for example, those in California (Huberty and Flock 1959).

The range of possibilities for food production is restricted also due to the topographical characteristics of the soil. Steep slopes may produce some forest growths, but are not particularly suited for pasture or crops. On the other hand, some soils have a wide range in use and management potential.

Function of Organic Matter

The dry matter in soil is composed of two components, one, the organic matter, and two, the inorganic matter. The organic matter is produced by living organisms and is composed of many carbon compounds. In soils, this organic matter is mixed with the inorganic constituents which were derived from rocks and their decomposition. One of the benefits conferred to a soil by its organic matter is due to its decomposition and the release of simple compounds which are then useful to subsequent plant growth. Another function of the organic matter in soils is that it improves the physical characteristics of the soil, by making it easier to work and easier for plants to grow. Organic matter also improves the colloidal properties of soils, which permits the holding of water and nutrients, adds buffering power against toxic levels of nutrients, and feeds micro-organisms.

Farmers have long been aware of the importance of soil organic matter, and no doubt saw that when manure was turned under the soil, the manure decomposed quickly. One of the keys in the management of soils is to control organic matter and its decomposition so that desired by-products from the decomposition are obtained.

Soil Fertility

The nutrient supplying power of a soil is called its fertility and involves the amount and availability of plant nutrients. The maintenance of soil fertility is concerned with adjusting the supply of available nutrients to optimum levels for economic crop production.

The inherent fertility of a soil is related to factors operating during its formation. The fertility of virgin soils, i.e., soil that has been undisturbed, reaches an equilibrium so that the nutrients added approximately equals those which are lost. The fertility of soils, which vary greatly, may become depleted when brought under cultivation, through crop removal and by leaching and erosion (see Fig. 2). Nutrient losses may be replaced by adding fertilizers and manures. Nitrogen levels may be increased also by the use of leguminous crops, providing nitrogen-fixing bacteria are present.

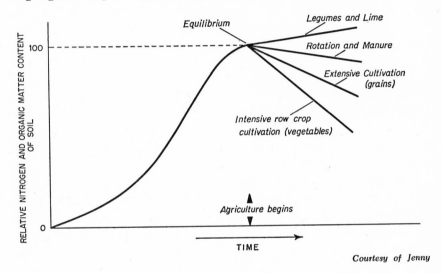

Courtesy of Jenny

Fig. 2. Natural Build-up of Soil Fertility and its Modification by Agricultural Practices

An important aspect of soil fertility is the acidity of the soil. This is so essential to nutrient availability and root growth that it is of prime concern in soil management. While plants vary in their response to pH, most crops do best with pH values near 6.5. A group of acid-loving plants does occur, which includes blueberries.

The natural reaction of soils is due to the interaction of climate with the parental materials of the soil. In general, soils are acid where the precipitation is high enough to reach appreciable amounts of exchangeable bases from the surface layers of soil. Thus, in humid climates (the areas of most intense agriculture), soil becomes more acid and may limit crop production. Soil alkalinity occurs generally in the more arid regions where there is a comparatively high degree of base accumulation. Alkaline soils are a problem also in the irrigated areas.

Soils become acid because the basic cations on the soil colloids are replaced by hydrogen ions. This process can be reversed and the soil pH increased by the addition of basic cations, i.e., calcium and magnesium. Calcium is the most economical cation to use to increase soil pH. In addition, calcium has other benefits that are essential for plant nutrition; it promotes good soil structure through granulation of the soil, and encourages certain soil organisms, especially the nitrifying and nitrogen-fixing bacteria.

The addition of calcium compounds to reduce the acidity of the soil is known as liming. While lime refers to CaO, the term is used in agriculture to include oxides, hydroxides, bicarbonates and silicates of calcium or calcium and magnesium. Liming of soils has resulted in significant increases in soil productivity.

The amount of liming required depends on the degree of pH change desired, the base exchange capacity of the soil, the amount of precipitation, and the liming material and its physical form in relation to particle size.

Soil may be made more acid by replacing hydrogen ions on the soil colloid. This can be done by adding substances that tend to produce strong acids in the soil. While nitrogen fertilizers tend to increase soil acidity, elemental sulfur is the most effective substance. It converts to sulfuric acid in warm, moist, well-aerated soils by bacterial action.

Food production in regions where rainfall is adequate (or irrigation water is available) can be limited by the amount of nitrogen present in the soil more often than not. Improved agricultural methods and better crop varieties are demanding more and more nitrogenous fertilizer applications. Because of heavy cultivation over many hundreds of years, many soils are low in their native nitrogen supply. Replenishment solely through the biological cycle is slow. Soils seldom can meet the increased demand placed on them by modern intensive agricultural methods.

Soil management is of special importance because plants need nutrients in large quantities. Potassium and phosphorus and the trace elements required by plants in growth must also be supplied and kept in balance with the total nutrient supply and demands of the plants under cultivation.

Because the air is approximately four-fifths nitrogen, it is estimated that approximately 35 thousand tons of nitrogen exists in the atmosphere above every acre of land. The supply is inexhaustible because nitrogen is constantly being returned to the atmosphere through the nitrogen cycle.

Some nitrogen in the air is fixed by lightning, during which oxygen and nitrogen are combined to form oxides of nitrogen, subsequently to be washed from the air by rain or snow and deposited on soil. This source of nitrogen for the soil is not large, amounting to perhaps two pounds per acre per year (U. S. Dept Agr., 1957).

Nitrogen fixations through the agency of plants in the soil is nature's principle method of fixing nitrogen from the air. Legumes may fix as much as 200 pounds of nitrogen per acre per year under suitable conditions. An average value is 20 pounds per year or less, depending upon the kind of legume employed, and the quality of the soil. The amount of nitrogen fixed in nitrogen deficient soils follows very closely the photosynthetic activity of plants growing on the soil. The soils with the least supply became increasingly poorer without good soil management techniques. The soils in the areas with the greatest concentration of people in Asia are some of the poorest. These could be improved by fertilizer applications combined with good soil management practices. Nitrogen is often the limiting factor. (U. S. Dept. Agr., 1957.)

Large quantities of nitrogen are fixed by industrial processes. Synthesis of ammonia in which nitrogen and hydrogen gases are combined under pressure in the presence of a catalyst constitutes the main source of nitrogen used in agriculture in industrial nations. This ammonia can be applied in the form of ammonia or ammonium salts. In the United States the production of ammonia for this purpose has expanded from 1.8 million tons in 1951 to 4.1 million tons in 1956. Nitrate of soda from Chile, formerly the world's leading source of nitrogen fertilizers, in the present day has to compete with synthetic fertilizer production.

Insofar as managing soils is concerned, the U. S. Department of Agriculture recommends first that soil should be managed to yield the greatest fertility possible, and second, supplementary additions of commercial fertilizers should be undertaken to maximize crop growth.

How Productive Is the Soil and How Good Is the Soil?

In general it is possible to tell if the soil is deficient by the health and vigor of the plants which grow in it. Knowledge of the soil and the nutrient requirements of the crop being grown are essential. There is adequate knowledge of both of these by soil scientists in the world to make gigantic strides in improving the productivity of soils. Again, the people who need the most help are least able to help themselves. Tests of the nutrient availability in soils can be used to predict the amount of plant growth which can be anticipated. The effectiveness of adding fertilizer to a soil can be measured in terms of the crop response.

Crop responses are limited also by environmental factors, particularly the kind of soil, the climate, and the water supply. Farming is a regional affair because these conditions must be accepted as they are, for the most part.

Plant responses in a soil are influenced by cultural practices which would include the kind of crop grown, the crop rotation system employed, the kind and amount of fertilizer used, its placement in the soil, and the time of its application. The effectiveness of fertilizer application is dependent not only on the nature of the fertilizer added but also on where it is placed in the soil and the way it is used.

Successful application of fertilizers in crop production can not only increase the yield of the crop but also maintain and improve the soil itself. The kind of crop under consideration determines how much nutrients will be used. One crop may use more of one nutrient than another to produce a yield in a soil. Obviously more of this nutrient must be supplied to the plants for their growth. Crops use only a part of the nutrients available in the soil each year. Many of the food crops will recover between 20 and 70 per cent of the nitrogenous fertilizer that is applied to the field. Recovery of phosphorus fertilizer is more slow and is thought to be about 10 per cent per year. Potassium, another important soil nutrient, is in the intermediate position (Bear 1953).

Farm manure is an important by-product where livestock populations occur. In the United States, for example, each year approximately a billion tons of manure are produced annually on farms and added to the soils. Manure helps to maintain the soil, improves its nutrient content, and adds to the organic matter. However, in industrialized nations, manure is no longer an economical fertilizer.

A ton of manure contains about 10 lbs. of nitrogen, seven pounds of phosphate, and four pounds of potash and is worth about two dollars a ton. A ton of 12-12-12 fertilizer contains 240 lbs. of each of these nutrients and is worth about 70 dollars a ton (Tukey 1960).

Caring for Soil for Food Production

Soils are tilled for three reasons: one, to prepare a suitable bed for the seed; two, to kill the weeds which are growing; and three, to manage last year's crop residue (U. S. Dept. Agr., 1957).

Weed control is necessary to eliminate competition for water, nutrients, and sunlight. Management of residues from previous crop growths is necessary to provide suitable conditions for seeding and managing the following crop.

Plowing is the method employed to break land. The loosening and granulation actions of plowing improved soils structurally, if the plowing is done when the soil is workable (good moisture content level). Deep plowing may be used to improve soil structures, especially during flooding, when the top layer of soil may contain much sand and clay, and also for insect, disease and nematode control, and mixing fertilizer into the lower depths of the soil (Bear 1953).

Soil Losses on Slopes

A major undertaking in soil management practices is to protect soil from erosion. Erosion is slow in soils that are covered with grass and trees. Very little, if any, loss occurs in woodland soils, for example, which are adequately covered. Fields which are cropped annually and not covered may lose an inch of top soil in a few years.

Tillage methods, as well as the type of crops grown, affect the soil condition, therefore influence the run-off of excess waters and erosion of soil. Some of the newer methods that have been found include mulching, contour tillage, waterway construction for sloping lands to channel the water without erosion of soil surfaces, and strip cropping has been used for centuries to protect cultivated land against erosion.

The conservation of the top fertile soils is a major problem. The losses that can be anticipated from soils on slopes of various degrees

TABLE 6

AVERAGE ANNUAL SOIL LOSSES IN TONS PER ACRE A YEAR[1], USING A ROTATION OF R—O—H[2]

Slope Per cent	No Practices				Contouring				Stripcropping				Terracing
	100'	200'	300'	400'	100'	200'	300'	400'	100'	200'	300'	400'	
2	1.7	2.4	3.0	3.4	1.0	1.4	1.7	2.0	0.5	0.7	0.9	1.0	0.6
4	3.3	4.6	5.7	6.6	1.7	2.3	2.9	3.3	0.8	1.2	1.4	1.7	0.8
6	5.3	7.6	9.3	10.7	2.7	3.8	4.7	5.4	1.3	1.4	2.3	2.7	1.2
8	8.0	11.2	13.7	15.8	4.7	6.7	8.2	9.5	2.4	3.4	4.1	4.7	2.0
10	11.0	15.5	19.0	22.0	6.5	9.3	11.3	13.1	3.3	4.7	5.7	6.6	2.7
12	14.5	20.5	25.0	29.0	8.7	12.3	15.0	17.3	4.4	6.2	7.5	8.7	3.5
14	18.5	26.0	32.0	37.0	14.8	21.0	25.5	30.0	5.5	7.3	9.1	10.5	..
16	23.0	32.0	40.0	46.0	18.0	26.0	32.0	37.0	6.7	9.5	11.0	13.0	..

[1] From U. S. Dept. Agr. (1957). R—corn, O—spring grain, H—hay.

of incline are shown in Table 6. The effectiveness of various soil management techniques is also clearly indicated.

Insect and Disease Control in Soils

Important considerations in soil management are the control of insects and plant diseases. Insects and plant diseases may completely frustrate our attempts to obtain good yields of crops from fertile soils. The same applies to nematodes.

Crop varieties resistant to these agents, tillage, time of planting, fertilization, irrigation, crop rotations, field sanitation and the applications of insecticides and fungicides are important in controlling insects and disease organisms in soils. The availability of insecticides and fungicides improves our ability to effect a widespread control over insects and soil pests.

Adequate knowledge exists for the control of these crop damaging entities, and a discussion on these subjects can not be undertaken here. The reader is directed to cited references (Bear 1953; Bailey 1951; Leach 1940; Martin 1953; U. S. Dept. Agr., 1952, 1953).

KEY TO FOOD PRODUCTION AREAS

The key to food production is vegetation. The potential of the earth's surface to produce food is tied in part to the type of vegetation than can grow in a particular area. There is a natural distribution of vegetation on earth which gives a key to the potential uses of areas for food production (see Fig. 3).

Tundra

Starting in higher latitudes, the tundra (and high mountains) is limited in food production potential for reason of climate. These

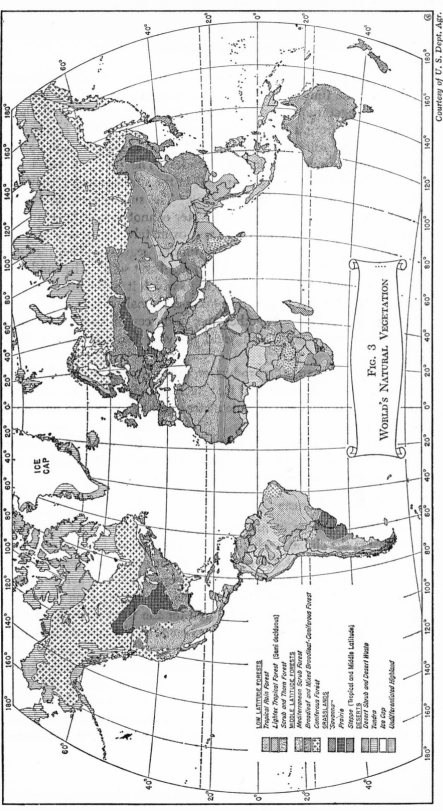

LOW LATITUDE FORESTS
Tropical Rain Forest
Lighter Tropical Forest (Semi deciduous)
Scrub and Thorn Forest
MIDDLE LATITUDE FORESTS
Mediterranean Scrub Forest
Broadleaf and Mixed Broadleaf-Coniferous Forest
Coniferous Forest
GRASSLANDS
Savanna
Prairie
Steppe (Tropical and Middle Latitude)
DESERTS
Desert Shrub and Desert Waste
Tundra
Ice Cap
Undifferentiated Highland

FIG. 3
WORLD'S NATURAL VEGETATION

Courtesy of U. S. Dept. Agr.

areas form a broad band across the northern parts of Asia and North America. The tundras lie beyond the temperature limit for growth of trees. Vegetation consists mainly of lichens, mosses and short grasses. The ground is often swampy. Freezing injury breaks the structure of the soil in much the same fashion as does frost in poorly constructed highways at lower latitudes. The pores or small depressions in the tundra which are left in the surface during thawing trap and hold water much of the time. The subsoil remains frozen during the summer, hence ground water cannot escape by evaporation. Rain and snow contribute approximately ten inches of precipitation a year in much of the tundra regions. The rainfall, although generally low, is sufficient to yield wet soils. The tundra is wet during most of the 2 to 4 months in which it is not frozen at the surface. Vegetation is scant, yet some animals are found in the more grassy regions. Together the resources of the tundra and high mountainous areas can yield a living for very few people (Fig. 3).

The secret to good crop production in the tundra is annual fertilization. The climate is so cold that bacterial action in the soil is too slow to break down dead organic matter, and hence release nutrients for plant growth.

The tundra can be made productive by the applications of a nitrate as fertilizer and the adaptation of crops to the cold soil, for example, plants having a low phosphorus demand.

Cool Coniferous Forests

Cone bearing trees including furs, pines, spruces, and hemlocks grow best in the climates where there is a long snow filled winter and a cool humid summer. The main part of the coniferous forest belt is north of the limit of agricultural activity generally. The average temperatures may be 55°F. or lower and the winters are long and cold. There is no demand for heavy rainfall for the tree's growth. However, precipitation in these areas does come in the summer when it is useful for vegetation especially in the interior sections of a continent. In Norway and Chile for example, on westward facing slopes near oceans, the mild winters and heavy rainfalls, due to the west winds from the ocean, result in increased sizes of trees. This is important in the Pacific coast area of North America from Alaska down through British Columbia to Northern California. In the southern half of this area, trees are enormous in size. The gaint sequoias and redwoods in Northern California are examples. An interesting observation made by the Canadian Forest Service is that there is less timber fit for sawing in all of Canada than in the state of Oregon in the United States. Most of the good Canadian timber land is in British Columbia.

Cool coniferous forests are generally found in climates close to or beyond the limits of adaptability to agricultural purposes (Jenny 1959; Huntington 1940).

From the standpoint of use in food production the cool coniferous forests rank low, although agriculture can be undertaken in the southern margins of these areas. They are at the upper limit for growth of wheat, oats, and potatoes. There are areas in Canada and in the USSR thousands of miles long and hundreds of miles wide that are of this type of soil and vegetation (Fig. 3).

The Temperate Deciduous Forest

Given an imaginary continent, extending from the North Pole to the Equator and without mountains, a general scheme of vegetation types to be found can be outlined. Starting with the tundra at the north and passing south through the coniferous forests, both sides and the center of this imaginary continent will have different types of vegetation (Huntington 1940; Jones 1941).

Along the coastal areas the coniferous forests become mixed with broad-leafed deciduous trees including maple, elm, oak, ash, and beech. (Deciduous trees are those which shed their leaves in the fall.) Proceeding further south, the conifers disappear and deciduous trees become more dominant. *Agriculture is most highly developed in the areas of mixed and deciduous forests.* Climatically this is an area within which a large variety of plants and animals can successfully pass through their life cycles. The useful grains including corn and wheat, fruits including apples and pears, and vegetables including potatoes and beans, grow best in this region. Cattle and poultry thrive well. The climate is intermediate between cool and cold winters, and the summers are warm enough to encourage the growth of plants and crops. Rainfall is adequate throughout the year and crops are not limited generally by this factor. When the trees are cleared from the land in this area, a rich soil is generally found, shown in Fig. 3.

The Mediterranean Dry Forest

On the west side of this imaginary continent, the broad-leaved forest growths familiar in Western Europe do not continue as far south as they do on the east side of the continent. The climate closely resembles that found in the Mediterranean area in Europe. Winters are rainy and moderately cool and the summers are hot and dry. Southern California along the coast is somewhat different than this due to the influence of the Pacific Ocean. Two general types of vegetation are found in Mediterranean type regions. One, a bushy vegetation and the other, an open forest. Bush-type growths cover the dry slopes. In the older part of Western Europe, ancient forests have been cut and bushy growths have taken over. Trees from this type of area grow roots to great depths in search of water in the dry summers. Olive trees are common. The Mediterranean-type of vegetation is found in Southern California east of the Sierra Nevada Mountains and extends up into the Sacramento Valley area. The agricultural products of such an area are more numerous than areas of mixed and deciduous forests. Some crops, including potatoes, apples and oats do not give good yields in the regions of ordinary mixed forests. Grapes, oranges and walnuts, however, are at their optimum in such regions. The major areas in the world of Meriterranean-type dry forest is found in areas of California, South Australia, Italy and the region surrounding the Mediterranean Sea, areas in Chile and South Africa (see Fig. 3).

Interior Grassland

In the center of the imaginary continent, the cool coniferous forests are bordered on the Southern edge by prairie lands instead of a belt of mixed forests. In the prairie area, grass will grow tall and thick, often more than two feet high. Agricultural activity can be undertaken with good success (Jones 1941).

Generally grasslands replace forests in the interiors of continents because of the unreliability of rainfall in the spring and winter. Short grasses replace the longer prairie grasses. As we progress further south in the interior of the continent, dryness becomes a more important factor. In some areas, prairies yield to steppes. In the steppe we find short grass often six inches high or less, growing in bunches instead of forming a thick turf. Agricultural activity in steppes is hazardous. There is an abundant yield potential in one year and little in another because of drought. The prairies and forest areas are seen in Fig. 3. The dry western plains are the American steppes and contain typical short grass in bunches.

Deserts

Moving further south in the interior of a large continent, deserts are found in latitudes where Mediterranean type growths occur along coastal areas. Such deserts occur here because high mountains along a coast cut off the moisture potential of westerly winds. When this happens, Mediterranean type soil and vegetation can be changed into a desert type.

In the desert, three types of vegetation are found. One consists of grasses and flowering plants that require but a few weeks to grow after one of the infrequent rains which will occur during the growing season. This water will dry quickly and disappear. With heavy rain, a desert may take on the appearance of a well-managed meadow and flower garden.

The second type of vegetation found in the desert is a bushy growth including cactus and sagebrush. The leaves are thick and thereby have some protection against drought.

The third type of vegetation found in deserts is something like that found in the prairie and in forests. When underground water supplies approach the surface a prairie-like grass may grow. If the water supply is continuous for a sufficient time trees may appear. Vegetation in desert areas is thought to be more varied on the whole than that of other regions in the same latitude. Desert type soils are found not only in the interior of continents but also on the west coasts of continents at latitudes of 20 to 30 degrees. In a subtropical belt a permanently high atmospheric pressure system may produce deserts and vegetative growths much like a desert located in the interior of a continent. Irrigation is required in these areas for crop production. Some deserts have been brought into cultivation, for example, the Imperial Valley in California. Nevertheless, on the whole, deserts have not made an important contribution in supplying products to the world.

Tropical Vegetation from Desert to Selva

Continuing south on the imaginary continent, the sub-tropical deserts in latitudes of 20 to 30 degrees yield to savanna on their

eastern margins and approaching the equator. The savannas pass
from a scrub forest growth to some kind of rain forest. All of these
growths near the equator are relatively useless to man at the present
time. Although they have an abundant vegetation, there is a scarce
population, the areas are very large, and the poverty of the inhabitants of these areas is wide-spread. Up until the present, man has
been unable to meet the challenge of this area (Huntington 1940).

Tropical vegetation is wide-spread in the southern continents of
the earth. Africa has the largest such development. Huntington
has reported that the following transition from the Sahara Desert to
the forests of Central Africa along the Nile valley. Starting at the
mouth of the muddy Nile, traveling south from Egypt one passes
through a desert country with a sandy, rocky landscape. Occasionally some tufts of grass and small bushes break the monotony of the
sand and rock landscape. The desert comes to an end at about 15½
degrees North latitude. A short rainy season is found at this latitude
beginning in July and yields about five inches of rain in a ten week
period. Rain occurs during a hot season when the temperature
averages approximately 90°F. To the south, the rainfall increases
and tropical steppes with short grass extend nearly across Africa
from east to west yielding a grazing ground for animals such as the
camel and the donkey and supporting some cattle. Passing south-
ward toward the equator, there is an increase in the amount of rainfall. The wet season ranges from 2½ months to 12 months. Rainfall ranges from 4 inches to 58 inches. Vegetation changes from desert type to short grasses, then to tall grasses then to grasses with
trees. The next stage is a jungle forest, then the equatorial forest or
selva, approaching the equator itself.

From bare desert where no vegetation is found, going toward the
equator, there is an increase in the size of vegetation found from an
inch or two high grass to equatorial forest trees ranging from 100 to
200 feet in height.

Where the season in tropical scrub forests is dry, grasses turn
brown and the soil dusty and dry. These forests occupy a larger
area of land than other tropical types. In Africa they are widespread
on both sides of the equator. In South America they comprise a
huge central area in Brazil. In Australia they cover the least-de-
veloped Northern part of the country. In Asia and North America
these are relatively unimportant except in the central part of India

where the trees commonly have an umbrella shape. In the wet season there is good growth of grasses. Heavy showers daily swell
the streams and muddy the soil. Travel is made difficult. At the
end of the dry season, grasses turn brown and have a burned appearance. Most of the trees are bare. The grass becomes as stiff and
coarse as dried corn stalks. The vegetation has been of little value
in food production (Huntington 1940).

In the interior of India, agriculture has been carried on where
tropical scrub forests once existed. The length and severity of the
rainy season in this region makes crop production risky. The possibilities of the grassland of the Savanna and scrub forest areas have
not been fully utilized at present.

Tropical jungles are found at low altitudes near the equator,
normally getting large amounts of rain. Long dry seasons do not
exist which would give rise to the tropical scrub forest. Rain in
tropical jungle areas is brought by the trade winds, which come from
the northeast in the Northern Hemisphere, bringing airs laden with
moisture from the sea to the area marked with jungle forest. When
a dry season in low latitudes does not exist, a rain forest develops.
One of the characteristics of a tropical jungle is that plants crowd
each other so closely that it is difficult to walk through it.

Agriculture is easily practiced and, in these areas, tropical plantations are found. The area is useful in the production of bananas,
mangos and coconuts. Wet tropical agriculture can be practiced in
the windward side of the Caribbean Islands and the neighboring
mainlands on the east coast of Brazil and along the eastern base of
the Andes. In Africa there is a large tropical jungle along the
borders of the Equatorial Forest and in Abyssinia and Madagascar
and along the Eastern coast of Africa. Because of the high altitudes
which are found in many parts of Africa, a true jungle is not found as
in other continents with equal climates. In Asia, jungles are found in
southeastern India at the foot of the Himalayas in Indo-China. Many
parts of the East Indies and small sections of the northeast coast of
India also are covered with jungles (Fig. 3).

In the equatorial rain forest, there is a constant growth of vegetation due to the warmth of the soil and the moisture in the ground.
The Amazon and Congo River basins are characteristic of this condition. These areas can be cleared but with difficulty. Agriculture is
difficult to practice due to the presence of constantly moist and warm

soil which favors the growth of weeds and the sprouting of trees. At present, little domestic animal production is found here because there is little or no grass growth. Human populations are very limited.

Vegetation yielded in the lowest latitudes on earth, as well as in the tundra, are presently of little use to mankind. The vegetation growing in intermediate ranges between the equator and the tundra are the places in which agriculture can be practiced with great success.

There are at least four grades of land utilization (Huntington, 1940). First is the unproductive ground. This would include areas where the temperatures are too low, the climate is too dry or the landscape is too rough to be used productively in agriculture. This includes Antarctica, the Sahara Desert and the true deserts of the earth, and the inaccessible portions of mountains and plateaus such as in Tibet, Chile, and northern Siberia. These lie beyond the limits where man can make a permanent living at the present time and, at the same time, contribute to the production of more food for others.

The second realm is that of non-agricultural production, composed mainly of grasslands and forests, largely unfit for crop production. These include the steppes of Asia, the great north woods of Canada, the equatorial rain forests of Brazil. Crops can be produced usually along the southern edges of these areas.

The third realm is that of uncertain agriculture. There are vast areas on earth where crops can be raised but with danger of failure due to uncertain climatic factors. This region includes the limit of growth of many of the best crops including corn, cotton and potatoes. Even if crops can grow in these areas they yield adequate harvests only every few years. Central parts of India, Northern China, the Sudan region, Southeastern Russia near the Caspian Sea, and the drier parts of the great plains of the United States are of this type. Such areas are generally very poor and have a low subsistence economy as in much of India and China. If human populations on such land are scarce, such as in the Western Dakotas, a progressive economy can develop.

The realm of high productivity is the fourth category. In this zone, agriculture is not only possible but probable. The areas are divided into three main types. One consists of the tropical plantations that flourish in Java, and along the coast of Brazil and Cuba.

The second consists of the warm temperate regions such as South-eastern United States, Mediterranean area, Japan, and South and Central China. The third region is in the cool temperate zone such as northern United States and western Europe.

These three regions together support 80 per cent of the people and a large percentage of commerce and industry of the world on only one-fifth of the earth's land.

NEW LANDS FOR FOOD PRODUCTION

The amount and quality of the land on earth available for food production is a fundamental factor to be considered. With a total land surface on earth of about $33^1/_2$ billion acres, the potential crop land estimates vary from four billion acres to 15 billion acres, The latter is thought to be an unrealistic estimate. There are wide variations in assumptions concerning the importance of and the value of untried soils. Technical opinions regarding the forest areas which could be cultivated also vary widely. All estimates include the assumption that there will be no change in climate which would influence the availability and utility of land.

A commonly accepted figure for the land surface capable of adequate food production is four billion acres and four-fifths of this area is already under cultivation. The distribution of the other one-fifth of this land, according to the United Nations Food and Agriculture Organization, finds one-third in Asia, one-fourth in North and Central America (largely in Canada), a quarter in Africa and small amounts in other parts of the world. The land which could be cultivated, which at the present time remains otherwise, would require major capital expenditures for its use. The Political and Economic Planning (P.E.P.) group in England, studying these areas, lists the following possibilities: (1) Certain areas of forest or scrub land can be cleared and land could be cultivated. However, real dangers would exist thereafter in soil erosion; also, the process of making or preparing the land for agricultural purposes is very difficult. (2) There are desert areas which could be cultivated, providing irrigation is available. (Irrigation development projects require major capital investments.) (3) There are many potentially fertile areas in the tropics. Improved technology is required to control pests and diseases of man, plants and animals. Control of human diseases including malaria, now capable of being controlled, can make an important contribution in opening a number of fertile tropical areas to food production. (4) The recovery of new farm land from the wild, and placing these in cultivation, requires industrious farm populations. This is not a widely distributed characteristic in the areas where the new land exists.

Much of the undeveloped agricultural lands of the present day remain so for good reasons. A variety of difficult conditions must be overcome for their exploitation. Most of these are marginal areas and the settlement by human beings and the development of agriculture in these areas are genuine barriers to the application of the technology available. The investments needed for the technological exploitation of these lands is very great. It is thought that the expenses and risks involved in making these lands productive will be far greater than that which has already been expended in developing the lands which are presently under cultivation.

Nevertheless there are vast potential agricultural land masses which could be brought into food production. These include the tropical rain forest areas, the semi-arid grass land, dry lands which could be irrigated, and lands of colder areas of the temperate zone (P.E.P. 1955).

Tropical Rain Forest

Rain forests of South America along the Amazon valley and in Africa along the Congo river and in some of the islands of the Pacific have potentially arable lands, estimated to be in the billion-acre quantity. The agriculture which is practiced now in these areas is often primitive, existing in small clearings which have been burned out of the forest or bush. After a few years of use, when the soil becomes depleted, the occupants move to a new plot.

To recover such land for agricultural use would first require the clearing of the land of the trees and dense undergrowth which exists. Drainage systems must also be installed. Equitorial rains and the heat of these areas have depleted the soils. Their fertility is poor due to the rapid decay of the organic matter which is deposited annually on the soil. When rain forests are cleared, the high temperatures of the area cause the rapid oxidation or burning of the topsoil. The heavy rainfall which occurs in these areas further bleaches the soil. The cleared areas are subject to rapid water erosion. Planted to rice or to yams this land is worn out in a few years with present systems. New techniques in soil and farm mangement would have to be developed to insure a continuing production of food.

The climate need not be an obstacle to human settlement in these areas with modern technology and sanitation. Serious problems at the present time are the human pathogenic diseases including malaria, yellow fever, dysentery, typhus, etc., which, in spite of advanced medical technology still infest these areas. Included also are diseases and pests of plants and animals which require active combat.

The reason these areas are in rain forest at the present time is because of their climate. The forests themselves are able to provide some part of the organic matter which is required by the poor soil to sustain forest growths. However, it has been found by Osborne that the developments in the Belgian Congo have demonstrated that tropical rain forest can be recovered successfully in plantations without upsetting the biological complexes of the area. Production of specialized agricultural products including cocoa, bananas, and nuts, for commerce can improve on the standard of living of people in these areas (P.E.P. 1955).

Semi-Arid Grassland

The largest units of land which can be cultivated are the semi-arid grasslands, such as are found in Africa. The main limiting factor at the present is a steady water supply. The dry season is 6 to 8 months long, a period during which little or no rainfall occurs. In this area, due to baking in the hot sun, soils develop a hard crust. In the rainy season much erosion occurs. The land is alternately drenched in rain then baked in the sun, which is not conducive to food production, either plant or animal. Clearing the soil of bush is a major undertaking, due to their root system. There is also a lack of information on the nature of the soils in the area and their responses to present day agricultural technology (Jenny 1959).

Dry Lands Which Can Be Irrigated

Each continent has some soil masses which cannot produce crops because they lack rainfall or the rainfall which occurs is irregular or comes at the wrong time of the year. Some of this land can be brought under cultivation by irrigation. In the densely populated areas of the world, irrigation has long been developed and near to the uppermost limits with past and present technological systems. Already one-fourth of the world's population lives from land that is irrigated. India, China and Egypt have highly developed irrigation systems, practically all of the land under cultivation in Egypt being irrigated.

There is an abundance of good land which could be brought under cultivation by irrigation in the United States, the Soviet Union, and some regions of Africa and Australia. In California, for example, there is an indication of the potential of such systems. Recent technological developments make it possible to bring water to areas which are now in short supply. An entire river valley may be shifted, or river channels altered. However, most of the irrigation which is required is more difficult to install and more expensive to construct than the systems presently in use around the world. The costs of maintenance for such systems are very large as well.

A recent survey has concluded that a great portion of the earth's 10 million square miles which now have less than ten inches of rain a year is beyond the conceivable range for artificial watering systems sufficient to produce plant food crops in continuous systems within the limits of economic possibilities (P.E.P. 1955).

Cold Areas of the Temperate Zone

It is possible to move cultivation further and further into the upper fringes of the temperate zone, in Northern Asia and Canada. There are two major problems: the length of the growing season, and the uncertainty of the soil. Because the growing season is 100 days or shorter in length there is a need for new varieties or types of plants which can grow and mature within the nature imposed time limitation. Yet, due to the warming trend in the earth's temperature at present, slowly, in the near future, large amounts of arable land may become available in the northern latitudes. If the earth is undergoing a warming trend, these new land mass areas may become very suitable for cultivation. If, on the other hand, a turn of events occurs and the world's climate becomes more severe or cold, areas which are presently under cultivation will be frozen out.

SUMMARY

In summary, most of the lands which could be recovered for agricultural purposes require expensive modifications prior to their being brought into cultivation. Many of the soils which could be available are poor soils, soils deficient in the nutrients required by plant and animal life. Most areas require development of new crops and crops varieties, and special strains of animals. Most of the areas which could be exploited have uncontrolled public health hazards for human beings at the present time. Temperature and climate cycles also may not be conducive to inhabitation by people.

The widespread disease infected tropical areas are not entirely under control. More than two-thirds of Africa is under attack periodically by locust invasions. The tsetse fly makes large masses of land uninhabitable at the present time by man or animal. Many areas that are not presently under cultivation, which have high potential for development, also have all the problems relative to man and public health (P.E.P. 1955).

Any effort of exploitation of these areas must include first an evaluation of the soil situation, then the establishment of pilot areas where testing programs can be undertaken. These areas have very complex communications and transportation difficulties, involving the spanning of jungles and swamps and mountains. These areas now are inaccessible. Even if food production became efficient, the above problems would be a great handicap in the movement of the food produced to areas of food shortages.

The reclaiming of or the extension of agricultural technology into presently non-used areas would involve elaborate projects and great investments of capital resources. *Furthermore, the production from these areas must be surplus food to add to the volume available to the people in the world.* If the land would slowly become at best a subsistence type of agriculture, then the whole purpose of the project would be defeated. It would be tragic to have more people living as poorly as before, or even worse, due to an attempt to bring sub-marginal areas under cultivation. There are human, social, and cultural problems which must be faced.

The potentially usable land of Africa and South America, some-times estimated to be nearly a billion acres, could provide the space for migration from the heavily populated areas and take care of some of the present world problems. However, due to political and social conditions at the present time, such land masses are closed to the millions of Asiatics who might find a livelihood there.

While the agricultural land of the earth is a clue to the progress of people living on earth, the resource it represents is probably the most abused. The major attention must be given to the land already available and under cultivation. Millions upon millions of acres of once fertile soils have been so depleted that man cannot gain a livelihood from them anymore.

Application of good management practices to the agricultural lands which presently are in production could markedly increase the yield of food in the world. For example, in Denmark, which was once described as the smallest and poorest country in Europe, now has more than four million people who are among the best fed in the world, on $10^1/_2$ million acres. A little over one-half of this land is available for productive agricultural use.

The consensus at the present is that we must realize that the agricultural land available on earth is limited both in quantity and quality. The extension of agriculture into lands which are now submarginal will yield poorer land than that already available, and everything that is required to improve the productivity of submarginal soil is very expensive. The people with the biggest needs who live on this soil are least able to carry on the processes which must come into play and are least able to afford the cost of such activity.

As we noted earlier, the yields of food from land already under cultivation is variable. The highest yields generally are found in northern Europe and the lowest in the under developed countries of Asia and Africa. Therefore, some improvement in the present situation is possible by improving on the use and the yields of land.

There are a number of factors which may be exploited to increase the current yields of cultivated land. Better seed and better seed stocks are available. Improved grain varieties can produce more food per acre than poor quality seeds with the same fertilizer foundation in the soil. Cows vary in their ability to yield milk from the same quantity of food. Improvement of the seeds planted in the ground and improvement in the quality of animals fed could go a long way in increasing the food supplies within the land resources available. There are also many advances that can be made in more widely applying the presently accepted, improved agricultural technologies. These would include improved methods of cultivation, improved methods of fertilization, irrigation technology, and mechanization of farming activities.

Some idea of the potential is seen when we recognize that by using the best crop land available and culturing it intensively, to the degree to which the Japanese are using their crop land, it could be possible to feed two billion people solely from the products of the soil in the United States. This would assume that the acres that are available for food production would be as productive as the Japanese crop land and that the crops grown in the field would be eaten directly rather than refining this plant material into animal products.

But, there is already a food surplus in the United States, and means of controlling this surplus are being sought. It does not appear to be a solution to the problem of sufficient food for all people. Each continent in general must be nearly self-sufficient in food production.

Assuming that the land which is available but as yet uncultivated in the world were brought into production, it would be equal to the food required by the present underfed populations on earth. Unfortunately, only one-third of this land which could be available lies in Asia where the major problems exist.

The exploitation of the poorer agricultural lands at the present time involves great expenditures of resources. Most of the good farm land on earth has already been placed under cultivation.

In 1919, Professor Mosier wrote, "Because of the great increase in the population of the earth, consumption of foods so nearly equals production that there is no longer any large reserve. We are now rapidly approaching the time when every idle acre must be put to work and every working acre must be made to yield as much food as possible." In 1960 the United Nations reported that two-thirds of the human race is underfed. More than half of the world's population now exists in Asia on less than one-sixth of this planet's land surface.

CHAPTER 7

The World's Water Resources for Food Production

THE HYDROLOGIC CYCLE

Water is an inseparable component of life and although the world's water supply is fixed in terms of the amount of water present, the supply is enormous.

The oceans cover approximately seven-tenths of the earth's surface and oceans are the great reservoirs from which our fresh water supplies originate.

There is a natural movement of water through a hydrologic cycle, illustrated in Fig. 4. Energy from the sun evaporates water from the oceans. As the atmosphere becomes saturated it periodically loses its water vapor in the form of rain, snow, hail, and dew. As these reach land the water is infiltrated into the soil or runs off into a stream or accumulates as snow and ice. The infiltrated water may be stored underground where it can contribute importantly to the ground water supply. Movement of ground water creates springs and maintains stream flow.

An important part of the water which reaches the soil is lost by evaporation and transpiration from plants and soil surfaces. While the amount of water evaporated from the surface of oceans and the land masses of the world is unknown, it has been estimated that the volume amounts annually to approximately 80,000 cubic miles over the land masses of the world (Huberty and Flock 1959).

The rate of evaporation of water varies in the world. Evaporation from the Atlantic ocean varies from a high of 6.5 feet per year in the range of 30° to 8° North Latitude, to a low of two feet per year between 8° and 3° North Latitude. Evaporation from the North Pacific Ocean apparently is somewhat less (Tressler and Lemon 1951). This is found to be in the order of 4.3 feet per year at a latitude of 20° North to a low of 1.8 at 50° North.

ANNUAL RAINFALL

Circulation of the atmosphere above the earth plays an important role in determining the nature and the distribution of the precipitation that occurs.

88

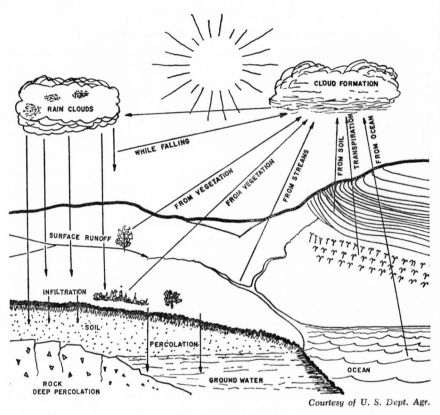

Courtesy of U. S. Dept. Agr.

FIG. 4.   THE HYDROLOGIC CYCLE

The moisture which reaches the land masses of the world varies in form, in amount, in intensity, in the time of year when it occurs and in its distribution over the land masses.

The average annual precipitation of water falling on the land surfaces of the earth is shown in Figure 5.   This is at best an approximation as large variations in annual precipitation occur even within small areas.   Storms of great intensity occur even in desert areas. Rainfalls from storms can range up to 20 inches in three hours, and examples of rainfalls of even higher amounts have been found in several parts of the world.   Because the capacity of the soil to absorb this amount of water is limited, the amount of run-off would be extremely high.

Considering the whole surface of the earth, there is a range in annual precipitation from practically no fall to over 500 inches.   As an

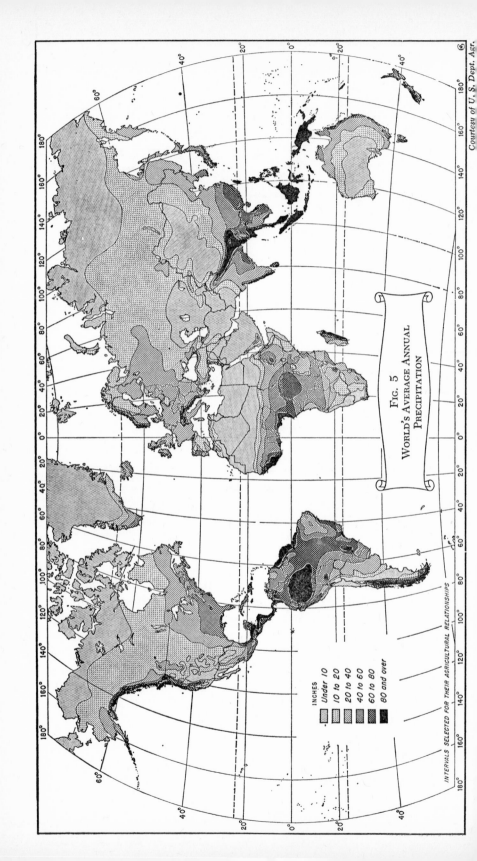

Fig. 5
World's Average Annual
Precipitation

INCHES
Under 10
10 to 20
20 to 40
40 to 60
60 to 80
80 and over

INTERVALS SELECTED FOR THEIR AGRICULTURAL RELATIONSHIPS

average value, the total amount of annual precipitation of water amounts to approximately two feet over every square inch of surface of the earth. For the United States about 20 inches of water is lost annually by evaporation from the land surfaces and through respiration. The amount of run-off that can be expected from a land mass is not only dependent upon the total precipitation but also upon its intensity, the duration of rainfalls that occur, the cover over the land and the characteristics of the soil and the rock underneath it as the drainage basin. In the United States the total flow from run-offs is estimated to be equivalent to a sustained flow of about 1.8 million cubic feet per second (U. S. Dept. Agr. 1955).

Dew Accumulations Variable

Dew is an important contribution to the water supply of land masses. Rather large amounts of water are condensed on plant foliage which is useful for plant growth, for example, in desert areas. In non-desert areas dew is also important as a water source. In Ohio, measurements show an average dew accumulation equal to three and a half inches of water a year, and upwards to ten inches are found in certain years (U. S. Dept. Agr. 1955).

SURFACE WATER SUPPLIES

Lakes, streams, and springs are surface water supplies of importance; however, the flow of springs and much of the low stage flow of water in streams are derived from ground water. Surface and ground waters are interrelated.

About ten per cent of the world's land surface is covered constantly with snow and ice. This amounts to about 5.8 million square

TABLE 7

AREAS ON EARTH COVERED WITH GLACIAL ICE[1]

Land Area	Square Miles
Continental Europe	3,880
Continental Asia	43,270
Continental North America	30,900
Continental South America	9,600
South polar regions	5,020,450
North polar regions	721,150
Africa	8
New Zealand	386
New Guinea	6
Total	5,829,650

[1] From Huberty and Flock (1959).

miles. Ice in some areas of the Antarctic has been found to be about one and one-half miles thick. The amount of water stored as ice is tremendous and, if it melted, large changes would be expected in levels of the oceans of the world. On the other hand, increasing ice caps on earth constantly remove some of the water from the oceans, therefore imposing a drop in the level of the oceans. The glacial ice present on earth has been estimated, and is shown in Table 7. Unfortunately, the great supply of water in the form of polar ice does not constitute a usable supply of water at the present time.

There are some 80 major rivers in the world which contain approximately 12 billion acre feet of water run-off annually. The world's total run-off of water from land is estimated to be about 20 billion acre feet annually (U. S. Dept. Agr. 1955).

The flow of water in the major world rivers varies widely as does the amount of water discharged during various times of the year. In semi-arid and arid areas a great part of the total run-off occurs a short time after the rainfall.

Those streams which have their major flow of water during the growing season are especially well suited for irrigation purposes.

MAJOR RIVERS IN WORLD

Africa

There are four major rivers in Africa—the Nile, Zambezi, Congo, and Niger. The Nile has played an important role in the history of mankind and is the longest river in the world, ranging for 4,100 miles. It drains approximately 1.1 million square miles and has an average annual discharge rate of about 75 million acre feet of water. The Zambezi river drains the east central portion of Africa and flows into the Indian Ocean. This is a major river which remains largely undeveloped. At the present time a water control system is under construction; the storage capacity of the new reservoir will be approximately 130 million acre feet (Huberty and Flock 1959).

This would hold about four times the water in Lake Meade on the Colorado River, which at the present time is the largest artificial reservoir in the world.

Asia

The major rivers of Asia are the Yangtze, Hwang Ho, Lena, Ob, Amur, Amu Darya, Aldan, Syr Darya, Tigris, Euphrates, Indus,

Ganges, Brahmaputra, Irrawaddy, and Mekong Rivers (Huberty and Flock 1959; Huntington 1940).

The Yangtze and the Hwang Ho Rivers are the main tributaries in China. The Yangtze drains an area of approximately 750,000 square miles. Both of these rivers contain extremely large amounts of silt, which is a handicap in the adequate utilization of the water. While extensive use is made of the rivers, the lack of silt control and flood control measures permits fluctuations in the water levels in the river by as much as 100 feet.

The Asian rivers that flow toward the North are ice bound for about four months a year. The interior portion of the Asian continent discharges its run-off waters mainly into the seas. The Syr Darya River has an annual discharge rate of approximately 17 million acre feet. The Amu Darya River discharges approximately 52 million acre feet of water annually mainly into Lake Aral. Both of these rivers are under extensive conservation development programs at the present time.

The Tigris and Euphrates Rivers make up the main run-off systems of the Near East. These rivers helped nurse the original civilization efforts of mankind and have been highly used since ancient times. The combined average flow of these rivers is in excess of 50 million acre feet and these rivers have immense potentials in water conservation and utilization.

The drainage of India and most of Pakistan occurs through the Indus River which has a peak flow of about 750,000 cubic feet per second. This river has been extensively developed during the past century and is important in the irrigation of large areas of farm land.

It has been estimated that the average annual run-off of water from Indian soil is about one and one-third billion acre feet annually. The Ganges waterway accounts for approximately one-third of this run-off. Approximately five per cent of the total amount of water available is being used for irrigation and power. A multi-purpose water project on a tributary of the Indus River is nearing completion. It should be a great importance in the area.

Southeast Asia is an area with a high average rainfall and land is drained by numerous minor streams. There is a great amount of water available which is not used (Huberty and Flock 1959; U. S. Dept. Agr. 1955; Huntington 1940; P.E.P. 1955).

Europe

The major rivers of Europe are the Volga, Dnieper, Danube, Elbe, Po, Rhine, Rhone, and Seine. The Danube River drains part of eight countries in Central Europe and has an annual rate of discharge of about 225 million acre feet of water. Flood dangers in this river are very great. Most of the upper reaches of European rivers have been controlled and developed into power production sites.

The Volga River runs into the Caspian Sea. The Dnieper River flows into the Black Sea. Both of these rivers are used for power and irrigation purposes.

Oceania

The Murray River is the major river of the Oceania area. The river is located in and is the principal river of Australia. It has a natural annual flow of about 11 million acre feet of water and drains about a half a million square miles of land. Of all the continents Australia has the lowest run-off of water. Australia has an area of approximately three million square miles and the run-off water is estimated to be about 200 million acre feet. About 40 per cent of the water is carried in minor rivers on the eastern slope of the ridge of mountains which line the eastern quarter of the continent.

New Zealand is in a better situation relative to water supply and rainfall distribution than is Australia. The major river is the Waikato River which is about 200 miles long. Power potentialities of the water in the north on the island are largely developed (Huberty and Flock 1959; Huntington 1940).

South America

The major rivers of South America are the Amazon, Plate, Orinoco, and Sao-Fransciso Rivers. The Amazon River is the world's largest. The river drains nearly three million square miles of land which has an average rainfall of between 60 and 80 inches. The annual discharge of water is about three and a half billion acre feet. Its main use at present is for navigation. This represents one of the major unexploited areas of the earth.

The Plate River forms an important drainage system for the southeastern part of South America. The Orinoco and the Sao-Francisco Rivers (although not as large as the two major rivers) are nevertheless important rivers of South America.

North America

The Mississippi, Yukon, Columbia, St. Lawrence, Fraser, Sacramento-San Joaquin, MacKenzie, Colorado, and Rio Grande Rivers are the major rivers of North America. The Mississippi River has an average flow of nearly a half billion acre feet a year and drains more than a million square miles of the central part of the United States. The Missouri, the Ohio and the Tennessee Rivers are tributaries of the Mississippi. The Yukon River in the northern part of the continent is the second largest river, and drains large areas of Alaska, discharging into the Bering Sea. The Columbia River has an annual discharge of nearly 200 million acre feet a year and is the third largest stream on the North American continent. Forty per cent of the water flow originates in Canada. Power and irrigation systems have been highly developed on the Columbia.

The St. Lawrence waterway is now an important international river. It is the fourth largest river of the continent with an annual run-off of approximately 150 million acre feet. An important part of the water resources of the United States is found in the Great Lakes. These have a storage capacity equal to the total rainfall of the whole United States for more than a two and a half year period.

Canada has very great resources in fresh water; more than six per cent of the surface area of Canada is composed of fresh water. The Fraser River in British Columbia and the MacKenzie River are important in the northern part of North America.

In Western United States the Sacramento-San Joaquin River system drains the central valley of California. Approximately 30 million acre feet of water are available annually and this is a highly developed irrigation and public water supply source. Extensive use of ground water has been made in this area in addition to the uses of surface water.

The Colorado River drainage system covers an area more than one-tenth the land area of the United States. However, because the precipitation in the area is low, the amount of water available is also low, estimated to be 16 million acre feet annually. The Colorado River basin system is important in that it is the fresh water resource for vast areas in the southwestern part of the country. Extensive development of the water resource of the Colorado River basin has been made and more has been planned. The Rio Grande is not too large a river yet it plays an important part in supplying fresh water supplies to the arid southwest. Discharge rate is something in the vicinity of five million acre feet per year. Water resources of the United States have been studied in great detail. (Huberty and Flock 1959).

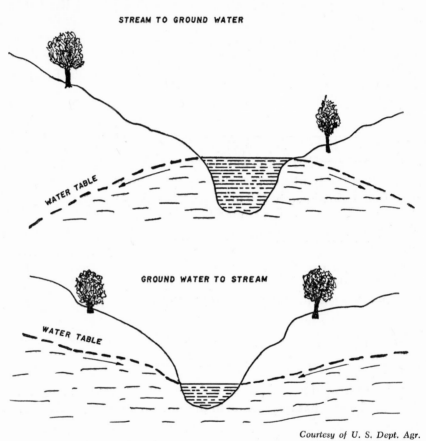

Courtesy of U. S. Dept. Agr.

FIG. 6. GROUND WATER CONTRIBUTES TO REGULAR FLOW OF STREAMS

GROUND WATER

Ground water is an important contributor to maintaining the flow of rivers and is a source of springs (Fig. 6). Ground water is characteristic in being relatively constant in composition and also in temperature. Obviously the losses of ground water by evaporation are of no consequence. It is to be expected that where bountiful surface water supplies occur the ground water resources are not normally very well developed. On the other hand, where the surface waters are not adequate to supply the needs, ground water supplies become increasingly important.

Importance of ground water resources can be seen from the fact that the volume of water presently available in the United States is equal to 35 years of run-off from the surface of the United States. Currently the United States is using the ground water basin resources for some 30 billion gallons per day which amounts to perhaps some 15 to 18 per cent of the total used. Sixty per cent of the supply is used for irrigation. In Germany, in contrast, 85 per cent of the water used is obtained from wells.

An important consideration in utilizing ground water is to maintain a balance between use and replacement. For example, in some areas of Texas the rate of withdrawl is estimated at 20 times that of recharge (U. S. Dept. Agr., 1955). In some areas of California water has been pumped to such a degree that sea water is beginning to invade the fresh water basins; a serious problem along coastal areas. Furthermore, by lowering the water table in an area it is possible to cause some ground settling. There is also the danger of pollution of water supplies. While with cheap electrical power it has been possible to develop adequate water supplies for farms and small towns using ground water supplies, larger communities seldom are able to draw their water requirements solely from underground water sources.

Usable ground water is often found in sand and gravel layers underground. Where water occurs in limestone formations underground some solution channels have been found through which water may flow. Such waters are usually very hard, in other words they contain large amounts of calcium and magnesium salts. It is important to note that in some areas solid rock formations containing large cracks and crevices have been used to store water underground.

Ground water movement may be as slow as a few feet a year, or move rapidly through coarse gravel basins (U. S. Dept. Agr., 1955).

Zones of Ground Water

Water which reaches the soil either increases the moisture content of the soil or it drains off. In dry soil the water successively wets deeper layers to the point of field capacity. Field capacity is the moisture content of soil to which each layer must be raised before water can drain through it. When the entire soil profile has been wetted to field capacity, the additional water which enters into the soil drains through it and into the underground layers. Here it emerges in springs and seeps into streams or adds to the subsurface water supplies in valleys.

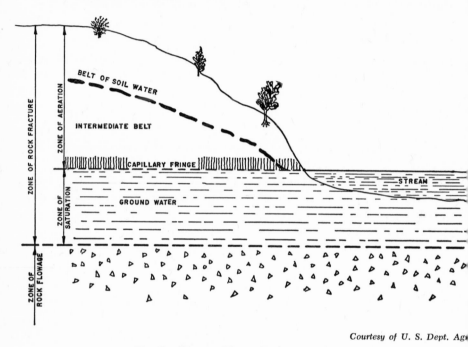

Courtesy of U. S. Dept. Agr.

Fig. 7.   Ground Water Zones and Belts

Water which filters down into the subsoil is known as subsurface water. This water may eventually evaporate from the soil or it may be absorbed by the roots of plants and then transpired away. It may also percolate further down to ground water reservoirs. Ground water supplies occur in a zone between the surface of the ground and lower depths to the point where rock formations occur (Fig. 7).

The bulk of the soil water found in the top soil and in the subsoil is water which can be returned to the atmosphere by evaporation from the soil or by transpiration by plants. Some water is pulled by gravity from the surface of the soil to the zone of saturation. The zone of saturation forms a huge reservoir of water which feeds the springs and streams and the wells. The zone of saturation has great importance, as it is capable of maintaining uniform flows in streams. Huge quantities of water can be stored in the depths of the soil, and since this water moves slowly into and out of the zone, it is discharged at a rather uniform rate. Another method of conceiving of the zone of saturation is to conceive of a water table, shown in Fig 7.

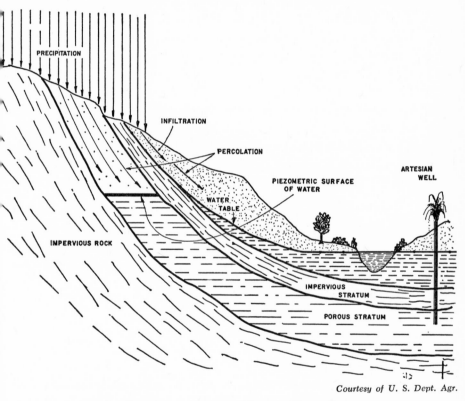

Courtesy of U. S. Dept. Agr.

Fig. 8. Diagram of Artesian Ground Water System

The run-off of water from soil occurs when precipitation is of such a degree that water does not have a chance to infiltrate into the soil, hence flows across the land surface. Most of this water eventually enters streams which carry the water into the oceans. In general, the run-off found on soil is composed of water from both the surface flow and from seepage flow. Part of the water that infiltrates the soil percolates downward to the water table and then enters channel streams and rivers through springs and seepage. About 20 per cent of all precipitation carried to the ocean by streams and rivers occurs from run-off (U. S. Dept. Agr. 1955).

This water is directly concerned with the agricultural activities in an area. Irrigation, water power and other industrial and domestic uses of water depend upon the flow of water in streams and rivers. As noted earlier, nine-tenths of the world's water needs come from surface water systems.

A diagrammatic sketch of artesian ground water is shown in Fig. 8.

There is a rather constant amount of water which is involved in the hydrologic cycle. Water is unique in this sense, since water can be used by man, allowed to escape, and then return in a never ending cycle.

WATER NEEDS OF PLANTS AND ANIMALS

Various studies have been undertaken to evaluate the amount of water required to yield various green crops. A typical analysis is shown in Table 8, which is useful in computing the amount of irrigation water needed for various crops.

TABLE 8

CONSUMPTIVE USE FOR CROPS IN THE MONTROSE AREA, COLORADO[1]

Culture	Growing Season	Consumptive Use
		Inches
Alfalfa	5/6–10/6	26.45
Grass hay	5/6–10/6	23.34
Corn	5/6– 9/6	19.66
Small grain	5/6– 8/6	14.87
Orchards	5/6–10/6	20.23
Seeped land	5/6–10/6	24.90
Natural vegetation	5/6–10/6	37.34

[1] From U. S. Dept. Agr. (1957).
The irrigation water required to satisfy consumptive use by each crop growing or to be grown on a farm is obtained by subtracting the effective rainfall from consumptive water requirements during the growing or irrigation season.

The irrigation water requirement to satisfy the needs of each crop is now adequately known (U. S. Dept. Agr. 1955).

Necessary information is also available relative to the amount of water required on the various types of soil under various climatic conditions.

In addition to the water requirements of plants it is also important to consider the requirements of various domesticated animals. A wide range in animal requirements also exists, as shown in Table 9.

TABLE 9

WATER CONSUMPTION BY ANIMALS[1]

Effect of External Temperature on Water Consumption

Water Consumption,

Hogs, Temperature (°F.)	Pounds per Hog per Hour		
	75–125 Lb. Hogs	275–380 Lb. Hogs	Pregnant Sows
50....	0.2	0.5	0.95
60....	0.25	0.5	0.85
70....	0.30	0.65	0.80
80....	0.30	0.85	0.95
90....	0.35	0.65	0.90
100....	0.60	0.85	0.80

Dairy Cows, Temperature	Gallons per Day per Cow		
	Lactating Jerseys	Lactating Holsteins	Dry Holsteins
50	11.4	18.7	10.4
50–70 ..	12.8	21.7	11.5
75–85 ..	14.7	21.2	12.3
90–100 .	20.1	19.9	10.7

Laying Hens, Temperature	Milliliter per Bird per Day	
	White Leghorn	Rhode Island Red
70........	286	294
80........	272	321
90........	350	408
100........	392	371
70........	222	216

Water Consumption of Pigs
(Pounds of Water per Day)

Conditions	
Body weight = 30 lbs.....	5–10
Body weight = 60–80 lbs...	7
Body weight = 75–125 lbs..	16
Body weight = 200–380 lbs.	12–30
Pregnant sows	30–38
Lactating sows...........	40–50

Water Consumption of Chickens
(Gallons per 100 Birds per Day)

Conditions	
1–3 weeks of age	0.4–2.0
3–6 weeks of age	1.4–3.0
6–10 weeks of age	3.0–4.0
9–13 weeks of age	4.0–5.0
Pullets..................	3.0–4.0
Nonlaying hens	5.0
Laying hens (moderate temperatures).............	5.0–7.5
Laying hens (temperature 90°F.)................	9.0

Water Consumption of Sheep (Pounds of Water per Day)

Conditions	
On range or dry pasture.............	5–13
On range (salty feeds)..............	17
On rations of hay and grain or hay, roots and grain.......................	0.3–6
On good pasture.................Very little if any	

In these experiments water was available for consumption.

Water Consumption of Growing Turkeys
(Gallons per 100 Birds per Week)

Conditions	
1–3 weeks of age..	8–18
4–7 weeks of age	26–59
9–13 weeks of age	62–100
15–19 weeks of age........	117–118
21–26 weeks of age	95–105

Water Consumption of Cattle

Class of Cattle	Conditions	Water Consumption (Pounds per Day)
Holstein calves (liquid milk or dried milk and water supplied)	4 weeks of age	10–12
	8 weeks of age	13
	12 weeks of age	18–20
	16 weeks of age	25–28
	20 weeks of age	32–36
	26 weeks of age	33–48
Dairy heifers................	Pregnant...................	60–70
Steers	Maintenance ration.........	35
	Fattening ration............	70
Range cattle	....	35–70
Jersey cows	Milk production 5–30 lbs./day.	60–102
Holstein cows	Milk production 20–50 lbs./day	65–182
	Milk production 80 lbs./day...	190
	Dry	90

[1] From U. S. Dept. Agr. (1957).

Water consumption by various animals is influenced by temperature, maturity and weight.

Water Holding Capacity of Soils Varies

Plants cannot use all the water stored in a soil. The plant will take soil moisture only to the wilting point of a plant. This point is the critical moisture content in which the forces holding the water to the soil particles themselves equal the maximum water absorbing force of plant roots present. The upper and lower limits of soil moisture range, between the wilting point and full field capacity are determined by the nature of the soil itself (Fig. 9).

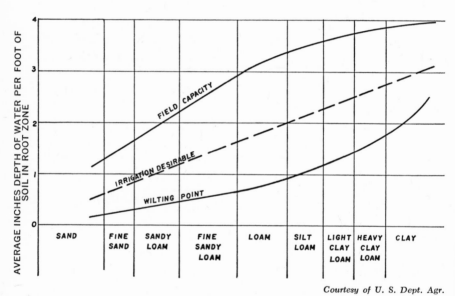

Courtesy of U. S. Dept. Agr.

FIG. 9.   MOISTURE RETAINED IN SOIL INFLUENCED BY SOIL TYPE

SOIL, WATER AND PLANT GROWTH

There is a general relationship between the feel and appearance of soil and its moisture content (Table 10). A crusted soil is a dry soil and moisture will move from the plant to the soil. When a soil contains less moisture than required to permit plant growth, the plants will wilt. Such soil taken into the hand will break down into a powdery condition. A high moisture tension exists in such soil which

TABLE 10

GENERAL RELATIONSHIPS BETWEEN SOIL MOISTURE AND THE FEEL AND APPEARANCE OF THE SOIL[1]

Moisture Between Wilting Point and Field Capacity	Feel or appearance			
	Coarse Soil	Light Soil	Medium Soil	Heavy and Very Heavy Soil
0	Dry, loose, single-grained, flows through fingers	Dry, loose, flows through fingers	Dry sometimes slightly crusted but easily breaks down to powdery condition	Hard, baked, cracked, sometimes has loose crumbs on surface
50 per cent or less........	Appears dry, will not form ball with pressure	Appears dry, will not form ball[2]	Somewhat crumbly, holds together from pressure	Somewhat pliable, balls under pressure
50 to 75 per cent........	Same as coarse under 50 per cent or less	Tends to ball under pressure but seldom holds together	Forms ball, somewhat plastic, will sometimes stick slightly with pressure	Forms ball, ribbons out between thumb and forefinger
75 per cent to field capacity	Tends to stick together, sometimes forms very weak ball under pressure	Forms weak ball, breaks easily, will not stick	Forms ball, very pliable, sticks readily if high in clay	Easily ribbons out between fingers, has slick feeling
At field capacity	Wet outline of ball is left on hand upon squeezing	Same as coarse	Same as coarse	Same as coarse
Above field capacity .	Free water appears when soil is bounced in hand	Free water released with kneading	Can squeeze out free water	Puddles and free water on surface

[1] From U. S. Dept. Agr. (1958).
[2] Ball is formed by squeezing a handful of soil very firmly.

attempts to take up water. Soil with about half of its moisture holding capacity fulfilled can be pressed in the hand to form a ball. This
soil could support some plant growth, yet the growth of plants will be
restrained by the amount of water available. When a soil contains
as much as it will hold, it will form a ball in the hand, and a wet
outline of the ball will be left after squeezing it. Soil containing

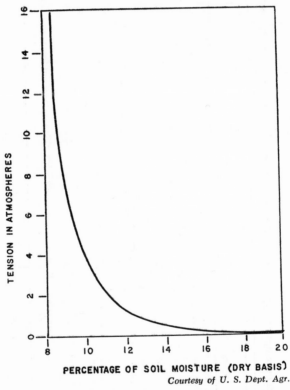

PERCENTAGE OF SOIL MOISTURE (DRY BASIS)
Courtesy of U. S. Dept. Agr.

Fig. 10.   Relation Between Soil Moisture Content
AND Soil Moisture Tension

more than this amount of water can be pressed in the hand and free
water will appear, showing that soil in such a condition does not hold
the extra water with much force. There is also a relationship between soil moisture content and soil moisture tension, shown in Fig.
10.
    A green plant will become dehydrated in a dry soil, water moving
from the plant to the soil. As the soil moisture tension is reduced,

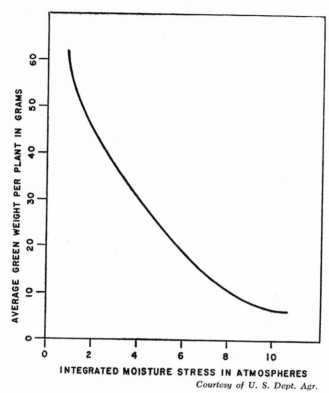

FIG. 11. RELATION BETWEEN SOIL MOISTURE TENSION AND
GAIN IN WEIGHT OF GREEN PLANTS

water can be taken up from the soil by a plant, and the plant can
then grow (Fig. 11).

Not only is the amount of moisture in soil important but the level
of the water table is also of great importance. Maximum responses
in plant growths are obtained with controlled water levels in soils
(Fig. 12).

IRRIGATION

One sure way to increase food production is to bring water to dry
but fertile soils, and the most important recent development in irrigation is its rapid acceleration everywhere under the pressure of hunger and necessity.

Irrigation is not new—it antedates recorded history of more than
one country on more than one continent. Whole civilizations have

flourished or fallen on the success or failure of their irrigation programs. In the United States about half of the available irrigation
water, under present standards, has been developed and put to work
irrigating more about 30 million acres. In the world there are some
300 million acres under irrigation and there may be water remaining
to irrigate an additional area the same size.

It is the wedding of land and water that produces food. While
the water resources of the world are fantastic in scope (95,000 cubic
miles evaporated over land and sea annually) generally in the world
there is more land that could be cropped than water available to it.
That means fresh water is the first fixed limit encountered in food
production.

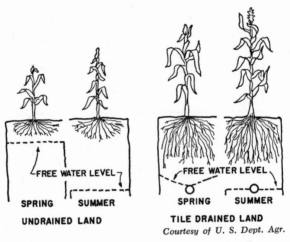

Courtesy of U. S. Dept. Agr.

FIG. 12. WATER LEVEL IN SOIL INFLUENCES GROWTH
OF PLANTS

When nations approach or encounter this limit, violent political
controversies may result. Such political arguments are merely the
symptoms showing that an area has reached its vital water-resource
ceiling. An increasing number of areas are reaching the dry bottom
of their water barrel (Straus 1949).

Countries with the greatest amount of irrigation at the present
time are indicated in Table 11. It is seen that China has approximately one-fourth of her cultivatable areas under irrigation. Egypt
is almost completely dependent on irrigated crop land. China and
India together have nearly one half of the world's irrigated farm land.

Irrigation in these areas is obviously very old and extensive use is made of small surface reservoirs.

In the United States 90 per cent of the irrigated land is found in the western states. Of all the states Arizona has the highest percentage of irrigated farm land (U. S. Dept. Agr. 1955).

TABLE 11

IRRIGATED ACREAGES AND LAND AREAS IN THE TWELVE COUNTRIES WITH THE GREATEST IRRIGATED AREA[1]

Country	Area, Thousands of Acres Total	Cultivated Annually	Irri- gated	Percentage of Irrigated Area to Total Area	Percentage of Irrigated Area to Cultivated Area
China.........	2,405,837	335,000	77,275	3.2	23.0
India	810,777	296,400	59,057	7.3	19.9
United States ..	1,934,256	340,998	26,233	1.4	7.7
Pakistan.......	230,000	45,000	21,310	9.1	47.4
Soviet Union...	5,502,917	—	16,062	0.3	—
Indonesia......	470,565	—	10,665	2.3	—
Japan.........	91,051	12,479	9,430	1.0	75.6
Iraq	109,821	—	8,150	7.4	—
Egypt.........	247,100	7,000	7,000	2.8	100
France	136,300	78,219	6,178	4.5	7.9
Mexico........	486,787	57,700	5,330	1.1	9.2
Italy	76,370	54,856	5,190	6.8	9.5

[1] From Huberty and Flock (1959).

The Soviet Union has about 16 million acres of irrigated crop land and 2.5 million acres of potentially irrigatable land. In the central Asian sectors of the Soviet Union about three-fourths of the cultivated land is irrigated, as in many sections agriculture is not possible without irrigation of the land. Because of the large supplies of surface water available in these areas of the Soviet Union, underground water resources have not been developed and are not a major source of supply (Huberty and Flock 1959).

WATER USE TECHNOLOGY

Water use technology does not mean the absence of use but rather the effective uses of the water resources available. Two steps are apparent: one, increase the efficiency of use; and two, attempt to increase the natural supply of fresh water in areas of deficiency.

Efficiency of Use of Water

Irrigation of farm land to improve the yield of food has been practiced for more than 5,000 years in the Tigris and Euphrates Valleys, in the Nile and in the Indus River Valleys. Some of the technologies developed in planning and installing irrigation systems have clearly demonstrated some of the technical skills by early people.

In spite of the long history of irrigation technology, the amount of water lost during irrigation (Fig. 13) is very great. Much can be done to improve the system and practices involved in irrigation. Possible improvements include reducing the amount of loss due to run-off and more efficient placement of the water for plant use.

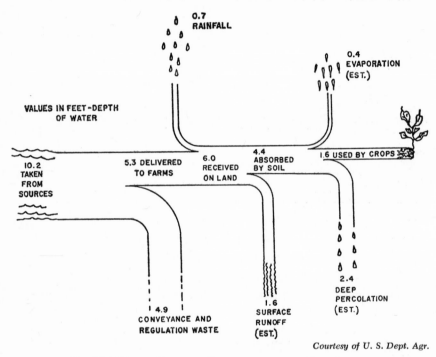

0.7 RAINFALL

0.4 EVAPORATION (EST.)

VALUES IN FEET-DEPTH OF WATER

10.2 TAKEN FROM SOURCES

5.3 DELIVERED TO FARMS

6.0 RECEIVED ON LAND

4.4 ABSORBED BY SOIL

1.6 USED BY CROPS

2.4 DEEP PERCOLATION (EST.)

4.9 CONVEYANCE AND REGULATION WASTE

1.6 SURFACE RUNOFF (EST.)

Courtesy of U. S. Dept. Agr.

FIG. 13. WATER LOSSES IN IRRIGATION CAN BE VERY LARGE

Major developments in irrigation in the future will be associated with great multi-purpose water projects in the major river basin areas of the world. (However, the widespread use of small dams and water collection ponds can have an almost equal impact for irrigation uses.)

An important aspect of water conservation is power production, and from these figures some indication of the degree of use of water resources by continents can be obtained (Table 12). Water is obtained from a renewable natural resource and therefore is considered in the plans for any wide scale development of fresh water resources. Based on the minimum flow of water in rivers in different areas of the world a U. S. Geological Survey estimated the potential for power production and the per cent to which it is developed, show in Table 12.

TABLE 12

INDICATIONS OF DEGREE OF USE OF WATER RESOURCES IN WORLD BY CONTINENTS[1]

Continent	Horsepower, Millions	Per cent Developed
Africa	274	0.5
Asia	151	9.6
Europe	58	86.0
North America	84	57.0
South America	67	6.6
Oceania	20	8.3
Total	664	20

[1] Fom Howe (1959).

It is seen that nearly half of the world's potential hydroelectric power is in Africa. It is to be noted that the values shown in Table 12 do not represent the full power potential. It is possible to increase the power potential over the minimum stream flow values by storage of peak flows and spreading the use over a longer period of

TABLE 13

SELECTED LIST OF MAJOR WATER STORAGE FACILITIES[1]

Dam	Country	River	Height, Ft.	Reservoir Capacity, Acre-Ft.
Hoover	United States	Colorado	726	32,000,000
Grand Coulee	United States	Columbia	550	9,645,000
Bhakra[2]	India	Sutlej	680	7,200,000
President Aléman	Mexico	Balsas	230	6,500,000
Shasta	United States	Sacramento	602	4,500,000
Falcon	Mexico	Rio Grande	160	4,000,000
Eildon	Australia	Goulburn	260	2,750,000

[1] From Howe (1959).
[2] Nearing completion. The Kariba Dam on the Zambezi River in Southern Rhodesia is now under construction. When completed, it will impound 130 million acre-ft of water.

time. Water storage projects are of such an order of magnitude that it is necessary that the resource serve more than one purpose. Some of the large water storage projects are listed in Table 13.

Danger of water pollution is now widely recognized in most countries of the world. Action is already underway to minimize the hazard. Salt and silt are important pollutions of natural water ways. Floods are important contributors to silt accumulation (U. S. Dept. Agr. 1955).

Multi-purpose water basin systems include the combination of irrigation, flood control, hydroelectric power generation and navigation. These factors each can contribute in an important way not only in food production but also in food distribution. The benefits can range from irrigation, to the production of fertilizers, to cheap transportation for food products.

INCREASING NATURAL WATER SUPPLIES

It has been a continuing goal of mankind from the beginning to induce rainfall, especially in the arid regions of the world. Various rituals of tribes and praying have been augmented by artificial induction of rainfall. Recent developments in seeding huge cloud formations with silver iodine crystals have had limited success. Although the practice of seeding clouds to induce rainfall is used in several parts of the world there is some discussion regarding its potential to increase the total precipitation available or the potential of the atmosphere. Only widespread application of the principle in time will yield an answer to this question (U. S. Dept. Agr. 1955).

Development of economically useful systems for reclaiming salt water would have a tremendous impact on the water supplies of the world, hence food production.

Recovering Water from the Seas

Men have died at sea and in desert areas when food was available but fresh water was lacking. Water is one of the most essential of the natural resources of the earth. The increasing world population's demand for high quality water is not beyond the capacity available from ground and surface water systems. The problem arises from the distribution of water over the earth. There are areas which have outstripped their water supplies, and these areas are often highly populated. For this reason, great interest is now centered on recovering fresh water from the seas.

Fresh water is low in dissolved solids, in contrast to sea water. There is a lack of definition as to the upper limit of salt that water may have and still be classified as fresh water. Water may have 500 parts per million of dissolved solids yet be considered as fresh water.

Chemical standards of the United States Public Health Service for satisfactory drinking water are shown in Table 14. In many parts of the world people have become accustomed to drinking water which contains five and more times the amount of total solids set by these standards. It is obvious that the quality of water is determined not only by the amount of solids present but by the chemical composition of the solids present and the organisms which the water contains.

TABLE 14

U. S. PUBLIC HEALTH STANDARDS FOR DOMESTIC WATER SUPPLIES[1]

	P.P.m.		P.p.m.
Turbidity (silica scale)	10	Iron + manganese	0.3
Color (platinum-cobalt scale)	20	Magnesium	125
Lead	0.1	Zinc	15
Fluoride	1.5	Chloride	250
Arsenic	0.05	Sulfate	250
Selenium	0.05	Phenolic compound	0.001
Hexavalent chromium	0.05	Total Solids	500
Copper	3.0		

[1] From Tressler and Lemon (1951).

Approximately the same kind of water and the same quality of water is required for both irrigation and for human consumption. While perhaps 500 parts per million of dissolved minerals can be tolerated in fresh water, sea water contains 35 thousands parts per million, of which nearly 30 thousand parts are sodium chloride, one of the most soluble materials found (Tressler and Lemon 1951). The challenge with sea water is to demineralize it cheaply enough so that it can compete with natural water supplies. There is a limit of practicability as to what water can cost.

Costs to Recover Water

There is a great demand for irrigation and domestic waters at the present time. Costs to obtain water at the present time for irrigation may be as low as one dollar per acre foot to as high as $1,000 per acre foot for distilled municipal waters on certain islands of the world. In the United States, maximum prices of the present day are about $40 per acre foot for irrigation water and $125 per acre foot for municipal supplies (Huberty and Flock 1959). Water recovery systems from sea water sources must be somewhat competitive with these values. Careful analysis of the possibilities of reusing water must also be made.

A lower trend in the cost to demineralize water is underway. Extensive research programs are currently in progress around the world on this problem. The United States government alone is investing in excess of 300 million dollars in 1961 on this research.

Types of Recovery Systems

Small systems for distilling and recovering water are found in many of the large cities in the United States, for example, used to develop water for storage batteries in automobiles. Water distilling systems are found on most of the large ocean going vessels. These systems are capable of producing perhaps 40 thousand gallons per day of fresh water from sea water.

There are various processes which have been developed to make fresh water from sea water. These systems can be classified as physical systems, chemical systems, and electrical processes.

Physical systems take advantage of the distillation, freezing, absorption and diffusion characteristics of water. Chemical processes include precipitation and the use of ion exchange systems. Electrical systems include various applications of electrolysis phenomena (Howe 1959).

The largest plants at the present time are found in the Persian Gulf and in the West Indies. The plant in the Persian Gulf consists of flash type distillation unit which yields about 2.5 million gallons per day. In the West Indies the plant at Aruba produces about the same amount per day (Huberty and Flock 1959).

In South Africa a large electrical dialysis plant for desalting water coming from mines is operating. This plant handles three million gallons of water per day, but only reduces the concentration of minerals in the water from three thousand to one thousand parts per million.

Distillation is the process of separating pure water from salt water brine by evaporating the water, removing the vapor then condensing it. This is possible because the salts dissolved in sea water are nonvolatile as compared to the water solvent. Economy in the use of heat used for evaporation can be made by regenerating systems, leading to multiple-effect distillation equipment. Each subsequent "effect" is operated at a lower pressure than the previous one. In England using six-effect distillation plants, the cost to produce water is approximately a thousand dollars per acre foot, the cost being predominantly fuel cost. Some have thought that it would be possible to increase the number of distillation stages and improve on the economics of the over-all costs. Using perhaps 15 to 18 effects, it is conceivably possible to produce fresh water from sea water at about $150 per acre foot. No such plants have as yet been built (U. S. Dept. Agr. 1955).

Other systems involve flash distillation procedures which are thought to have an economy over the conventional multiple effect plant.

Flash vacuum distillation procedures are designed to take advantage of the variations in temperature of sea water. A warmer sea water can be passed into a vacuum chamber and evaporated. The vapor so produced can be condensed by circulation through a heat exchanger. Howe has reported that power must be supplied to remove the brine from the vacuum chamber, to eliminate the air from the system, to remove the condensate from the condenser, and to circulate cold water. With a temperature difference available of 35°F. or more, it appears possible to interpose a turban wheel in the vapor path between the evaporator and condenser. For such plants, producing 100 thousand gallons per day or more, a turban wheel could be installed and could produce sufficient power to operate the pumping machinery (Huberty and Flock 1959). Experiments to determine the efficiency of the rather unusual equipment involved are underway at the University of California. Preliminary estimates are that the process could operate at $100 per acre foot when the system is placed next to sea water supplies which would give a difference of temperature of 35°F. or more. Warm water can be obtained from the surface of the ocean and cold water from the depths, perhaps 1,500 feet or more, in the ocean. In some locations in the world, temperature differentials in excess of 35° can be obtained. These are areas which could greatly benefit from increased fresh water supplies.

Solar Distillation.—Systems have been developed for recovering fresh water from sea water without the use of fuel sources. Solar energy is collected and water heated with the collected energy. Water evaporates and the water vapor is collected and condensed. Tests have indicated that on a year-round basis about 50 per cent of the solar energy that hits the surfaces can be accounted for in the latent heat of the distillate produced from these simple stills. Its production capacity is about one gallon per eight to ten square feet of collector surface. First cost estimates were in the order of $10 per gallon per day of capacity. Using the most advanced system it is estimated that costs of water so produced would be in the order of $1,000 per acre foot at best.

The use of *freezing* as a means of recovering fresh water from the oceans has been proposed. When water is frozen only the pure water crystallizes and dissolved salts remain in solution in a brine. The energy relationships seem attractive since the latent heat of fusion is only one-seventh that of the heat of vaporization. Some schemes for separating ice from brine involve compressing the ice to squeeze the brine from it or centrifuging and washing the flaked ice formed.

At its best this system has been estimated to cost between $100 and $160 per acre foot of water produce which would indicate this system has considerable promise.

There are a number of *chemical processes* for the separation of salts from sea water; most would precipitate the unwanted materials from solution and use ion exchange systems. Such systems are satisfactory for small quantities of water. Ion exchange processes in general are effective for waters containing less than 2,000 parts per million of dissolved minerals. At the best it is thought that cost to purify water by such techniques is in the vicinity of $1,000 per acre foot (Howe 1959).

Electrolysis

Because sea water is a solution containing ionized materials it is capable of carrying electric currents. One system uses a series of semi-permeable membranes, separated from one another in compartments. The application of an electric potential at the ends of the compartments causes the ions to migrate out of the center compartment and toward the end compartments. The water in the center compartment becomes demineralized. This type of system requires too much power to be used with sea water.

It has recently been thought that by having a large number of compartments in a series between two electrodes the efficiency of the system might be improved. This became possible very recently with the development of electrically positive and negative membranes. The power requirement is proportional to the amount of ions to be removed. It appears now that brackish water can be converted into acceptable irrigation water from supplies which contain 35 hundred parts per million of dissolved salts at a cost of less than $50 per acre foot.

According to Howe (1959) the lowest reliable cost estimates a decade ago for demineralizing sea water was about $470 per acre foot for vapor compression systems. During the last two years investigations have shown that figures as low as $100 are possible. In order to reduce this figure to $40, it would require some radical modifications of existing systems or more likely the development of new processes, as yet unknown.

IMPROVED PRACTICES REQUIRED

Present knowledge of the water requirements of plants and animals is adequate to achieve a much greater production of food. The potential of water use technology is tremendous but limited at present by economics. As the demand for water increases, further improvements will undoubtedly take place.

The opportunity to increase the available water supply for irrigation purposes leaves something to be desired. It would seem that an immense potential exists in making better use of the available surface fresh water sources of the world. Considered as a whole the water sources of the world certainly are adequate to meet the needs of agriculture providing the technology available is applied.

The efficiency with which farmers apply irrigation water to their crops is poor (see Fig. 12). A small portion of the water diverted for irrigation is available to plant roots; the remainder is lost as run-off, deep percolation or evaporation.

The use of waters for irrigation usually results in a rising water table in the soil. When the water table rises too near the surface it can produce drainage and salinity problems which must be corrected if cropping is not to be limited. Furthermore, water level variations during growing seasons alter the growth of plants (see Fig. 13).

In certain parts of the world, ground water supplies were once thought to be limitless. Before 1910 many of the wells of California had pressures of more than ten lb. per square inch and flowed at 900 gal. per minute. The pumping rate in 1950 dropped in some cases to ten gal. per minute. In some parts of California the water level in wells has been declining at the rate of three feet a year (U. S.

Dept. Agr. 1955). Elsewhere industrial waters are fed back into the soil through return wells.

The water supplies available can be extended by adopting controls which tend to conserve surface and ground water resources for beneficial uses. Good water laws establish a control of use among competitive needs, protecting water rights of the users and reduce wastage. Planning is usefully undertaken for all river basin systems. There can be more efficient reuse of industrial waters. Much water which is currently not useful may be reclaimed. There can be improvements in land-use practices to conserve natural precipitation and reduce the movement of sediment. There could be an improvement in the handling and use of irrigation water to reduce the losses in transportation and increase the efficiency of application. There can be an intensification in drainage, irrigation and flood control activities. Recent development has found that by applying thin chemical coatings over water reservoirs the rate of evaporation of water from the surface can be reduced. This may have some bearing in the future in areas where water is in very short supply.

SUMMARY

In summary, fresh water is often a limiting factor in food production in the world. Although the supply of water on earth exceeds the demand, the problem is that the distribution of water resources on the land of the world is uneven, and can not be easily manipulated.

There are areas where water shortages occur in serious proportions. Furthermore, the water resource problem becomes larger each year due to increasing human populations, hence water demands.

Some progress can be made by organized efforts in nations and between nations to apply the water-use technology available, consistent with good conservation practices.

Data available showing the extent of irrigation (Table 11) indicates that the countries with the most irrigation (China, Pakistan, and India) also have the greatest gap between the food needs of their peoples and the food supply available.

The potential of planting crops ecologically adapted to the conditions in local areas, with less general technology being required, has not been adequately explored.

The uneven distribution of water resources in the world becomes more serious each year.   Some progress can be made by organized efforts by the nations of the world.

The application of water to crops is a major factor in agriculture. The productivity of agriculture is a major limiting factor for the peoples of the world.

The moisture which reaches the land masses of the world varies in form, in amount, in intensity, in the time of year when it occurs and in its distribution.   For the most part, man remains at its mercy.

CHAPTER 8

Food from the Seas

There are two major food supply sources for men on earth—agriculture and fisheries. While at the present time only about three per cent of the world's food comes from marine sources, in some areas the products from the seas constitute ten per cent and more of the food supply of a nation (Tressler and Lemon 1951).

WORLD CATCH OF FISH

The total catch and landings of fish, crustaceans, and shellfish by the countries of the world are shown in Table 15. Included in this data are the trends in the catch over a twelve year period.

More than three million men are employed in the fishing industry around the world (United Nations 1957).

WORLD FISH HARVESTS

The world's fish catch is approximately 40 billion pounds a year, of which 98 per cent is taken in the northern Hemisphere (Fig. 14). About 47 per cent of the harvest is obtained in the North Pacific and 46 per cent in the North Atlantic. Five per cent is obtained in the Indian Ocean and one per cent in the South Pacific and the South Atlantic Oceans. The Asiatics catch about half of the total catch, Europeans a third, and North Americans about 15 per cent. Although fish are caught in fresh waters and along coastal areas of land of the earth, the great commercial fishing is in the Northern oceans at high middle latitudes (Tressler and Lemon 1951; Anderson 1959).

Oceans—A Major Food Source

As a biological system, sea water contains approximately one part of living or dead organic matter in 100,000, which would amount to about 20 thousand tons of organic matter per cubic mile.

About 140 million square miles of the earth's surface is occupied by the oceans, which have an average depth of slightly more than two miles. The volume of the ocean is approximately 330 million cubic miles.

About 70 thousand cubic miles of sea water are evaporated annually. These eventually return in the form of rain, surface water and ground water. As this water returns to the sea, nearly three billion tons of dissolved salts are carried to the oceans.

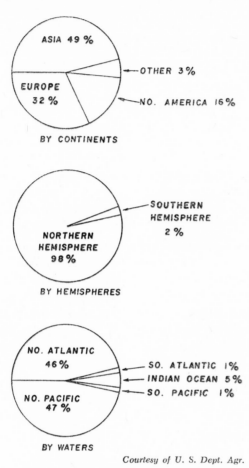

Courtesy of U. S. Dept. Agr.

FIG. 14. COMMERCIAL FISH CATCH BY CONTINENTS, HEMISPHERES, AND WATERS

Composition of Sea Water

Sea water contains about 3.5 per cent of dissolved salts, which are mainly the chlorides and sulfates of sodium, magnesium, calcium and potassium. Appreciable amounts of bromine, iodine, iron, silicon, carbonate and phosphate also occur. More than 30 other elements are found in some quantity.

TABLE 15

TOTAL ANNUAL CATCH AND LANDINGS OF FISH, CRUSTACEANS, MOLLUSKS, ETC., BY SELECTED
COUNTRIES; 1938 AND 1947–56[1]

C—Catch (live weight),
L—landings (landed weight),
CL—catch and landings identical

Country	1938	1947	1948	1949	1950	1951	1952	1953	1954	1955	1956
					Thousand Metric Tons						
Major Producers:											
Canada (including Newfoundland)											
.... C	837	988	1,053	1,000	1,048	1,013	940	925	1,026	954	1,077
L	761	878	960	899	962	927	858	851	956	884	997
China (Mainland)											
............CL	1,500[2]	...	...	440	910	1,300	1,667	1,890	2,290	2,520	2,550
Japan........CL	3,562	2,206	2,431	2,642	3,086	3,666	4,820	4,522	4,545	4,913	4,763
Norway....... C	1,153	1,196	1,504	1,297	1,468	1,839	1,815	1,557	2,068	1,813	2,129
L	1,017	1,032	1,318	1,084	1,279	1,669	1,670	1,398	1,905	1,647	1,960
United Kingdom											
.... C	1,198	1,172	1,206	1,159	989	1,086	1,105	1,122	1,070	1,100	1,050
L	1,098	1,047	1,098	1,049	926	993	1,038	1,030	980	1,004	975
United States (including Alaska)...... C	2,253	2,283	2,410	2,504	2,590	2,365	2,391	2,438	2,706	2,739	2,936
L	1,930	1,967	2,041	2,172	2,216	2,002	1,950	2,019	2,151	2,087	...
U.S.S.R.......CL	1,523	1,427	1,486	1,827	1,627	1,977	1,888	1,983	2,258	2,498	2,617
Medium Producers:											
Angola........CL	26	51	113	131	136	177	154	220	261	290	...
Brazil.........CL	103	140	145	153	153	158	175	161	172	...	...
China (Taiwan).CL	90	63	84	80	84	104	122	130	152	180	193
Chile.........CL	32	61	65	77	88	94	119	107	144	214	188
Denmark...... C	97	206	226	258	251	293	324	343	359	425	463
L	89	195	217	245	241	281	312	331	353	418	456
France[3]....... C	530	476	468	474	454	528	488	520	500	523	538
L	463	441	422	426	408	482	426	459	445	459	479
Germany, Western..... C	777	...	409	501	552	679	663	730	678	777	771
L	714	270	368	459	511	636	621	693	642	734	681
Iceland....... C	274	484	478	408	373	418	402	425	455	480	517
L	...	433	414	343	324	371	335	361	384	407	444
India.........CL	...	662	...	570	817	751	744	819	828	839	1,012
Italy.........CL	181	160	157	178	184	185	212	208	218	218	219
Korea, South...CL	832	302	285	300	216	265	278	257	247	259	341
Malaya........CL	...	119	139	162	148	144	136	147	137	137	...
Morocco[4]......CL	31	51	56	93	123	91	122	128	93	82	99
Netherlands.... C	256	295	294	264	258	294	314	343	339	320	298
L	226	256	258	234	230	262	277	311	301	276	264
Pakistan.......CL	...	...	...	...	...	239	243	249	260	271	277
Peru..........CL	...	31	48	45	74	97	113	118	146	183	250
Phillippines..... C	81	251	195	238	226	299	318	312	365	386	416
Portugal....... C	247	282	292	281	307	307	363	425	439	425	471
L	218	230	221	214	229	233	255	293	307	287	321
Spain......... C	409[6]	581	547	571	598	604	612	635	650	760	749
L	388[6]	541	504	518	538	547	549	569	578	676	668
Sweden........ C	129	165	194	182	187	183	204	197	193	209	...
L	124	156	184	173	176	173	194	187	184	200	165
Thailand.......CL	161	151	161	154	178	187	192	205	230	213	218
Turkey........CL	76	...	...	...	...	110	100	103	119	112	140
Union of South Africa (including S.W. Africa)...... C	68	118	191	233	306	465	652	651	634	621	582
L	59	103	171	208	272	441	629	627	610	595	550
Selected Smaller Producers:											
Argentina......CL	55	65	71	65	58	78	79	77	78	79	75
Australia......CL	34	38	39	35	33	38	46	52	54	52	50
Belgian Congo..CL	1	14	18	25	43	37	49	67	66	81	...
Belgium....... C	43	81	71	68	59	57	71	74	72	80	69
L	41	81	66	63	54	52	65	69	66	73	62
Ceylon........CL	...	...	24	36	43	37	26	26	30	31	40
Egypt.........CL	38	47	43	55	44	50	54	52	57	63	70
Faeroes.......CL	63	97	92	100	98	93	87	89	89	106	116
Finland........CL	44	46	46	66	66	66	58	62	66	63	60
Greece........CL	25	22	34	35	52	43	43	46	53	60	65
Hong Kong.... C	...	...	34	...	...	35	41	40	47	46	...
L	...	14	25	27	31	31	36	35	43	43	...

Country	1938	1947	1948	1949	1950	1951	1952	1953	1954	1955	1956
Ireland........ C	13	22	26	18	17	17	19	19	22	24	31
L	12	20	25	16	16	16	18	18	20	23	29
Mexico........CL	17	54	68	68	74	75	58	67	...	...	...
Morocco⁶......CL	...	11	11	10	9	9	11	11	10	13	9
New Zealand... C	27	34	36	37	35	35	36	37	37	39	...
L	25	31	33	34	32	32	33	34	34	36	...
Poland........CL	...	40	...	74	81	88	92	84	106	113	127
Tunisia........CL	10	10	12	11	12	15	13	12	...	...	...
Uganda........CL	...	9	11	12	15	20	23	23	24	25	34
Venezuela......CL	22	76	92	75	78	75	62	63	52	70	61
Yugoslavia.....CL	17	11	21	27	26	25	24	26	23	23	28

1 From United Nations (1957). ² 1936 data. ³ Includes Algeria. ⁴ Data refer to former French Protectorate. ⁵ 1934 data. ⁶ Data refer to former Spanish Protectorate. ... Data not available.

While sea water is relatively constant in salinity, there is a slight increase in the polar regions of the earth brought about by concentration through freezing. Ice is removed from the salt water by freezing, leaving somewhat larger proportions of salts behind. The sources of the salt content of the seas is thought to be the weathering of the rocks and land of the earth.

It has been estimated that if the soluble salts present in the oceans were removed and recovered, they would form a layer nearly 500 feet deep over the surface of the land of the earth. A constituent of sea water occurring in the proportion of one in a billion would amount to 150 billion tons of the substances in all of the sea waters of this world.

Plankton—Primary Food Supplies of the Oceans

The oceans of earth receive seven-tenths of the radiant energy incident on the earth's surfaces. Most of the solar energy is absorbed near the surface of the oceans. The first 100 to 150 feet of the surface of the oceans is occupied by minute photosynthetic plants. They are extremely numerous in types and amounts found. Those microscopic plants and microscopic animals found to occupy the oceans are called collectively the plankton—the primary food supplies of the oceans. During the times of the year when sunlight intensity is at its maximum, plankton may grow to such concentrations in sea waters that the waters may appear slightly muddy. It is estimated that 400 tons of vegetable matter are produced annually per square mile of sea water in the English channel, for example.

Cycle of Life in Oceans

The minute plants which grow in the ocean are consumed by the various species of organisms present. The herring, menhaden, shad, sardines, and mackerels consume plankton, and subsequently are fed upon by the larger fish. Dead plankton settle in the bottom of the oceans to become food for macroscopic animals, which in turn become the food supply of crabs, lobsters, cod, and haddock for example. There is a cycle of living organisms from the surface to the bottom of the oceans. One end product of this cycle is the production of fish which become sufficiently large to be suitable as food for mankind.

Major Fishing Areas of the World

The important fishing areas in the world are concentrated near land; a small portion of the total ocean surface contributes most of the fish taken for food. The chief fishing regions appear to be along the ocean currents.

The major fishing areas are located generally in cooler waters of high and middle latitudes, and can be divided into (1) commercial fisheries in fresh water, (2) fishing along the coastal areas, and (3) fishing in the open sea or banks. In general, the fresh water fisheries are less important than the coastal or open sea fisheries. Coastal fisheries are perhaps the most common at present.

Fresh Water Fishing

The fish taken in fresh water are of two general types, one migrating from salt water to fresh water streams for a portion of their life cycles, and those that spend their entire life cycles in fresh water streams and lakes. The most significant fresh water fisheries are those in the large lakes and river systems: in North America, the Great Lakes; in Southeastern Europe, the river and inland sea fishing areas; the salmon fisheries of the rivers flowing in the northern Pacific; the inland fisheries in China and Japan.

Great Lakes fishermen in the United States and Canada catch lake herring, trout, pike, white fish, yellow perch, and chub, which together amount to more than three-fourth of the total catch. These fish are usually near, or within a few miles from shore. Lake Erie, Michigan, and Huron yield three-fourths of the quantity of fish taken in the Great Lakes. The northern lakes are beginning to contribute a larger proportion of the total as the other lakes are becoming over fished. In the United States the Mississippi River system waterway and the eastern rivers of the United States yield fish in amounts nearly equal to that of the Great Lakes. Fresh water fish taken from these rivers include the catfish, carp, sheep's head, and buffalo.

Fresh water fisheries of Southeastern Europe include the river-sea systems of the Danube, Dneiper, Don, Volga, and Ural Rivers and the Black, Azov, and Caspian Seas. Two major types of fish are caught —those that spend their lives in salt water, then move into rivers during the spring and summer to spawn and feed, and those that are fresh water fish year round. The herring, sturgeon and salmon are important members of the salt water fish that migrate into the fresh water, and the carp, perch and pike and the sterlet sturgeon being members of the latter type. Fresh water inhabitants amount to one-third of the total fish catch in southeastern Europe. Fishing is concentrated in the lower ends of the rivers and in the great deltas and shallow waters of the inland seas. The great river systems of Southeastern Europe drain vast expanses of rich soils. In rapidly moving rivers, because rich plankton populations present do not have time or the conditions to develop, this food for fish accumulates mainly in the inlets to the major shallow seas, and in the lower levels of tributaries. Seas having no strong currents such as those in the oceans, cannot distribute plankton over large areas. Hence in river deltas, large areas of shallow water with soft muddy bottoms occur. With warm temperatures a rich plankton supply develops and a large variety and number of fish exist upon this supply.

There is a large salmon fishing area in the northern Pacific area, rivers emptying into the northern Pacific having notable populations of salmon. Although large depletions in salmon populations have taken place, the salmon remains one of the most important commercial fish crops in the world. Salmon fishing now exists from Oregon north to Alaska around to Siberia and down to northern Japan. Salmon is the third most important commercial fish, exceeded only by the herring and the cod. About 100 years ago, the Pacific Coast states in the United States and British Columbia supplied nearly all of the salmon consumed. In recent years Alaska, Siberia, and Japan have supplied more than 75 per cent. Strict regulations regarding salmon fishing are presently enforced. There is a need to improve conservation systems internationally between Russia, Japan, and the United States to protect the salmon in this area (Tressler and Lemon 1951).

In southeast Asia and Japan fresh water fish are grown by fish farming systems. Large quantities of carp and other fish are grown in lakes, ponds, and canals. Waters are stocked, fertilized, and harvested.

Commercial Coastal Fishing

Nearly every inhabited coast on earth has some fishing activity. The fish obtained are used either for local consumption or commercial distribution. There is a three mile limit along the coasts of oceans which, by general agreement, yields the rights to fish offshore areas to the inhabitants of the country. People from other countries are excluded from fishing these areas.

The better of these fishing areas usually occur at low and middle latitude areas. The waters of cooler areas contain the largest concentration of this type fishing activity. The warmer waters seem to hamper the development of great fishing systems. A part of the explanation is that plankton are less plentiful in tropical warm waters. It is thought that bacterial invasion in warmer waters is an important limiting factor to the growth of plankton. Plankton in the tropical areas appear to be concentrated in cool water currents in the oceans, along land. Another limiting factor to good coastal fishing can be the absence of a continental shelf.

While the fish populations in warm seas appear to be rather large, it is currently thought that there are fewer of any one type and certainly it has been found that there are fewer useful species of fish. Furthermore, the perishable nature of fresh fish in the high temperatures and humidities, and the lack of refrigeration facilities in tropical areas makes fish preservation most difficult.

Low latitude fishing is carried on extensively in the tropical Americas and in Southeastern Asia. Coastal villages usually have fresh fish available daily. In the channels of the Gangese, in India, for example, commercial fishing is an important component of the food supplying system.

In the United States, one-third of the fish products are obtained from California coastal fishing areas.

Large populations of shell fish are found along sea margins and bays and in enclosed waters. Because shellfish have a limited migration range and they live in shallow waters, an abundant supply of oysters, lobsters, clams, shrimp, crabs, and scallops is commonly available.

The oyster is the most valuable of the shell fish. The chief oyster areas in the United States range from Cape Cod to the Rio Grande River area, in Western Europe from the North Sea area to Northern Spain, and in Eastern Asia from Northern Japan to Southern China. Three-fourths of the oyster supply of the United States comes from the Chesapeake Bay area.

Oysters can be cultivated as a crop. They require a breeding place in shallow stream-fed bays whose waters are less salty than those in the open oceans. Wave movements should not be too great and a food supply must be abundant. For best results, the bottom of the oyster bays must provide a place where the oysters can attach themselves.

A female oyster yields many millions of eggs each season. To reach maturity an oyster requires five years in cold water and two or three years in warm water (Allen 1953). Shells that are removed from the oysters can be put back into the oyster bays to form a part of the bed for the crop.

Lobsters are found in the cool waters of the middle latitudes, and range in North America from Newfoundland to the Delaware Bay and from southern Alaska to northern Mexico. In Europe they range from the coast of Scotland to northern France. In eastern Asia they range up near central Japan. There are also some lobster populations in the southern Hemisphere.

Shrimp and crabs are inhabitants of warm waters of the lower latitudes in sub-tropical areas. They grow well in muddy, soft, or sandy bottoms. Shrimp and crab harvests are well developed in western Europe, eastern Asia, the Mediterranean Area, and along the south Atlantic and Gulf Coast of the United States.

In addition to the above coastal fishing activity, there are some fish which roam widely in schools through the coastal waters and feed near the surfaces. Characteristic of these are tuna and tuna-like species including bonita, and bluefish. These form an important fish catch in eastern Asia, south of Japan, in the western Mediterranean, off the coast of France, and off the southern coast of California.

There are a number of small fish, including the sardine, anchovy, and pilchard. These exist in coastal waters off Japan and China, western Europe, the English Channel down to the western Mediterranean Area, and from British Columbia south to California. On the eastern coast of North America the menhaden is caught in

large numbers. At the present time this fish is used largely in production of fertilizer and oil.

Open Sea Fishing

The greatest catch of fish occurs in the northern oceans at high
middle latitudes. There are three major open sea fishing areas:
European North Atlantic including the North Sea and the White Sea
in Northern Russia; the American North Atlantic from New England
to Labrador; the Pacific Ocean from Southern China to Siberia.

The fishing banks are concentrated in shallow indentation and
above and on elevated parts of the continental shelves the underwa-
ter extensions of land masses are called continental shelves, and are
found in large areas in the Northern Atlantic and Pacific Oceans. In
the North Atlantic the banks have an area of about 100,000 square
miles. Banks in the North Sea region comprise an area of nearly
300,000 square miles. The Eastern Asia banks are found to be approximately 100,000 square miles. The world's richest fish areas are
usually less than two hundred miles from land. The Dogger bank
located nearly in the middle of the North Sea is only 100 miles from
land. The Grand Banks off Newfoundland are 180 miles out.
Georges Bank is 170 miles from Boston. Most of the fishing occurs
in water less than 600 feet deep.

The distribution of fish in the ocean is related to the temperature
of the sea. Jones (1941) has found that cold water species such as
cod, haddock, halibut, herring and mackerel are not in the fish catch
in southern oceans in any quantity.

Major World Fishing Areas

Anderson (1951) reports the following major known fishery resources in the world and their location:

North America.—The Atlantic Ocean—waters around South Green-
land, Labrador, Newfoundland, the Maritime Provinces, and other
parts of Eastern Canada, the Atlantic Coast of the United States and
areas covered by the Davis Strait, the Grand Banks, and the Gulf of
Mexico; the Pacific Ocean—waters around Panama, areas covered by
the Bering Sea, from the Gulf of Alaska to Lower California, and the
off shore Central American area.

South America.—The Atlantic Ocean—waters around Venezuela,
the Guineas, Southern Brazil, Uraguay, Argentina, the Falkland Is-

lands, and Tierra del Fuego; the Pacific Ocean—the waters around Peru, Chile, and the Galapagos Islands.

Asia.—Waters around the Siberian Coast, the East Indies, and the areas covered by the Bering, Okhotsk, Caspian, Japan, and China Seas, and the Bay of Bengal.

Africa.—Waters of the Atlantic Coast of South Africa and Angola, areas covered by the Gulf of Guinea, the waters in the Region of the Cape Verde and the Canary Islands, and the Mediterranean Sea.

TABLE 16

1958 FISHERIES CATCH: QUANTITIES BY GROUPS OF SPECIES[1]

Groups	Quantities Million Metric Tons
Freshwater fish	5.28
Salmons, trouts, smelts, etc.	0.70
Flounders, halibuts, soles, etc.	0.76
Cods, hakes, haddocks, etc.	4.33
Herrings, sardines, anchovies, etc.	7.10
Tunas, bonitas, mackerels, etc.	1.96
Mullets, jacks, sea-bass, etc.	3.49
Sharks, rays, etc.	0.32
Unsorted and unidentified fishes	6.51
Crustaceans	0.75
Mollusks	2.01
Aquatic animals and plants	0.51
World Totals	33.72

[1] From United Nations (1958).

Europe.—Waters around the coasts of Norway, the British Isles, Bay of Biscay, and the North, Baltic, Barents, Kara, and Black Seas.

Australia, New Zealand, and the East Indies.—Waters of the Central and Southern New Zealand Coast, Tasmania and the Southern and Central Australia Coasts. Anderson has reported that the promise for greater developments of fishery resources is apparent in Southern Hemisphere areas off South America, Africa, and Oceania. Asia also has unexploited possibilities. He also has reported that the Northern Hemisphere has untapped potentials in migratory species and species in deep untested waters.

Important Fish Species

The important fish can be divided into four groups. The *bottom dwelling* fish including cod and related species such as haddock, hake, and pollock (also called white fish); flatfishes such as sole.

flounder, and halibut; rosefish and related species; mollusks such as oysters, clams, and mussels; and crustacea such as shrimp, crabs, and lobsters. *Surface swimming:* the herring, and species such as pilchards and menhaden; tuna and tunalike species including bluefin and bonita; mackerel and related species; sharks and sharklike species. *The third group migrates from sea to fresh water to spawn.* This group includes the salmon, the shad, and the smelt. *The fourth group migrates from fresh water to sea water to spawn.* This would include the eels.

TABLE 17

RELATIVE RANKING OF SPECIES ACCORDING TO VALUE OF FISHERIES IN THE UNITED STATES[1]

Position	Species	Approx. Per Cent of Total Catch
1	Salmon	9.7
2	Oysters	9.5
3	Tuna	8.2
4	Shrimp	8.0
5	Haddock	4.1
6	Pilchard	3.6
7	Lobsters, northern	3.6
8	Crabs	3.5
9	Cod	3.5
10	Clams	3.4
11	Flounders	3.2
12	Croakers	2.6
13	Halibut	2.6
14	Mackerel	2.3
15	Sea Trout	2.3
16	Menhaden	2.3
17	Rosefish	1.9
18	Mullet	1.7
19	Lake Trout	1.5
20	Sharks	1.5
	All Others	21.0
	Total	100.0

[1] From Tressler and Lemon (1951).

The herring and related species are the most important in volume of all the fishes taken from the waters of the world. The salmon are considered to be the most valuable (see Tables 16 and 17).

Fish Uses

Two-thirds of the world catch is marketed as fresh, frozen, canned, or cured fishery products for human food. The other third is made into fish meal and oils. Of an approximately 40 billion pound catch, 41 per cent is eaten fresh and frozen, 10 per cent is canned, 16 per cent is cured, and 33 per cent goes into meal, oil, and fertilizer production.

Rates of Production and Consumption

Of all the fish products produced in the world, on an average about five pounds are eaten a year per person. However this value varies greatly. In Canada and the United States, people consume about eleven pounds a year per person. In the Caribbean area it is estimated that about 40 lbs. per person are eaten. People in Norway and Sweden consume about 60 lbs. per person. In the African,

TABLE 18

FISHERY PRODUCTION PER PERSON IN CERTAIN COUNTRIES[1]

Country	Approximate Pounds Per Person
Iceland	6,200
Newfoundland	1,500
Norway	700
Japan	120
Canada	100
Denmark	60
Sweden	50
United Kingdom	50
Netherlands	40
Portugal	40
Spain	40
United States	40
Venezuela	30
Germany	30
France	30
Soviet Union	20
Phillippine Islands	15
Argentina	10
Mexico	10
Italy	10
China	10
India	5
Brazil	5

[1] Adapted from United Nations (1945, 1957, 1958).

Asiatic, and Oceania countries it is estimated that consumption is as high as 100 lbs. per person per year in some areas.

On the other hand, the production of fish per person per country varies over a much larger range (see Table 18).

Need For Research

Tressler and Lemon (1951) report that research is a relatively new activity in the fishing industry, having existed for less than three decades. In the United States more than five dollars is spent in agricultural research per ton of human food compared to less than one dollar per ton of fish products. Realizing the potential of reseach in improving fisheries resources it would seem appropriate to consider favorably the exploitation of our resources of oceans, lakes, and streams. Jul (1951) has reported of the great potential of southern hemisphere waters. He reports that 95 per cent of all marine products (excluding whales and whale products) are caught in the northern hemisphere, but that this does not mean that the southern hemisphere has extremely limited fisheries resources. It is perhaps natural to assume that the catch could be increased in southern hemisphere areas if fishing activities were intensified. In recent years Chili, Peru, and the Union of South Africa have increased their catch, confirming reports that have indicated the existence of unused fishing resources. Jul predicts that there is substantial room for development not only in the southern hemisphere but also in areas where heretofore, little fishery activities have taken place.

Knowledge of the fish resources of the ocean is limited today. One of the significant contributions which could be made to increase the supply of marine products would be through extensive explorations of the less known fishing grounds. Research, according to Jul (1951), should be aimed at determining not only the existing resources but also how these can best be maintained and the extent to which they can be continued to be exploited.

While it is true that certain areas of the ocean are over-fished at the present time there are hundreds of species of fish which occur in large quantities which are seldom utilized. Possibilities of fish culturing systems would also appear worthy of exploitation.

There are many banks north of Eurasia and North America which have fertile fishing grounds and these are as yet untouched. However, these are very distant from markets and in seas which are open only a few months each year. Catching fish on these banks would be somewhat more expensive.

Fish in the major banks of the present have been vigorously exploited over many years, and there are signs of marked declines in the fish catch. Realistic conservation practices are indicated and these are the subject of international meetings between nations.

It is a consensus of expert opinions that if fishing is to continue to be an important component in producing the food supplies of the people of the earth, investigation of the life histories and habits of the fish and some system of regulation must develop whereby fish are allowed to spawn sufficiently to reproduce themselves in adequate numbers. Improved methods of fishing might be developed to avoid the destruction of small fish which die after being caught in nets.

Some countries maintain huge fish hatcheries and seasonally stock coastal waters and inland waters, and some fishing can even take on the aspects of farming, for example.

Hertzler reports developments of great salt water ranches where portions of estuaries are fenced in and fish are fed on native plankton. Fish might be produced in great quantities, much as is done in present systems of raising livestock on land.

Fish are an important food supply for man, and fish can be very abundant in certain parts of the ocean. For example, more than two billion pounds of herring are caught annually in the North Sea. This is remarkable when we consider that the area has been fished for more than a thousand years.

Uses of Fish in U. S.

The commercial fisheries in the United States and Alaska yield a catch of 4.6 billion pounds annually. They are distributed as follows: 903 million pounds marketed fresh; 579 million pounds marketed fresh or frozen in the form of fillets; 211 million pounds marketed frozen not filleted; 100 million pounds cured; 1,459,000,000 lbs. canned; 1,348,000,000 lbs. as by-products; and 650,000,000 lbs. occurring as waste for fresh and processed fish. Salt water fin fish make up 85 per cent of the catch, salt water shell fish about 1 per cent, and fresh water fish about five per cent in the United States. Twenty varieties of fish accunt for most of the catch (see Table 17).

Changing Demand for Fish

New species of fish are being consumed rather than new uses for species that are available. It was not long ago that the rosefish was of no commercial importance. It was actually thrown overboard by fishermen sorting the rosefish from cod and haddock which they sought. Recently the rosefish has been marketed in fillets, skinned and frozen and sold as ocean perch. Since its introduction following World War II, consumer reaction has been very favorable. Demand now exceeds production possibilities in this former trash fish which now finds ready use. Another example is with the rock fish which formerly was not considered suitable for food but which now is being exploited with some success. There is an abundance of carp in many fresh water lakes and streams and there are many other possibilities in the future for other fish types.

Any attempt to establish new fishing industries or to increase the production of existing industries depends on the existence of markets for the catch. This is particularly important in areas where fish have been heretofore limited. Several projects which attempted to introduce fish into the diets of people not accustomed to consuming fish have been unsuccessful. These local inland populations were not accustomed to eating fish.

Adequate distribution of the catch is an important consideration. Fish is a highly perishable commodity. However, adequate technology exists for handling perishable fish in dried, frozen, canned and pickled forms. It is thought that research which would contribute to improving or extending the distribution or utilization of commercial marine products is equally as important as research into fisheries resources or fishing methods.

According to Jul, in the long run the trend will undoubtedly go towards the development of more staple fish products. Salting of fish has been for many years the main method of preservation. With interest in salted fish products on the decline it is not unlikely that staple fish products could be made more palatable than products that now make up the bulk of the salt fish trade.

Increased Food From The Seas

Fish are excellent sources of protein in human diets, and fish have always been a substantial part of the world's supply of high quality protein. From a nutritional standpoint fish protein is as useful for mankind as protein from meat animals.

Fish as noted earlier are eaten fresh or preserved by canning, salting, smoking, pickling, and freezing. Fish which are considered non-edible are made into fertilizers, meal, and oil. Fish liver oils are important commercial products. There are also a number of by-products from the fresh fish industry. Are there non-fishing possibilities?

In addition to fish, there are vegetable products from the sea, including seaweed. Yet, when we consider the tremendous quantity of products produced in the seas of the world, our use of these appears very small. Plankton is mentioned commonly as a marine food of almost inexhaustible supply. Their composition is about 50–60 per cent protein, 5–15 per cent fat, around 15 per cent carbohydrates, and also rich in minerals and vitamins. (The vitamin A value of cod liver oil for example comes initially from plankton.)

There is a potential in *utilizing plankton* in the oceans. The natural rate of conversion of plankton to fish is not a highly efficient one. Plankton themselves are highly nutritious, and can be good sources of the nutrients man needs.

Plankton could be an important feed for land animals which in turn could be added to the human diet.

At first glance the 400 tons of plants produced per square mile of ocean surface would seem an easy catch. We find, however, that what we have available is an unexploited source with mixed potentials.

As so aptly stated by Tressler and Lemon (1951) sea water is water only in the sense that water is the dominant substance present. Sea water can be considered as the self-replenishing homeland of the plankton. How to harvest the plankton resources of the oceans remains the challenge. The only workable system of the present time is to harvest plankton in the form of fish, and this method is most inefficient. The successful harvesting of plankton themselves could have an immense impact on the food production capability of men.

The oceans of the earth, while recognized as a great natural resource, remain an unexploited wilderness at present.

CHAPTER 9

The World's Food Production

The preceding chapters in Part II were designed to explore the fountainheads of man's foods and the limits of natural resources and present practices in generating his food needs.

In Chapter 5 we saw that indeed a technology of food production has evolved with man. We also saw that modern man has failed to produce any new crops in the past 450 years and this perhaps has contributed to his present dilemma.

In Chapter 6 we saw that there is more land available in the world for food production but that this land is of less productive capacity than the land already in use, the extension of localized successes of modern scientific agriculture to the other areas of the world would require capital resources that are not presently available, and that there is little hope for a spectacular change in this situation in the near future.

In Chapter 7 we saw that the world's water resources are much greater than the needs of man, but these water resources are not equally distributed over the surface of the world we inhabit and as a result water *is* a limiting factor presently in the expansion of efficient agriculture. Further, the three countries with the greatest amount of irrigation already have the greatest problem in attempting to expand food production.

In Chapter 8 we saw that the world's fish harvests conceivably could be increased but that further expansion requires cooperative research and development on a rather wide scale by many nations. Since this is slow in occurrence at best, if it occurs at all, then a significant expansion of fish harvests from the seas must not be anticipated in the near future.

Considering the above, it would be useful to know how successful man is in producing, harvesting and gathering foods with present practices. An indication can be found by looking into the nature of the world's food supplies. After studying the nature and rate of increase that is occurring in these gross supplies, we could compare them with the rate of increase in human populations on earth. From such an analysis we should be in a position to make certain judgements about the adequacy of present practices, and perhaps pinpoint areas where progress could be made.

HOW MUCH FOOD IS PRODUCED ANNUALLY IN THE WORLD?

One of the assignments of the Food and Agriculture Organization of the United Nations is to develop estimates of the world's food supply. A summary of results of a recent survey for the major food crops is shown in Table 19. The estimated stocks of major food com-

TABLE 19

ESTIMATED WORLD[1] PRODUCTION OF MAJOR FOOD COMMODITIES[2]

Commodity	1934–38 Average	1948–52 Average	1953–54	1954–55	1955–56	1956–57
			Million Metric Tons			
Wheat....................	95.0	111.3	130.2	118.6	123.4	121.5
Barley....................	28.5	36.0	43.9	44.8	46.4	52.6
Oats.....................	37.5	42.5	41.4	42.2	45.7	44.3
Maize....................	94.1	119.7	128.4	122.8	129.6	135.2
Rice (milled equivalent).......	70.2	74.8	86.4	82.2	88.0	91.6
Sugar (centrifugal)...........	20.0	26.6	30.8	31.6	32.0	33.3
Citrus fruit.................	11.1	14.9	17.0	17.5	17.8	17.7
Apples....................	11.0	12.6	13.0	13.8	12.8	13.7
Bananas...................	8.1	10.5	10.9	11.5	11.7	11.4
Vegetable oils and oilseeds (oil equivalent)...............	9.2	11.6	12.7	13.2	13.3	14.5
Animal fats................	2.97	4.10	4.52	4.65	5.05	5.25
Coffee....................	2.41	2.26	2.51	2.52	2.81	2.65
Cocoa....................	0.74	0.76	0.74	0.81	0.85	0.92
Tea......................	0.47	0.56	0.60	0.66	0.67	0.67
Wine.....................	18.0	17.6	20.7	21.2	21.3	20.6
Milk (total)................	193.6	205.6	225.6	229.3	232.4	235.7
Meat[3]....................	26.9	30.8	34.4	35.8	37.3	38.4
Eggs.....................	5.81	7.50	8.27	8.69	8.84	9.04
Index of all farm products.....	85	100	111	111	114	117

[1] Excluding U.S.S.R., Eastern Europe and China.
[2] From United Nations (1957).
[3] Beef and veal, mutton and lamp and pigmeat.

modities over a number of years are shown in Table 20. The quantities shown in the latter table include normal carry-over stocks.

FOOD PRODUCTION BY CONTINENTS

The production of food commodities in the world by continents is shown in Table 21 for North America, Table 22 for Latin America, Table 23 for Western Europe, Table 24 for Africa, Table 25 for the Near East, Table 26 for the Far East, and Table 27 for Oceania. The countries which are included in each of these major divisions of the world are shown at the bottom of each of the individual tables. Data

TABLE 20

ESTIMATED STOCKS OF MAJOR COMMODITIES, 1952–57[1]

Commodity	Month and Day	Stocks						Production, 1952–55 Average	Gross Exports, 1952–55 Average
		1952	1953	1954	1955	1956	1957		
		—Million Metric Tons (Quantities Shown Include Normal Carry-Over Stocks)—							
Wheat									
United States..............	1 July	7.0	16.5	25.4	28.2	28.1	24.5	29.9	7.9
Canada...................	1 Aug.	5.9	10.4	16.4	13.6	14.7	17.5	14.3	8.3
Argentina................	1 Dec.	0.1	2.0	1.6	2.2	1.1	...	6.7	2.7
Australia.................	1 Dec.	0.5	1.0	2.5	2.5	2.3	...	5.2	2.5
Total—4 major exports...		13.5	29.9	45.9	46.5	46.2	45.0	56.1	21.4
France...................	1 Aug.	1.2	0.8	1.0	1.4	0.9	0.7	9.6	1.3
Italy.....................	1 Aug.	...	...	2.1	1.4	2.7	2.9	8.4	0.7
Rice (milled equivalent)									
Asian exporters	31 Dec.	0.7	1.4	1.3	0.5	0.5	...	20.5	3.2
United States..............	31 July	0.1	—	0.4	1.4	1.0	0.5	1.7	0.6
Mediterranean.............	30 Sept.	—	—	0.2	0.3	0.2	...	1.5	0.3
Total...................		0.8	1.4	1.9	2.2	1.7	...	23.7	4.1
Coarse Grains									
United States..............	1 July	18.2	24.5	29.2	35.8	39.6	44.9	107.8	3.9
Canada...................	1 Aug.	3.6	5.1	5.6	3.8	4.5	7.2	12.6	3.0
Total—2 major exporters..		21.8	29.6	34.8	39.6	44.1	52.1	120.4	6.9
Butter									
United States..............	Dec.	0.01	0.03	0.01	0.02	0.02	...	0.70	—
Cheese									
United States..............	Dec.	0.10	0.11	0.09	0.09	0.28	...	0.60	—
Dried Skim Milk									
United States..............	Dec.	0.02	0.06	0.04	0.02	0.01	...	0.56	0.06
Liquid Edible Vegetable Oils									
United States..............	1 Oct.	0.24	0.58	0.56	0.33	0.28	0.43	2.41	0.39
Sugar (raw value)									
Cuba....................	31 Dec.	2.16	1.51	1.95	1.62	0.64	...	4.83	4.82
World Total............	31 Aug.	10.7	10.2	12.0	11.5	10.5	...	37.4	12.6

[1] From United Nations (1958, 1960).

TABLE 21

NORTH AMERICA: PRODUCTION OF SELECTED COMMODITIES[1]

Commodity	1934–38 Average	1948–52 Average	1953–54	1954–55	1955–56	1956–5 7
	Million Metric Tons					
Wheat......................	33.80	44.46	48.64	35.19	38.89	41.78
Oats.......................	65.60[2]	25.30	23.02	25.19	28.11	24.96
Maize......................	53.20	82.36	82.06	78.24	82.84	88.27
Rice (milled equivalent)........	0.62	1.25	1.59	1.89	1.65	1.40
Potatoes...................	11.94	12.83	12.38	11.41	12.14	12.90
Citrus fruit.................	3.62	6.41	7.45	7.32	7.45	7.51
Vegetable oils and oilseeds (oil equivalent)...............	1.19	2.66	2.75	2.87	3.21	3.71
Animal fats.................	1.29	2.37	2.52	2.52	2.79	2.85
Milk (total).................	54.55	58.59	62.18	63.20	63.94	64.83
Meat[3].....................	8.04	10.91	12.15	12.47	13.29	13.88
Eggs......................	2.42	3.77	3.85	3.95	3.94	3.95
Index of all farm products.....	73	100	107	104	108	112

[1] From United Nations (1957).
[2] 1937–41 average. Average production for 1934–38 was abnormally low owing to the effects of droughts in 1934–36.
[3] Beef and veal, pigmeat, mutton, and lamb.

TABLE 22

LATIN AMERICA: PRODUCTION OF SELECTED COMMODITIES[1]

Commodity	1934–38 Average	1948–52 Average	1953–54	1954–55	1955–56	1956–57
	Million Metric Tons					
Wheat.....................	8.62	7.94	9.78	11.70	9.52	11.58
Maize.....................	18.00	15.12	18.62	17.32	18.99	17.88
Rice (milled equivalent).......	1.33	3.07	3.56	3.79	3.83	3.88
Sugar (centrifugal)...........	6.89	12.33	12.72	12.84	12.73	13.84
Citrus fruit.................	3.28	3.64	3.81	3.92	4.02	3.92
Bananas...................	4.20	6.80	7.63	7.90	8.10	7.90
Coffee.....................	2.11	1.89	2.02	2.01	2.25	2.07
Cocoa.....................	0.24	0.25	0.26	0.31	0.29	0.30
Milk (total)................	12.22	14.72	16.70	17.08	18.01	18.69
Meat[2].....................	5.02	6.07	6.09	6.30	6.48	6.65
Eggs......................	0.48	0.59	0.69	0.74	0.79	0.84
Index of all farm products.....	82	100	108	113	116	119

[1] From United Nations (1957).
[2] Beef and veal, pork, mutton and lamb.

TABLE 23

WESTERN EUROPE: PRODUCTION OF SELECTED COMMODITIES[1]

Commodity	1934–38 Average	1948–52 Average	1953–54	1954–55	1955–56	1956–57
	Million Metric Tons					
Wheat.....................	31.07	30.32	35.14	35.69	37.79	31.80
Rye.......................	7.49	6.65	6.80	7.65	6.70	7.14
Barley.....................	9.08	10.93	13.86	13.72	14.74	19.16
Oats......................	16.44	14.84	15.66	14.58	14.78	16.28
Maize.....................	9.73	7.14	9.45	8.55	9.76	10.15
Sugar (centrifugal)...........	4.02	5.20	7.14	6.66	6.98	6.61
Potatoes...................	69.87	76.28	77.85	81.05	73.26	83.17
Citrus fruit.................	1.99	2.10	2.36	2.63	2.52	2.22
Apples....................	7.42	8.72	9.24	9.49	8.70	10.15
Olive oil...................	0.81	0.86	1.11	0.86	0.69	0.84
Animal fats................	1.05	0.89	1.08	1.19	1.26	1.33
Wine......................	14.13	13.09	15.84	15.32	16.09	15.08
Milk (total)................	77.02	77.15	88.64	91.08	90.33	91.23
Meat[2].....................	8.72	7.77	9.47	10.28	10.58	10.76
Eggs......................	1.94	2.09	2.45	2.65	2.71	2.79
Index of all farm products.....	93	100	115	115	116	118

[1] From United Nations (1957).
[2] Beef and veal, pork, mutton and lamb.

for the U.S.S.R., Eastern Europe and China are contained in a separate Table 28.

North America

Agricultural production in North America rose about four per cent in the years 1956–1957 reaching new record levels in Canada and the United States. In Canada the increase was as much as eight per

TABLE 24

AFRICA: PRODUCTION OF SELECTED COMMODITIES[1]

Commodity	1934–38 Average	1948–52 Average	1953–54	1954–55	1955–56	1956–57
	Million Metric Tons					
Wheat....................	2.50	2.98	3.58	4.11	3.64	4.03
Barley...................	2.09	2.56	2.98	3.14	2.33	3.07
Maize....................	4.50	6.95	8.54	8.45	8.48	8.79
Millet and sorghums..........	7.88	8.95	9.36	9.50	9.18	9.30
Rice (milled equivalent).......	1.11	1.74	1.87	1.90	2.02	2.02
Sugar (centrifugal)..........	0.95	1.36	1.59	1.71	1.89	1.85
Starchy roots...............	35.38	44.12	49.49	51.00	51.71	53.09
Pulses....................	0.56	0.88	0.99	1.02	0.97	0.94
Citrus fruit................	0.38	0.76	0.93	0.98	1.06	1.16
Bananas...................	0.25	0.30	0.41	0.37	03.7	0.37
Groundnuts (oil equivalent)....	0.56	0.70	0.89	0.80	0.92	0.89
Vegetable oils and oilseeds (oil equivalent)................	1.69	2.16	2.47	2.45	2.46	2.54
Coffee....................	0.12	0.26	0.33	0.37	0.40	0.41
Cocoa....................	0.49	0.50	0.47	0.49	0.53	0.59
Wine.....................	2.14	1.72	2.27	2.54	2.05	2.40
Milk (total)...............	5.21	6.25	6.85	7.24	7.42	7.72
Meat[2]....................	1.13	1.43	1.56	1.57	1.55	1.56
Index of all farm products.....	78	100	113	117	116	120

[1] From United Nations (1957).
[2] Beef and veal, pork, mutton and lamb.

cent. Grain crops were high in spite of further reductions in acreage, particularly in barley. There has been a substantial increase in the livestock production. The United States production of food for that year was a little above the level of the previous year although the total harvested acreage was down four per cent because of drought conditions in some areas and the impact of the soil bank programs in others. United States grain production rose slightly, including larger harvest of corn and wheat, offsetting declines in rye and rice. There has been an increase in production in the United States of soybeans and livestock. North American food production for selected commodities are shown in Table 21.

Latin America

Latin American food production is estimated to be increasing by three per cent a year. The rate of population growth has been so rapid however that the per capita production remains below the pre-war level. Weather difficulties, which commonly occur in these areas, have damaged food production in many countries. In Argentina, dry spells have recently reduced corn and seed production

TABLE 25

NEAR EAST: PRODUCTION OF SELECTED COMMODITIES[1]

Commodity	1934–38 Average	1948–52 Average	1953–54	1954–55	1955–56	1956–57
	Million Metric Tons					
Wheat	9.66	11.13	16.04	13.73	14.28	15.27
Barley	4.75	5.28	7.32	6.51	6.02	6.77
Rice (milled equivalent)	1.09	1.33	1.14	1.48	1.35	1.61
Total cereals[2]	20.80	23.96	32.49	29.31	29.26	31.41
Sugar (centrifugal)	0.22	0.43	0.57	0.62	0.73	0.76
Pulses	1.16	1.32	1.33	1.35	1.34	1.30
Citrus fruit	0.79	0.86	1.17	1.11	1.25	1.26
Dates	0.87	0.85	1.08	1.16	1.14	1.11
Bananas	0.10	0.13	0.16	0.17	0.18	0.18
Vegetable oils and oilseeds (oil equivalent)	0.35	0.46	0.54	0.60	0.55	0.63
Milk (total)	11.30	12.45	12.89	12.19	13.17	13.32
Meat[3]	0.99	1.28	1.40	1.44	1.52	1.58
Index of all farm products	83	100	119	119	121	125

[1] From United Nations (1957).
[2] Wheat, barley, oats, maize, millet and sorghums and rice.
[3] Beef and veal, pork, mutton, and lamb.

which then create cattle feeding problems. Changing weather, frost, droughts, and flooding have made inroads in the gains in food production. For the area as a whole, grain production is increasing, especially for wheat, barley and sugar. Livestock production appears to show a small increase. See Table 22.

Western Europe

Western Europe continues to have a slight increase in food production (see Table 23). The production of grain is increasing, the production of citrus fruits is maintaining itself, and there is an upward trend in livestock production in most of these countries. In the United Kingdom, the main importer of these commodities, there has been an increase in the production of meat, milk and eggs, by as much as ten per cent.

Africa

Agricultural production in Africa is rising slowly, see Table 24. Production of citrus fruits and olives have increased sharply in North Africa. South of the Sahara Desert, major crop productions are increasing. Food production in the Union of South Africa has been increasing steadily.

TABLE 26

FAR EAST (EXCLUDING MAINLAND CHINA): PRODUCTION OF SELECTED COMMODITIES[1]

Commodity	1934–38 Average	1948–52 Average	1953–54	1954–55	1955–56	1956–57
	Million Metric Tons					
Wheat......................	12.13	11.34	11.50	13.51	13.83	13.44
Millet and sorghums..........	14.94	13.35	18.44	18.20	15.93	17.00
Rice (milled equivalent).......	65.28	66.60	77.08	72.07	77.98	81.74
Sugar (centrifugal)...........	4.18	3.26	4.03	4.78	5.11	5.36
Sugar (non-centrifugal).......	3.67	3.86	4.09	4.30	4.19	4.13
Starchy roots................	21.62	26.27	30.11	31.87	33.62	34.10
Pulses......................	6.78	7.17	6.92	8.29	9.09	8.44
Vegetable oils and oilseeds (oil equivalent)................	3.96	3.99	4.44	4.91	4.79	5.02
Meat[2]......................	1.63	1.75	1.98	1.95	2.03	2.11
Milk (total).................	23.23	25.24	27.36	27.99	28.24	28.55
Index of all farm products.....	97	100	110	113	117	119

[1] From United Nations (1957).
[2] Beef and veal, pork, mutton, and lamb.

TABLE 27

OCEANIA: PRODUCTION OF SELECTED COMMODITIES[1]

Commodity	1934–38 Average	1948–52 Average	1953–54	1954–55	1955–56	1956–57
	Million Metric Tons					
Wheat......................	4.38	5.30	5.52	4.70	5.40	3.79
Sugar (centrifugal)...........	0.94	1.04	1.47	1.48	1.35	1.39
Milk (total).................	10.18	10.23	11.03	10.52	11.26	11.37
Meat[2]	1.42	1.58	1.74	1.79	1.87	1.86
Index of all farm products.....	88	100	108	108	115	114

[1] From United Nations (1957).
[2] Beef and veal, pork, mutton, and lamb.

The Near East

Agricultural production in the Near East which has previously been very rapid is slowing (see Table 25). There was a peak in grain production achieved in 1953. Most of the increases in grain output were in Egypt, Iran, Iraq and Syria. In Turkey, wheat harvests were slightly lower in 1957.

Production of fruits and vegetables has increased substantially in a number of these countries under the stimulus of great import demands in recent years by countries in the Persian Gulf area.

The Far East

Excluding China, present estimates indicate that about a two per cent increase in food production is being achieved per year. Per

A. U.S.S.R., Eastern Europe and China: Cereal production

Year	U.S.S.R.[2]	Eastern Europe	China[2]
	Million Metric Tons		
Prewar..................	79.5[3]	43.8	97.9
Average 1948–52..........	86.5[4]	40.1	116.6[4]
1953/54.................	84.6	38.7	145.9
1954/55.................	87.9	38.0	149.6
1955/56.................	108.0	41.5	153.4
1956/57.................	130.0	38.1	157.1

B. U.S.S.R.: Production of selected commodities

Year	Cereals[2]	Sunflower Seed[2] (Oil Equivalent)	Sugar (Granulated)	Cotton[2] (Raw)
	Million Metric Tons			
1940.....................	79.5	...	...	...
Average 1950–52..........	86.5	0.74	2.86	1.17
1953....................	84.6	1.03	3.43	1.22
1954....................	87.9	0.75	2.61	1.33
1955....................	108.0	1.45	3.42	1.23
1956....................	130.0	...	4.35	...

C. U.S.S.R.: Livestock numbers

Year	Total Cattle	Cows	Pigs	Sheep
	Million Head on 1 October			
1953....................	63.0	26.0	47.6	114.9
1954....................	64.9	27.5	51.1	117.5
1955....................	67.1	29.2	52.2	125.0
1956....................	70.4	30.9	56.4	129.8

[1] From United Nations (1957).
[2] Estimates.
[3] 1940.
[4] Average 1950–52.

capita production remains less than before World War II. Production in Japan is materially greater. The regions total grain output is increasing substantially. Record rice crops are being harvested in Burma and Thailand and good ones in many other countries in that area. Sugar crops are increasing in India, Japan and Taiwan. There is also an increase in the production of oil seeds (see Table 26).

Oceania

Data for Oceania indicates that production was slightly less in 1957 than in 1956. Australian wheat harvests fell by as much as one-third due to adverse weather conditions. In New Zealand the rising trend in production appears to be continuing for most products. Production details for Oceania are shown in Table 27.

U.S.S.R., Eastern Europe and Mainland China

Reliable data from this block of countries is difficult to obtain. That which is available is shown in Table 28. The U.S.S.R. is increasing substantially the production of potatoes and also the production of vegetables. The wheat harvest is reportedly improving at the rate of about five per cent a year since 1955. Grain harvest data for the U.S.S.R. are shown in Table 28. As a whole, cattle production was increased recently by five per cent, pigs by eight per cent, and sheep by four per cent. Milk production increased substantially, while the over-all production of meat and eggs increased slightly according to United Nations reports. In eastern Europe cereal harvests and potato production is increasing. Sugar beet production is maintaining itself. Fruit and vegetable production is reported increasing in Bulgaria and Romania. Potato production in eastern Germany and Poland have been reported by the FAO to be increasing markedly.

On Mainland China, due to the irrigation of large areas of virgin land, reports are that 5,000,000 acres have been added for food production. Total harvest of cereals, legumes, potatoes and soybeans is reportedly increasing. In spite of this improvement, however, the planned level of production has not been obtained and with a 2.2 per cent annual increase in population and rapid urbanization, per capita availability of food is declining. Livestock production is weak and little progress is apparently being made. Pig numbers have improved slightly, according to detailed United Nations reports.

WHAT IS RATE OF INCREASE IN FOOD PRODUCTION?

In Table 29, it is to be noted that in no crop was there an annual increase higher than two per cent. In terms of animal products, fruits and luxury food items, the average annual increase has been approximately 1.5 per cent. Rice production increased only about 0.1 per cent and rice is the basic foodstuff for more than a billion people in Asia alone.

There have been striking increases in food production in some countries, and some of these have come in less developed areas. According to the FAO, Thailand is increasing its rice production by an estimated 2.4 per cent annually. In Mexico production has increased by 2.6 per cent annually. While these are isolated

TABLE 29

ESTIMATED WORLD[1] PRODUCTION OF MAJOR CROPS, 1934–38 AND 1949–51[2]

Crop	Average Annual Output 1934–38 (Million Metric Tons)	1949–51 (Million Metric Tons)	Average Annual Increase (Percentages)
Wheat....................	129	144	0.8
Rye......................	21	20	..[4]
Barley....................	41	46	0.8
Oats.....................	45	49	0.6
Maize....................	110	133	1.4
Millet and sorghum..........	46	51	0.7
Rice, paddy...............	151	153	0.1
Total of the above grains....	543	596	0.7
Sugar....................	26	34	1.9
Potatoes..................	159	157	..[4]
Sweet potatoes and yams......	45	55	1.4
Pulses...................	21	22	0.3
Oilseeds..................	41	49	1.3

[1] Excluding U.S.S.R.
[2] From P.E.P. (1955).
[3] Including rape seed and linseed which, though eaten, are usually regarded as industrial oilseeds.
[4] Data not available.

examples they do indicate that some notable increases have occurred.

There have been average annual increases of more than one per cent per year in wheat, barley, rye, oats, corn, meat, nuts and soybeans, during the first sixty years of this century in the world. However, available reports indicate that between 1900 and 1950 India increased groundnut production by an average of 4.9 per cent annually and the U.S.A. by 4.0 per cent. Between 1900 and 1950 Canada increased its wheat production by an average of 4.5 per cent and Australia by 3.0 per cent per year. During this same period U.S.A. meat production has increased by 1.1 per cent (P.E.P., 1955).

While the above are examples of single food crop supplies and their increases, the production of food in selected countries is more meaningful. According to the FAO, Egypt has raised agricultural output by less than one per cent between 1910 and 1950. Food production in the United States has risen by 1.5 per cent per year, including all the profitable and luxury food items, between 1910 and 1950. Japan increased food production by two per cent a year since early in 1900. The rate of progress is slowing, however, in that area (P.E.P. 1955).

RATES OF INCREASE IN WORLD FOOD PRODUCTION AND HUMAN NUMBERS

World food supplies are increasing, and the general annual rates of increase for the various sectors of the world are given in Table 30.

The rate of increase in 1952–53 was 2.7 per cent a year, accompanied by an annual growth of 1.5 per cent in human population.

Since the end of World War II, through the assistance provided by the United Nations Agencies and the United States foreign agricultural programs, there have been underdeveloped countries which have made some long-term increases in food production potentials. Taking the world as a whole, food production has during recent years not equalled the rate required. Yet the situation is not hopeless. Rarely in the history of the world has so much conscious effort gone into growing more food.

TABLE 30

INDEX NUMBERS OF VOLUME OF AGRICULTURAL PRODUCTION AND AVERAGE ANNUAL INCREASE IN COMPARISON WITH GROWTH OF POPULATION[1]

Region	Pre-war Aver-age	1953–54	1954–55	1955–56	1956–57 Prelimi-nary)	Average Annual Increase 1948/49–1952/53 to 1956/57 Produc-tion	Popula-tion
	—Average 1948/49–1952/53 = 100—					—Percentage—	
Western Europe........	93	115	115	116	118	2.7	0.75
North America.........	73	107	104	108	112	2.0	1.8
Oceania..............	88	108	108	115	114	2.1	2.4
Subtotal above regions	82	110	109	112	115	2.3	1.2
Latin America........	82	108	113	116	119	2.9	2.3
Far East (excluding China)..............	97	110	113	117	119	3.0	1.4
Near East.............	83	119	119	121	125	3.8	2.2
Africa...............	78	113	117	116	120	3.1	1.9
Subtotal above regions	88	111	114	117	120	3.1	1.7
All above regions.....	85	111	111	114	117	2.7	1.5
World[2]............	..	110	111	114	117	2.7	1.5

[1] From United Nations (1957).
[2] Including estimates for the U.S.S.R., Eastern Europe, and China.

Three Retarding Influences to Producing More Food

P.E.P. (1955) gives three important reservations about the future production of food in the world. First, good weather has played a large part in recent crop increases. Good weather is not predictable, and it remains to be known how far the gains which have been registered can be maintained in less favorable growing season. This is thought to be particularly important in relation to the production of cereal crops.

Second, progress has been made in a number of countries but the rate of increase is below the average gain required. Whether or not the present rate of increase can be maintained in these countries depends on the views of their governments, their pursuit of food production policies, and on world economic conditions.

Third, the tendency for prices for food products to move against farmers continues to occur. On the world market this means that the sharp rise in the volume of agricultural trade yielded no increase in real purchasing power to agricultural exporters. On domestic markets the increase in farm product prices in most countries (from which data is available) were exceeded by the rise in prices paid by farmers for services and products. There have been declines in farm incomes in several countries although increases in the volume of production in many cases was sufficient to offset the effect of price changes.

Food prices at the retail level are rising in most countries, reflecting some inflationary pressures. Consumption appears to be keeping pace with the expanding food production. In those countries where active economic developments are under way, the demands have sometimes exceeded production and have necessitated a larger import of food. Surplus stocks of most commodities have shown no further rise and the surpluses for some foods are beginning to decline. There has been an exception with coarse grain stocks which have risen some in recent years (United Nations 1960).

Trends in Food Production

The United Nations reports that a significant feature of the trend of agricultural production in the last few years has been the rate of increase in economically less developed regions. Food production here has been greater than average while food production in the developed parts of the world has tended to increase at a slower rate. However, the benefits this could yield in less developed countries have been offset by their population growth, to be discussed later.

It has been reported that no matter what other improvements may be possible in currency and trade, the underfed parts of the world must increase domestic food production to form a basis for any real improvement in the food supplies available per person in any region. In the past, a major part of any increase in food consumption levels has come from the domestic production of food. It is to be recognized that, in countries which are largely agricultural, increased agricultural production is not only the chief means of improving trade balances but also is significant in raising the extremely low standards of living of rural populations. A United Nations report (1959) concludes that, in spite of the fact that there are surplus food stocks in the world, the importance of planning some programs to increase agricultural production in local areas is the paramount feature in improving the condition of the less developed regions.

In 1951 the FAO recommended that an increase of 2.0 per cent in food production in excess of the annual rate of population growth was desired for the world as a whole. This rate of growth has in some cases been achieved although the preliminary estimates of what was required indicated that this was a lower limit of development needed. However, world food production has increased but slightly over world population growth in recent years (Table 30).

The United Nations reports that between 1955 and 1957 world food production increased about three per cent but the increases were less than one per cent ahead of the rate of population growth. Yet, world food production in 1957 was estimated to be about 17 per cent over the average for 1950. Since 1950 the less well fed regions of the world have somewhat improved their position in regard to total food production. This is shown in Table 30. United Nations reports indicate that in Latin America and in the Far East, where population increases have been particularly rapid, recent production gains have matched those of the rest of the world, but these areas also had had great increases in population. The net result is that they have not been able to overcome the setback of the war years when production lagged behind population growth. In these two regions per capita production is still less than before the war.

INADEQUACY OF WORLD FOOD PRODUCTION

The United Nations Food and Agriculture Organization reports that there are probably few communities in the world whose daily minimum requirements are less than 2200 calories for members of these communities. Average supplies for more than two-thirds of the world's population fall below this level. In many countries the daily food supplies per person exceed 2,200 calories, but this still falls short of the human requirements of these areas.

Production of food around the world in general has recovered

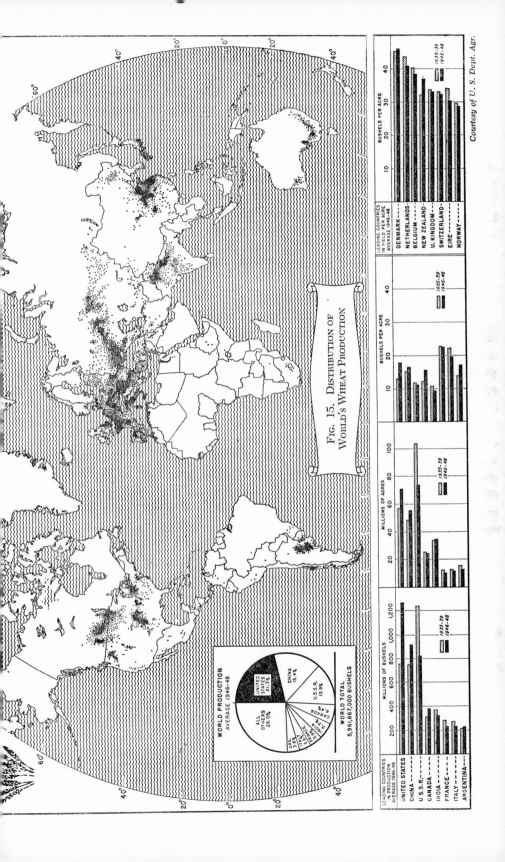

Fig. 15. Distribution of World's Wheat Production

Courtesy of U. S. Dept. Agr.

since the World War II decline. By 1952, the production of food
in the world in terms of calories available for human consumption
were eight per cent over prewar levels. However, during this time
populations increased 14 per cent.

One of the most significant features of recent trends is that the
well-nourished peoples of the world are becoming distinctly better
fed than people living in the under-nourished regions of the world
which are becoming less well off.

The food surpluses in some areas of North America, South
America, Oceania and in Western Europe are increasing. Where
supplies of food per person before World War II were low, they are
now lower.

The United Nations FAO estimates that to provide an adequate
food supply for the world population in 1980 there must be a global
annual increase in food production of about 2.25 per cent over the
rate of population growth. While this is an average figure for the
whole world, higher rates than this will be necessary in underdeveloped areas where all but a minority of the existing people are already
undernourished and where population growth is proceeding rapidly.
In Western Europe and North America, for example, lower rates of
increase in food production would suffice, for a while.

A large portion of the people who will make up the world's population in 1980 probably have already been born. The question is,
what likelihood is there of achieving a 2.25 per cent annual increase
in food production for them and the whole world with present practices.

There is a striking difference between technological capability
and possibility and what actually happens. One difficulty is that
there are social and economic climates which are necessary before
the successful application of the food production technology, which
is already known, can occur.

VARIATIONS IN CROP YIELDS

There is a wide variation in the yield of a crop per unit of land,
around the world. Comparisons between the yields of wheat, corn,
rice and potatoes in several countries are shown in Table 31.

In addition, the food crops are uneven in distribution over the
earth. This perhaps can best be shown in terms of world maps
(Figs. 15–18) for selected crops.

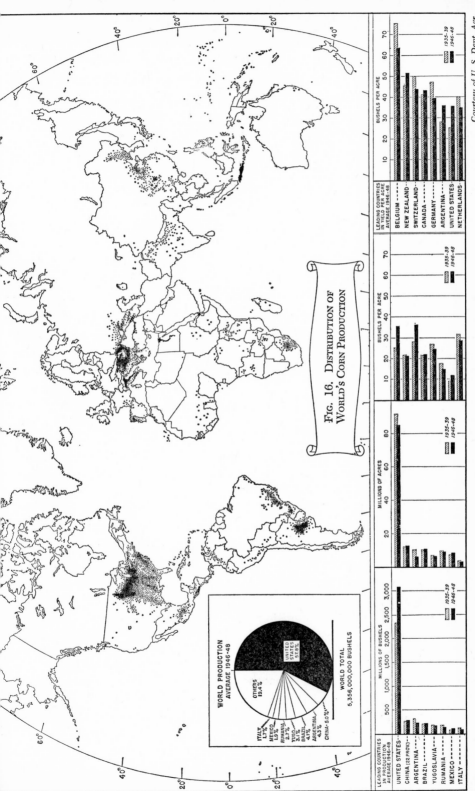

Fig. 16. Distribution of
World's Corn Production

Courtesy of U. S. Dept. Agr.

IMPROVEMENTS REQUIRED IN PRESENT PRACTICES

The ability with which past civilizations exploited energy sources is, for us, a measure of a given civilization. Prehistoric men consumed plants and animals and performed muscle work. Next, animals were domesticated and taught to perform work tasks; higher organizations than this require vast amounts of energy. After the invention of the water wheel, the energy of falling water was applied to work tasks, as the grinding of grains. Later, energy was obtained by burning the stored coal, oil and gas reserves in the earth's crust to produce mechanical power, which was followed by the production of electrical energy from both water and steam. All these are converted energy sources—energy from the sun. Even the water wheel took its power from water evaporated by solar energy from the earth's surface.

TABLE 31

ESTIMATED YIELD OF PRINCIPAL FOODS IN SELECTED COUNTRIES[1] (AVERAGE 1949–51 IN 100 KG. PER HECTARE[2])

Wheat		Maize		Rice		Potatoes	
Country	Yield	Country	Yield	Country	Yield	Country	Yield
United		Italy	18.3	Thailand	13.0	Netherlands	250
Kingdom	27.3	U.S.A.	23.5	Burma	13.9	United	
Denmark	35.0	Canada	30.4	India	10.8	Kingdom	188
France	17.9	Argentina	12.8	Pakistan	13.6	U.S.A.	163
U.S.A.	10.6	India	6.0	Japan	39.6	Argentina	65
Canada	11.8	Java		U.S.A.	25.9	India	67
Argentina	10.1	Madura }	8.2	Australia	48.7		
Australia	11.0			Italy	47.8		
India	6.5						
Algeria	5.8						

[1] From P.E.P. (1955).
[2] One hectare equals 2.47 acres.

The energy requirements of current societies can be foreseen to be exhausting the existing fossil fuel reserves, which are not quickly regenerated. The shrinking energy sources are being drawn upon by the rapidly increasing industrialization of the nations of the world. At the height of competition for these fossil fuel reserves has come a discovery—one capable of changing the course of recent events. This discovery is atomic energy.

Atomic Energy Not a Panacea

It is not the intent of the above to indicate that the applications of atomic energy are a cure for all of man's ills, yet the successful

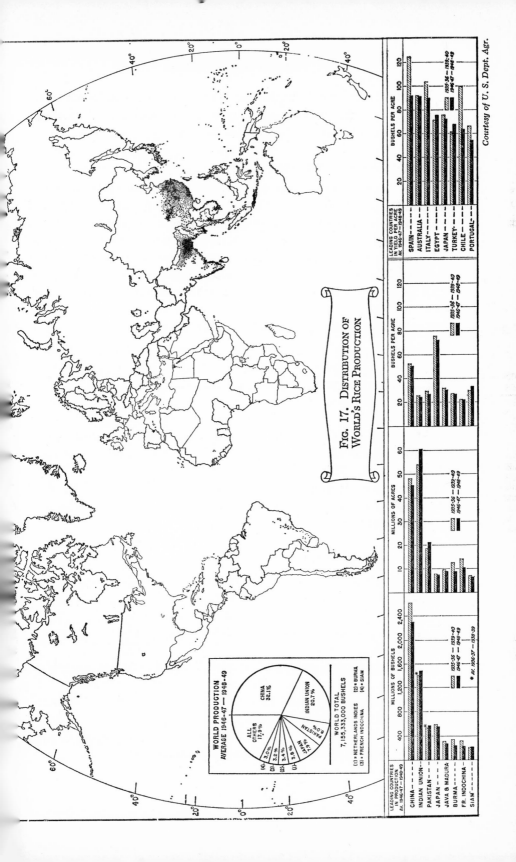

FIG. 17. DISTRIBUTION OF WORLD'S RICE PRODUCTION

Courtesy of U. S. Dept. Agr.

application of atomic energy for our mutual good can indeed improve the lot of mankind by helping in the attack on starvation. Hence, it may be useful to briefly explore this subject.

Water and Power Limiting Factors

Plants grow in moist soil, and water is a generally limiting factor to plant growth. This can be corrected by irrigation. But to irrigate we must have water to pump and power to pump it. Atomic energy facilities are already successful in demonstrating their ability to produce electric power. Several cities are now being serviced with such power, and nuclear powered ships have circled the world. The technical "know-how" required is therefore available.

Nitrogen Fertilizers as a Limiting Factor

If water is supplied, the next limiting factor is the nutrient supply in the soil. Depleted soils must be rebuilt if plant growth is to be successful. The most critical nutrient which is in short supply is nitrogen fertilizers. Currently they are either mined from natural deposits (in Chile for example) or synthesized.

The passage of nitrogen gas with oxygen gas through intense radiation yields nitrogen compounds which are functional as nitrogen fertilizers. This is a well recognized radiation induced synthesis. Operating a reactor to produce power to pump water can at the same time lead to the synthesis of nitrogen fertilizers, which are a limiting factor in plant growth in the world.

Power Plus Radiation

The power potential of a pound of uranium-235 even with present knowledge is more than a million times that of a pound of coal. Obviously, the application of paramount importance is power production to perform much of the work load currently undertaken by other means.

But, when atomic energy is released, intense radiation sources are created as a by-product. The one pound of uranium-235 yields approximately one pound of fission products which are intensely radioactive. These can be dumped in the ocean and buried in the ground at great expense or they may be usefully employed, thereby actually making power production more economical.

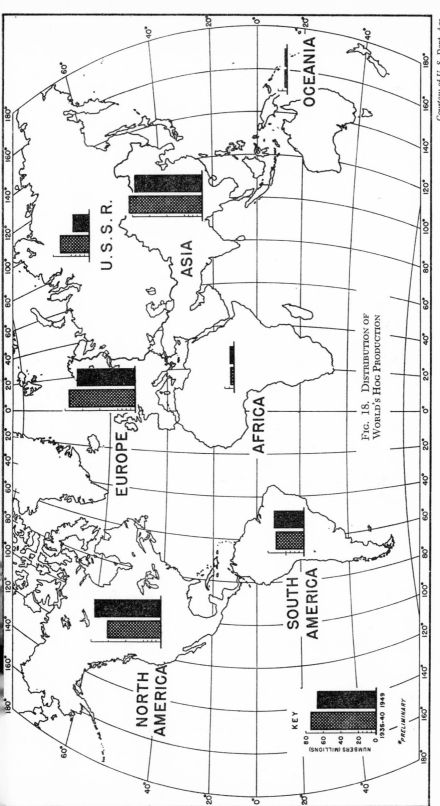

Fig. 18. Distribution of World's Hog Production

KEY

1936-40 1949

*PRELIMINARY

NUMBERS (MILLIONS)
0 20 40 60 80

Useful Radiations

Of the particular types of radiations available, gamma rays and beta radiation from radioactive elements (and machine-generated electron beams) are the most applicable at present for most radiation uses. Because of their great penetrating power, gamma rays have widespread radiation applications. Gamma radiation can be obtained either from fission products or from reactor-activated elements. Beta rays are also available from fission products and reactor activated elements. Although beta rays have limited penetrating power, for special applications this is a distinct advantage.

USES OF RADIATIONS

There are many beneficial applications to be made of radiation, and the list is growing daily, including uses in the field of food production.

It has been noted that plantings in radiation fields at increasing distance from ground zero yield a maximum plant growth greater than the controls which have not received the radiation treatment. Increased height and weight are found.

Studies with many varieties of seeds have lead to the conclusion that low doses of radiation can increase the yield of edible crops over control untreated seeds (Vidal 1959). For example, it is reported that the irradiation of radish seeds produces not only double the yield of radishes, but the roots which are obtained are fleshy and tasteful, which is not common in large radishes. The yield and the quality both are improved by this treatment. Similar results with spinach found a doubling of the quantity of edible leaves. While this work is in its infancy, the opportunities for increasing the yield for edible plants from existing seeds may be significant.

Improved Varieties of Plants and Animals.

Programs of study have evolved using mutated material in plant pathology, plant breeding, and entomological studies in fundamental evaluations in the field of genetics. A number of improved crop varieties have appeared. Some varieties are found resistant to disease organisms, others with desirable growth characteristics, such as stiffer straw, or higher yield. A radiation-induced, mildew-resistant barley mutant of high yield potential has been found in several countries. A barley mutant of equal interest has been found with a shorter straw than the parent and with more round kernels. A four-rowed mutant has been produced from two-row fly-resistant barley. The four-row kernel plants also give a higher yield.

Animal research has not been as successful although there are indications that some useful mutations are possible. When combined with desirable traits of standard breeds of animals these might yield improved livestock.

Elimination of Whole Insect Populations

The screw fly worm is a parasite of warm blooded animals, the flies depositing eggs in and on living animals. If the host dies before the larvae have developed almost completely, the larvae also dies. The fly is widely distributed in tropical and sub-tropical areas. In the course of studying the phosphorus metabolism of this fly with radioactive phosphorus it was found that the treatment sterilized the fly in the process.

It is the practice of this insect that the males mate often but the females only once. If a female mates with a sterile male, sterile offspring result. This initial discovery led to attempts to control the fly in a small area such as an isolated island where infestations could be measured. The reason for interest was that in the United States alone the annual economic losses from this pest have been set at 16,000,000 dollars. No effective control measures were available.

From 1951 to 1953 studies were undertaken by the U. S. Department of Agriculture in Florida. Late in 1953 the Netherlands Antilles government requested assistance from the U. S. Department of Agriculture in the control of the screw fly. The insects were extremely abundant on this island isolated 40 miles from the coast of Venezuela; it was an ideal opportunity to field test information developed on the sterilized males.

Sterile males were released at the rate of 100 per square mile per week for eight weeks. Prior to the experiment there were as many as 15 egg masses per goat per week for example. The first test results obtained were negative; the number of radiation sterilized males released was increased to 400 per square mile. By the end of the next eight weeks the normal fly activity had ceased. Only two egg masses were collected a few months later; all were sterile and failed to hatch. There had been an eradication of the pest from Curacao

Island. Similar activities have been undertaken in the U. S. Because of the size of the area to be treated in southern United States, it required more than 50 million sterile male flies per week. A technical problem was created in how to generate this number of males.

Studies have now been started to attempt to eradicate other insects in other countries with this and modified techniques (Desrosier and Rosenstock 1960).

Soils

Our civilizations are built on a broad foundation of fertile soils. If the earth were a vast sand dune, life as we know it could not exist. There is a complex interplay between the earth and the living systems it supports.

Green plants draw their energy from sunlight, and convert a portion into useful biological compounds, which then serve as a broad food supply base for the animals which roam the earth. On the other hand, plants draw their nutrients mainly from the soil, which is teeming with life. A spoonful of very fertile soil may contain a billion living organisms.

An understanding of the soil is of great practical value in our attempts to generate adequate food supplies for all men. Of great advantage to soil scientists in their attempts to delve into the mysteries of the soil are the radioisotopes.

Using radioactive elements, it has been possible to learn how minerals are solubilized and taken into plants. With radioactive phosphorus, for example, it is possible to follow this essential plant nutrient from rock through soils into plants.

Radioactive tracers permit the study of leaching of essential plant nutrients from soils, which is of ultimate importance in agricultural technology. Much greater assurance of the biological significance of a fertilizer application is now available by checks with tracers.

The discovery of atomic energy and its application to plant research has permitted a substantial gain in knowledge over that possible in the past. Not only are the results obtained more accurate, but the time involved in experiments is condensed. Field experiments were extensively used in the past. Field experiments now usually constitute but the first and last steps in such research. Rapid accumulation of knowledge not obtainable before can now be anticipated in shorter time and with substantial reductions in costs.

Economic Benefits

The economic benefits from this research have been assessed to have already returned ten times the costs. The work on fertilizer placements and applications have led to savings ranging from 10 to 50 per cent. This is rather significant considering that in the United States more than a billion dollars is spent annually for fertilizers. Consider also the benefits to underdeveloped countries whose supply of fertilizers is limited. If one were to predict an increase in fertilizer availability from 10 to 50 per cent in a short period of time prior to these discoveries, such predictions would have been seriously challenged.

Added to these advantages are the improved production of crops with newly developed fungicides, pesticides and fumigants. All together, these are yielding the largest food supply ever developed on earth, and promise even more.

Plentiful Power

On a more broad scale, the hope for atomic energy is to yield cheap power. While the information available today does not warrant such hope, the nature of the source of the energy is so fundamental to the universe we inhabit that perhaps we must alter our concepts of economics. Atomic energy is here and it is only a matter of time before it will be used and used widely. Economics take peculiar turns—for example, Iceland is fortunate in having hot springs beneath the island which can be piped to cities to heat homes and operate factories. Perhaps it is not surprising to find that the cost of heating homes with natural hot water is about the same as using natural gas, or coal, or oil in other countries. People are obviously willing to exchange a certain portion of their life's energies to keep warm. The same applies to the relative amount of a man's energy he is willing to exchange for good food, and full stomachs.

Plentiful power is what is needed to pump water and make fertilizers, and these could increase the food supplies in the world. Cheap power would permit lower manufacturing costs of food products. Cheap power would mean cheaper transportation, important in improving the economics of food distribution. With more good food available to people, we could except them to want to know more about the world they live in, to take up a civilized life and this can be achieved only through better education. And, educated people have a by-product of new technological achievements which could yield more good food as needed.

Adequate Food for Man

There is hope that atomic energy can help solve or ease the gigantic problem of feeding the people on earth. While there are tremendous amounts of food produced annually on the face of the earth a major portion of that food never helps mankind. This will be explored in the next chapters.

There is no doubt that there is a great opportunity to expand present systems of food production and distribution as currently practiced around the world. These systems can be forced to yield more good food. But, there is a limit to how much food agriculture can yield, i.e., a population problem with plants and animals.

Average Food Supplies Available Per Person Per Year

The production of food in the world amounts to about 2.4 trillion pounds distributed approximately as follows: cereals, 1.0 trillion pounds; potatoes, 450 billion pounds; sugar, 73 billion pounds; tree fruits, 94 billion pounds; fats and oils, 43 billion pounds; milk, 519 billion pounds; meat, 85 billion pounds; eggs, 20 billion pounds; fish, 40 billion pounds.

For the world's 3.0 billion people, this amounts to an average per person per year of the following: cereals, 333 lbs.; potatoes, 150 lbs.; sugar, 25 lbs.; fruits, 32 lbs.; fats and oils, 15 lbs.; milk 173 lbs.; meat, 28 lbs.; eggs, 7 lbs.; and fish, 13 lbs.

Assume that the average weight of all the people in the world were about 120 lbs. and that a man eats about ten times his body weight a year in good food. Each person would need about 1200 lbs. of food a year, or a supply of about 3,600 billion pounds a year for the world's 3.0 billion people.

If the world's food supply is about that given above at present, then on the average there is about 800 lbs. of food produced per person per year.

It is estimated that at least 25 per cent (some estimates as high as 50 per cent have been made) of the food produced is lost in storage and distribution. Then the world food supply figure of 2,400 billion pounds would have to be cut by one fourth, leaving a supply of about 1,800 billion pounds, or about 600 lbs. per person per year.

To meet the food needs then even in terms of bulk, we must double food supplies over that available today to feed us tomorrow with good food.

And, doubling present supplies would not be enough as a goal because during the time it would take to achieve this, there would be the hundreds of millions more people on earth.

Evolution in Food Production Required

Suppose we could achieve a doubling of food production by improving present practices, then agriculture would be terminal insofar as expecting further increases in food supplies is concerned. There is a physical limit to agriculture.

For example, planting tomatoes in fields in the same manner as wheat could yield at its maximum about 70 tons to the acre. This would be with a concentration of 200,000 plants to the acre, compared to the 5,000 presently employed to yield 25 tons. The limit here is population densities—the physical limits of plants having a place in the sun.

But doubling food production would in effect allow us to feed just the people on earth yesterday with good food. What about those new members of the human race that will be added during this development? These would take up almost all of the new production that would occur. This would in effect maintain the status quo, which is inadequate.

What appears necessary is an evolution in the means employed in food production. Can we further pinpoint the problem area? It is not difficult to add carbohydrates to food supplies. It is more difficult to produce fats and oils. It is harder still to produce high quality protein, which is the nutrient so critically short in the world.

Men in the past were able to meet the challenge of populations and hunger—first with natural husbandry, then they evolved this into naked fallowing, then added the legume rotation, which gave way to grassland agriculture, which yielded to scientific crop rotation, which yielded modern scientific agriculture.

At each stage in this evolution of food supplies, men no doubt thought that the stage they were in was the ultimate only to find that food production continued to increase due to new technological achievements. The important improvements in the past were for the most part, up to modern scientific agriculture, simply management changes which were easily accepted and put into practice. The challenge was to accept the new technique, then successfully apply it.

But the latest advancements require large outputs of capital and this is a commodity drastically short in this world. It would seem that expecting high capital investment agriculture as a solution fails to meet the requirement of a good solution—one which people are able to take with the resources that are available. All the legume rotation meant was adding new seed and better scheduling of land resources, factors available to intelligent men. To be useful, a new technology must be functional, and it must be such that people can make use of it.

An evolution appears needed in food production and specifically in generating high quality proteins. Unfortunately complete proteins are not available in any one plant.

It is relatively easy to increase carbohydrate supplies and if this is done they become the food available in greatest supply, and this is what people will eat. We then have full stomachs but starved people just as before.

To refine these starchy foods into animal flesh is not sufficiently efficient at present to allow men to have generous amounts of high quality protein in diets. Therefore, some other solutions must be found, and several are available. Proposals in another and non-terminal direction will be presented in Part IV in the discussion of world starvation and its control. If we seek to increase the amount of high quality protein available to people, growing seeds in the ground and then feeding these plants to animals is but one of the means.

Objective Views of Man's Dilemma

The inadequacies of the world's food supplies have been succinctly summarized by Sen (1961), Director General of the United Nations Food and Agriculture Organization. He said, "Today more than half of the world's population suffer from varying degrees of under-nourishment and malnutrition. Undernourishment means plain hunger. Malnutrition has been called hidden hunger, an expression which implies that people who have enough to eat may nevertheless be unhealthy, seriously ill and die because the diet does not provide all the elements for satisfactory growth and health."

Viewed another way, modern man has created his present dilemma by inadequate action. *For the past 450 years, civilizations have added no new food crops of any significance.* Modern man has been content to refine and extend the discoveries of earlier man. In the meanwhile the human population on earth has increased beyond the ability of inherited systems of food production to nourish them.

PART III

Spanning the Harvests

CHAPTER 10

The Composition of Plants and Animals and Their Storage Stability as Foods

INTRODUCTION

Man must digest the food he eats if the nutrients present are to become available to him. The digestion of food is accomplished for the most part by enzymes present in his mouth, stomach, and intestines. The useful foods of man are those that he can profitably digest.

It turns out, however, that he is not the only form of life on earth with a digestive process. All living entities have somewhat similar processes. All living organisms generally compete for energy and they take it where they can. As a result, there is a competition between many forms of life on earth for energy and nutrient sources, and this competition includes man.

Since foods are harvested for the most part only during certain times of the year, it is critical that man retain parts of the harvests and store them for subsequent use. Mankind requires a daily food supply and because of the nature of the food harvests, we must exert some control over the products we have accumulated lest these become attacked by other biological forces, and at our expense.

Toward this end, man has accumulated a technology of food preservation. This is the subject of Part III and it is divided into

163

two chapters. In the first, the composition of plant and animal tissues and the influence of their chemical composition on their storage stability is discussed. In the next chapter, the methods available to store and distribute foods for short or long periods is presented and analyzed.

THE COMPOSITION OF PLANTS AND ANIMALS

We draw our foods from the plant and animal kingdoms. An understanding of the composition of plants and animals leads to an understanding of the composition of our foods.

Foods Alike in the Elements They Contain

The general life chemistry of plants and animals has much in common, and it is to be expected, and indeed found, that living entities require much the same chemical elements. These include hydrogen, carbon, oxygen, nitrogen, calcium, phosphorus, sulfur, sodium, potassium, iron, and a list of minor elements.

Foods Differ in Molecular Constituents

An important difference is found, however, in the molecular form in which these specific elements occur, and this varies between the various plants and animals.

Because animals are incapable of the elementary syntheses performed by plants, the animals require specific, rather complex, molecules as nutrients, and this is reflected in the chemical composition of their tissues. Information concerning the composition of plant and animal tissues in terms of molecules is recognized to be more useful than their composition solely in terms of the chemical elements they contain.

Components of Universal Nutrient Called Food

The idea that foods vary in terms of molecular structure developed in 1834 when the universal nutrient for man called "food" was found to contain three major molecular groupings or components, the carbohydrates, proteins and fats. Since then, and up to the recent discovery of vitamin B-12, there have been more than 50 essential molecules or nutrients identified in foods. These 50 chemical compounds, which include the vitamins and minerals, comprise the material present in living substances of plants and animals which man requires in his food. These materials are: arginine, histidine, iso-leucine, leucine, lysine, methionine, phenylalanine, threonine, tryp-tophane, and valine, all of which are essential; three components of fats; sugar, a carbohydrate; the fat soluble vitamins A, D, E, and K; the water soluble vitamins of the B complex, and vitamin C; the minerals calcium, chlorine, cobalt, copper, fluorine, iodine, iron, mag-nesium, manganese, phosphorus, potassium, sodium, sulfur and zinc.

Foods Generally Water Systems

From an over-all view, plant or animal tissues are generally water systems of carbohydrates, proteins and fats. Dissolved in the water phase are the water soluble carbohydrates, proteins, fatty acids, mineral salts, vitamins, physiologically active compounds and pigments. Proteins are held in a colloidal state in the water system, and fat in an emulsion. Dissolved in the fatty phase are the fat soluble vitamins, physiologically active compounds and pigments.

Proximate Composition of Foods

The chemical composition of a food is usually described in terms of its content in per cent of carbohydrates, proteins, fats, ash (mineral salts), and water. Important differences between plant and animal tissues are found in terms of their composition in this sense. Plant tissues are usually rich sources of carbohydrates; animal tissues are usually rich sources of protein. For example, an apple may have 16 per cent carbohydrate, 0.2 per cent protein, 0.8 per cent fat, 2.0 per cent ash, and 81 per cent water, while lean muscle may contain 2.0 per cent carbohydrates, 20 per cent protein, 2.0 per cent fat, 2.0 per cent ash, and 74 per cent water.

Small Difference Important

While foods are found to vary substantially in terms of their major and minor nutrients, usually the composition of closely related plants or animals is similar. There may be important differences, for ex-ample in vitamin content between various varieties of a fruit or vegetable. Those differences are sought and selected to yield foods of improved value to man.

Foods from Lower and Higher Plants

The plant life found on earth can be classed either as lower or higher from a standpoint of molecular complexity and degree of organization. The higher plants are those commonly seen and which generally produce flowers and seeds.

A number of lower plants, including mushrooms, truffles and algae, are eaten by man; though some types contain toxic components. These lower plants, if eaten as a steady diet, measurably lower the satisfaction of eating. Yet, such materials can be important additives to our diets, and, as will be shown, important to consider in future food production systems.

Dry Fruits and Seeds Most Important Plant Foods

The most important higher plant structures used as food are the dry fruits and seeds. These would include all the cereals and small grains, the legumes and nuts. Because they are dry, they store easily and are not difficult to transport. Roots, tubers, bulbs, and other so-called "earth" vegetables are next in importance to us although their food value is lessened because of the increased moisture content over dry grains. The leafy parts of plants contain little stored or reserve food and, although very perishable due to their high moisture content, are eaten as sources of vitamins, minerals, and roughage. The fleshy fruits such as peaches and apples are very perishable, are good sources of carbohydrates and vitamins and, further, add pleasure to eating.

Cereals and Grasses

Cereals are the dry seeds of those members of the grass family grown for their grains and are by far the most important plants eaten by man. Of the cereals, wheat, corn, and rice are the most important. One or more of the cereals is adapted to each type of climate on earth: barley and rye grow in the northern regions, wheat in the temperate regions, corn and rice in the warmer temperature regions and in the tropics. Cereals have a wide range of requirements of moisture and soil types. They can be grown with little labor and the yield of food is high for the work involved. Cereals are a principal source of carbohydrates although they contain proteins, fats, and some vitamins, and minerals. Cereals in their native dry state are alive. They respire just as we do, giving off carbon dioxide, water and heat. Grain with about 12 to 14 per cent moisture can be stored for long periods of time. The optimum range in moisture content varies somewhat for the different grains.

Wheat

Wheat is the most important annual grass. The mature grain is a germ covered with a starchy quilt. The germ is a good source of vitamins, fat, and protein. The germ and starchy cover is packaged in a bran or husk which is also a good source for protein and vitamins. There are eight important types of cultivated wheats and they grow from 2 to 4 feet in height.

The spring wheats are sown in the spring, harvested in the fall. Winter wheat is sown in the fall and harvested in the early summer. The yields from the winter types are higher. In the United States about half of the wheat crop is hard, red, winter wheat; one-fourth is soft, red, winter wheat; one-fifth is hard, red, spring wheat; one-twentieth is durum wheat, and part of the rest is white wheat. These wheats are the most widely used item in human diets.

Corn

Indian corn is America's only contribution to the important group of cereals and is the largest of the cereals grown, sometimes reaching 15 feet. Two kinds of flowers are produced—the tassel or male flowers, and the ear or female. Each kernel is a fertilized ovary. The silks are pollen tubes. The ovaries and consequently the mature kernels are produced in rows on the cob, which is surrounded by an inedible husk. No wild species of corn has ever been found. Corn is considered the most difficult and spectacular of the isolations of food crops from nature. Dent corn is the type grown in the largest amounts. The inside of the kernel is somewhat soft, and there is an indentation found at the crown of the kernel as the inside dries and shrinks. Corn has been bred to have ears of a type and location that can be yanked from the stalk by a mechanical harvester, and is an example of the possibilities available to manipulate plants. Sweet corn is an immature form of corn of varieties selected for sweetness. When at prime eating quality, the kernels are easily punctured with the thumb nail, yielding a milky exudate of 73 to 76 per cent moisture. At 68 to 70 per cent moisture, the exudate is thick and pulpy, the corn chewy and rather tasteless.

Rice

Rice is the most important cereal grown in tropical areas and is indispensable as a food for about half the people on earth. About

95 per cent of the world crop is grown in the Orient. The rice plant is an annual grass and instead of an ear, produces a number of fine branches which terminate in a single grain, covered with a husk. Commercial polished rice has the husk removed. Most of the vitamins in rice are in the husk, hence lost in this practice. Enriched, polished rice is husked rice to which the vitamins and minerals lost by removing the husk are returned. Unpolished rice is best for human nutrition or, as a substitute, polished rice which has been enriched.

Legumes

Legumes are second to the cereals as important sources of human food. Legumes are the "meat" of the vegetable world and are close to animal flesh in protein food value. Soybeans are one of the oldest known food plants. The seed is the richest in food value of all the vegetables consumed throughout the world. It is used in the fresh, fermented, or dried form. Field and garden peas are also legumes of high value as food. Field peas are mainly livestock feed, while the garden peas in an immature state are eaten fresh, or preserved by freezing, canning, or drying for later use. The entire young pods of string or snap beans, and many types of cultivated beans are edible. The peanut is also a legume and is a good source of protein and oil. Lentils are also legumes.

Nuts

A nut is a one-seeded, one-celled fruit with a hard shell. Hazelnuts, chestnuts, and filberts are truly nuts. Other plant tissues may be called nuts, for example: Brazil nuts (seeds), peanuts (legumes), or walnuts, coconuts, pecans, and almonds (dry fruits). We distinguish three groups of "nuts" . . . those with high fat content, those with high protein content, and those with high carbohydrate content. High fat "nuts" are the Brazil nuts, Cashew nuts, coconuts, pecans, and walnuts. The high protein "nuts" are the almonds, beechnuts, and pistachio nuts. High carbohydrate "nuts" are acorns and chestnuts.

Roots and Tubers

Plant roots and modified roots are storage organs for plants and also are important to us as food. We enjoy fleshy tap roots such as carrots, beets, radishes, and turnips. Roots are dependent upon plant growth above ground to synthesize the chemical compounds to be stored and in general a large top growth usually indicates a large root. Certain plants have large, fleshy lateral roots, such as found with sweet potato. One sweet potato plant may have from 6 to 8 large fleshy roots.

Underground Stems

The white potato is an underground stem and is the most widely grown of the earth vegetables. The potato is not a root, as it has nodes (eyes) and other stem characteristics. From 6 to 8 large potatoes are obtained per plant. The potato was cultivated for centuries by the natives in Peru, and was introduced into world commerce following the discovery of the Americas. The fruits produced by the plant are not edible.

Vegetables

In comparison with the cereals and sugar plants (cane and sugar beets) the vegetable food crops are very numerous and usually limited geographically in production. Many vegetables, for example, are grown in Asia which are unknown in the United States. Vegetable growing is a highly local affair, unlike cereal growing.

Tomatoes, peppers, and eggplant serve to demonstrate this point. The first two are widely eaten in the United States, while eggplant has never achieved wide acceptance. In the Orient the eggplant has the widest acceptance of the three.

Onions represent an important class of bulbs grown as food crops. Members of the cabbage family, including cauliflower, broccoli, Brussels sprouts, kale, collards, and kohlrabi are also widely eaten. Turnips, rutabaga, radishes, beets, carrots, and parsnips are perennial plants. They store rich supplies of carbohydrates in their roots during the first season to support growth during the second season, when they produce seeds. The salad crops of lettuce, celery, endive, chicory, cress, and parsley are important foods in all parts of the world.

Fruits

Fruits are ripened ovaries of a flower; the edible portion is usually the fleshy covering over the seeds.

Fruits and vegetables can also be divided into groups mainly according to their uses. Fruit vegetables (pumpkin, cucumbers, tomatoes) are technically fruits but are eaten as vegetables. In food value and other properties, fruit vegetables resemble the other vegetables.

When speaking of fruits in general we usually mean tree fruits or berries. Tree fruits are grouped into those from fruit trees which shed their leaves in the fall (apple, pear, peach) and those which shed their leaves in the spring (citrus fruits). The former are called decidous trees and the latter evergreen trees.

TABLE 32

TYPICAL COMPOSITION OF FOODS OF PLANT ORIGIN[1]

Food	Per cent Composition—Edible Portion				
	Carbo-hydrate	Protein	Fat	Ash	Water
Cereals					
Wheat flour, white	73.9	10.5	1.9	1.7	12
Rice, milled, white	78.9	6.7	0.7	0.7	13
Maize (corn) whole grain	72.9	9.5	4.3	1.3	12
Earth Vegetables					
Potatoes, white	18.9	2.0	0.1	1.0	78
Sweet Potatoes	27.3	1.3	0.4	1.0	70
Vegetables					
Carrots	9.1	1.1	0.2	1.0	88.6
Radishes	4.2	1.1	0.1	0.9	93.7
Asparagus	4.1	2.1	0.2	0.7	92.9
Beans, snap, green	7.6	2.4	0.2	0.7	89.1
Peas, fresh	17.0	6.7	0.4	0.9	75.0
Lettuce	2.8	1.3	0.2	0.9	94.8
Fruits					
Banana	24.0	1.3	0.4	0.8	73.5
Orange	11.3	0.9	0.2	0.5	87.1
Apple	15.0	0.3	0.4	0.3	84.0
Strawberries	8.3	0.8	0.5	0.5	89.9
Melon	6.0	0.6	0.2	0.4	92.8

[1] From Food Composition Tables, Food and Agricultural Organization of the U. N., Rome.

Strawberries, blueberries, gooseberries, cranberries, currants, blackberries, and raspberries are important fruits, due to their being valuable sources of nutrients as well as their having a pleasing taste.

Peaches, plums, cherries and apricots are members of a class of fruits which are widely cultivated. Apples and pears belong to another class of useful fruits, as do the orange, lemon, and grapefruit.

The composition of selected important members of the plant kingdom which are eaten as food by man are presented in Table 32.

Foods from Animals

The mammals have long been recognized as useful to man as food. Cattle, hogs, goats, and sheep have been widely cultivated as food crops. Cows, sheep, and goats yield meat and milk, while hogs yield meat and lard. In addition to these animals, there are many birds and fish useful as food.

Beef Cattle

Beef cattle have been selected for milk and meat yield. In dairy herds, there are selections for high milk production and high butter-fat yield. The Hereford and Angus are meat animals, the Holstein cow is a high yielding milk animal, the Jersey cow yields high butter-fat content milk, the Brown Swiss yields meat and milk. Artificial selection and breeding have perpetuated the characteristics of animals most useful to man in food. In addition to the dairy cow, milk is obtained successfully from goats, sheep, mares, reindeer, camels, zebras, llamas, yak, and buffalo.

Milk

The origin of the practice of drinking the milk of mammals is not known, although it is a very ancient practice. Well developed dairy herds were tended at least five thousand years ago. It is believed that first sheep, then goats, and finally cows, were cultivated for this purpose. The milk that was collected was carried in pouches made from the stomachs of animals. A stomach of a goat, for example, was cleaned, tied at one end, and filled with milk. It is now known that the stomach of a young goat or sheep has an enzyme called rennin, which is currently used in making cheese. A pouch of milk carried in the sun also yielded adequate conditions for the growth of micro-organisms. At the end of a short storage period, the pouch of milk contained a ball of "cheese" in a watery whey. This cheese was found edible and tasteful.

Butter

Churning or violently agitating milk yields butter. In fresh milk, butter fat is present as small globules which strike one another and coalesce. There is a change in physical condition from tiny fat globules in water to tiny water globules in fat—the latter we call butter. It was eventually learned that butter is easiest made from cream, the present day practice.

Poultry and Eggs

The contribution of birds to man's welfare has been improved by the domestication of birds to yield flesh and eggs. The wild hen of India was a bantam-sized slender bird laying a dozen eggs a year. Through breeding and selection, improved usefulness has been incorporated in the hen. Present day varieties produce more than 200 eggs a year. In addition to egg production, the production of broilers in ten weeks, weighing three pounds, has become the most efficient means of producing flesh. The conversion of grain to flesh is now at the rate of two and a half pounds of grain per pound of chicken. This is to be compared with the conversion of four pounds of grain per pound of pork, and 10 lbs. of grain per pound of beef.

Fish and Shellfish

Fish and shellfish are the major sources of protein in diets of people living along many coastal areas. Fresh water and salt water fish have been major and minor food sources for man. As noted earlier of the Roman Empire, live fish were carried in tanks on wagons from ponds and lakes to Rome. There the fish were kept alive until ready to be eaten. Trout are similarly handled in some American markets. Along our coasts we find lobster pounds.

Meat and Fish Equally Nourishing

The flesh of fish and shellfish is nutritionally as effective in human diets as is the flesh of animals. In addition, fish livers are excellent sources of the fat soluble vitamins.

Problem of Raw Fish as Food

Clams, lobster, mussels, shrimp, and cockles contain an enzyme, thiaminase, which can destroy vitamin B_1 if they are eaten raw. Frogs, birds, toads, and mammalian tissues do not contain thiaminase. Whitefish, carp, catfish, and herring do. Salmon, trout, perch, blue gills, eels, bass, wall-eyed pike, cod, haddock, and halibut are thiaminase-free. Carp and clams contain high levels. Thiaminase also occurs in leaves of many trees, in mustard seed, wheat germ, ground fern, and linseeds. Fortunately, thiaminase is easily destroyed by heating or cooking.

Insects as Food

Insects are eaten in cooked form. Men eat grasshoppers, beetles, crickets, caterpillars, the pupae of butterflies and moths, termites, ants, and bee larvae.

Edible Portions of Animals

The head, body, and limbs of animals are composed of muscle, bone, cartilage, fatty-tissue, nerve, and skin. Nearly half the weight of the animal body is muscle, which is eaten as food. Muscle is about three-fourths water, one-fifth protein, and the remainder fat, carbohydrates, vitamins, and minerals. There may be large amounts of fat associated around muscle tissues. Fat tends to accumulate just beneath the skin, around muscles, and in the body cavities. Muscles vary in their thickness and length, from animal to animal.

Muscles are covered and held together with a tough connective tissue, which is not digestible, and contributes to the toughness of meat. The tenderness of animal flesh is directly related to the amount of covering tissue present. Aging meat by storing the carcass in a cool room tenderizes the meat. This is due to the degradation of some of the connective tissue by the enzymes in the dead flesh in a self-digestive process. Gelatin may be made by boiling the skin, bones and connective tissue in water, which explains in part why cooking meat tenderizes it. The tougher the meat, the longer it is necessary to cook it, to tenderize.

Animal Flesh Varies in Protein Content

Animal flesh varies somewhat in its protein content. The edible portions of beef contain approximately 17 per cent protein; flank has 15 and round steak 19 per cent protein. During roasting, some water is evaporated from the meat, and some of the fat has dripped. The result is a greater per cent of protein in the weight that remains, i.e., roast beef has about 25 per cent protein.

Pork has a somewhat greater variation in protein content. Bellies may have only 9 per cent while tenderloin may have 20 per cent. Most pork chops, roasts, hams, and shoulders have about 15 per cent protein, slightly less protein than found in beef flesh.

Chicken, geese, turkey, and quail are relatively high sources of protein, containing about 20, 16, 20, and 25 per cent, respectively. Fresh fish and shellfish are good sources of protein, and have the same biological value in our diets as other animal flesh. Edible fish and shellfish contain approximately 18 per cent protein, including trout, haddock, smelts, scallops, lobster, and crab, for example. Tuna has some 25 per cent protein. Smoked herring, because it is partially dried, has nearly 37 per cent protein.

TABLE 33

GENERAL COMPOSITION OF FOODS OF ANIMAL ORIGIN[1]

Food	—Per cent Composition—Edible Portion—\ Carbo-hydrate	Protein	Fat	Ash	Water
Meat					
Beef, medium fat..............	...	17.5	22.0	0.9	60.0
Veal, medium fat..............	...	18.8	14.0	1.0	66.0
Pork, medium fat..............	...	11.9	45.0	0.6	42.0
Lamb, medium fat.............	...	15.7	27.7	0.8	56.0
Horse, medium................	1.0	20.0	4.0	1.0	74.0
Poultry					
Chicken......................	...	20.2	12.6	1.0	66.0
Duck........................	...	16.2	30.0	1.0	52.8
Turkey......................	...	20.1	20.2	1.0	58.3
Fish					
Non-fatty fillet................	...	16.4	0.5	1.3	81.8
Fatty fish fillet................	...	20.0	10.0	1.4	68.6
Crustaceans..................	2.6	14.6	1.7	1.8	79.3
Dried fish....................	...	60.0	21.0	15.0	4.0
Milk					
Cow, whole..................	5.0	3.5	3.5	0.7	87.3
Goat, whole..................	4.5	3.8	4.5	0.8	86.4
Cheese					
Hard, whole milk.............	2.0	25.0	31.0	5.0	37.0
Soft, partly whole milk.........	5.0	15.0	7.0	3.0	70.0

[1] From Food Composition Tables, Food and Agriculture Organization of the U. N., Rome.

Blood Products

Blood collected under sanitary conditions from healthy animals is eaten and may be made into blood sausage and similar products, or converted into by-products such as albumin and adhesives. Barbarians of 20,000 years ago in Northern Europe rode horses and drank their blood, an important source of vitamin C in their diet.

Composition of Animal Products

The composition of selected important members of the animal kingdom which are eaten as food by man are presented in Table 33.

Animal vs. Plant Food Sources

It is clearly seen from the preceding tables that foods of plant sources are generally high in carbohydrate content, while foods of animal sources are rich in protein. However, careful selection of diets from exclusively plant or exclusively animal sources have yielded good health to men.

TABLE 34

USEFUL STORAGE LIFE OF PLANT AND ANIMAL TISSUES AT VARIOUS TEMPERATURES

Food	Generalized Average Useful Storage Life (Days) at:		
	32 °F.	72 °F.	100 °F.
Animal flesh............	6– 10	1	less than 1
Fish....................	2– 7	1	less than 1
Poultry................	5– 18	1	less than 1
Dry meats and fish........	1,000 and more	350 and more	100 and more
Fruits..................	2–180	1–20	1– 7
Dry fruits...............	1,000 and more	350 and more	100 and more
Leafy vegetables..........	3– 20	1– 7	1– 3
Root crops..............	90–300	7–50	2–20
Dry seeds...............	1,000 and more	350 and more	100 and more

A particular problem with food sources relates to their storability, i.e., how long food from either source can be kept and eaten without repercussion from consuming spoiled foods. A brief summary of the useful storage life of plant and animal tissues at various temperatures is presented in Table 34.

These food storage characteristics are still limiting factors in obtaining uniformly good food throughout the year, throughout the world.

CHAPTER 11

Food Storage and Distribution

INTRODUCTION

Plant and animal tissues that are dead are consumed by biological forces one way or another. There is a contest between man, the animals, and the micro-organisms as to which will consume the nutrients first. Because of this situation, man must engage in competition with these other forms of life to survive and live effectively.

In addition, although foods which are rid of micro-organisms and kept so will not undergo microbiological spoilage, some chemical deterioration occurs. Sterile foods are subject to chemical reactions which cause losses in flavor, texture, color, and nutritive value. These must also be controlled.

During the past 150 years, a technology of food preservation has been generated. Man has learned to control some of the natural destructive forces and withhold the fruits of nature as his own food supply. These methods of food preservation are the refrigerated storage of perishable commodities, the freezing of foods, preservation by drying, canning, fermentation and pickling, preservation as sugar concentrates, with chemical additives, and with atomic radiation (Desrosier 1959).

THE REFRIGERATED STORAGE OF PERISHABLE COMMODITIES

The metabolism of living tissues is found to be a function of the temperature of the environment, and living organisms have a small temperature range which is optimum for growth. Higher temperatures are injurious; lower temperatures greatly retard metabolism. Temperatures near the freezing point of water are effective in reducing the rate at which respiration occurs in living tissues. Such temperatures have been found to be valuable in short-term preservation of foods. For every 18°F the temperature is lowered, it may be estimated that the rate of reaction will be halved or the storage life doubled. The storage of foods at temperatures near 32° and 34°F prolong the period in which foods may be stored, and this turns out to be very useful. Not only is the respiration rate of such foods as

176

fruits decreased, but the growth of food spoilage micro-organisms is retarded as well.

There are generally considered to be three types of micro-organisms: those with an optimum temperature for growth at 130°F, called thermophiles; those with an optimum at 98°F, called mesophiles, which include the human pathogenic organisms; and those with an optimum growth temperature near 40°F, called the psychrophiles. Lower temperatures are a positive means of controlling the growth of food spoilage micro-organisms. However, it is quite clear that their growth is retarded at these temperatures, not stopped.

Ice has been employed since early times to prolong the storage life of foods, and was one of the early export items from the American Colonies to the tropics. Ice has a disadvantage in that when all the energy deficit of ice is supplied, the ice melts and water remains. The temperature of the water-food begins to come into equilibrium with the environment. Protective mechanisms (insulation) prolong the process. When the temperature of the water-food reaches that where micro-organisms can multiply, the food deteriorates very rapidly. One important feature of ice in cooling foods is that ice does not desiccate the food by cooling it. Ice is therefore used presently where this characteristic is of value. Mechanical refrigeration has many more desirable characteristics and temperature control of food storage chambers is within the presently available refrigeration technology, without the inherent problems associated with the use of ice. However, mechanical refrigeration not only cools foods, but it also condenses moisture on the evaporator of the refrigeration system. This moisture comes from the food. It is therefore necessary to protect the food material in such a way that the temperature is controlled yet moisture losses are held to a minimum. This may be accomplished by controlling the humidity of the atmosphere in the refrigerated storage chamber, by packaging of the food, or by both.

The length of time foods can be kept edible is increased by storage of foods at temperatures below 40°F with the exception of melons, cucumbers, squash, eggplant, sweet potatoes, okra, tomatoes, and certain tropical fruits (bananas, pineapple).

Meats must be refrigerated at all stages from butchering to eating. If it is desired to hold meat for a week the meat must be rapidly cooled to below 35°F, otherwise the meat will begin to spoil. Most commercial fresh meat is consumed within a week or ten days from the time it is slaughtered, although some beef is sometimes "aged" for a few weeks. To keep meat for longer periods, it is necessary to use more drastic methods of preserving (freezing, canning, drying, curing, etc.).

The heat present in freshly killed animal must be removed rapidly to avoid decomposition and retard losses in body weight. It is desirable to remove this body heat in less than twenty-four hours. The temperature of the carcasses entering a cooler are usually about 100°F. The thickest section of the carcass should be cooled to a temperature of 32 to 34°F. Beef at this temperature can be stored successfully for eight days, lamb for six, and veal for six, before entering retail distribution channels. For delayed marketing, meat is commonly frozen and held at 0°F or lower. The humidity of the storage room is a factor requiring attention. The carcass will lose nearly two per cent of its weight in the chilling process, due to loss of moisture. Vapors rising from a warm animal carcass are principally water vapor. If the relative humidity of the storage room is about 90 per cent, the meat will mold. If the relative humidity is less than 85 per cent, the carcass will lose excessive weight.

Mold and slime formation on chilled carcasses can be retarded by using ultra violet lights in the storage chamber, ultra violet light at a wave length of 2700Å having germicidal power. If the carcass is exposed thoroughly to the germicidal rays, the meat will not mold; however, the exterior fat may turn rancid sooner with this treatment than without.

Fresh fish is more perishable than meat. Storage of fish in ice slows the process, but the flesh may still become soft and flabby. The bright color of the skin dulls, the sweet fresh fish flavor is lost, and unpleasant, strong odors develop. When caught at sea, fish is packed quickly into crushed ice, and iced again along the distribution channel from the sea to our tables. Soft fish like the whiting will not keep long under any circumstance. On the other hand, if cod is kept at 32°F it can be held for up to three weeks. For inland markets, much of the fish is frozen and distributed in that condition.

Shellfish may be kept for a week if cooled to ice temperatures. However, shrimp, lobster, and crab are very perishable, keeping in storage for a few days at the most. Lobster can be held alive in cool sea water, but immersion in fresh water causes their quick death.

Eggs should be stored at the lowest temperature possible without permitting the interior of the egg to solidify. When this occurs, the resulting expansion may cause shells to crack. Eggs with firm, thick albumen solidify at a higher temperature than thin-albumen type eggs. Shell characteristics also affect the storage quality of eggs, as thick shells withstand solidification better than thin-shelled eggs. It is considered that 29°F is the most acceptable storage temperature for eggs, the storage room being maintained at constant temperature for best results. A relative humidity between 82 and 85 per cent is generally considered optimum for egg storage. Lower humidities result in desiccation and hence enlargement of the air cell, which is undesirable.

Eggs absorb odors during storage and are not usually stored commercially in the same room with other commodities with distinct odors, such as onions, fish, or even potatoes.

Fresh fruits and vegetables that are alive maintain life processes during cold storage. They will keep only so long as they are alive and able to resist attack by spoilage organisms. Being alive, they oxidize sugar, and this produces heat. This heat reverses the benefits of refrigeration. So, more refrigeration capacity is needed for living tissues than is required by dead tissues. Sufficient refrigeration is needed to remove the heat produced by the fruit, and more still to cool the fruit to retard their respiration.

Fruits must be of suitable maturity (less than dead ripe) for best storage life. While the conditions for the successful storage of fresh fruit are well established, new technology is being evolved. For example, the storage of apples in flexible film containers creates a micro-environment, one bushel large. With this technique fruits can be held in improved condition for longer periods of time. Respiration is allowed to proceed in such film containers at reduced rates, due to the preferential carbon dioxide exchange properties, low moisture vapor transmission rates, and good oxygen exchange rates. Moisture losses with this technique are greatly reduced. After a year of storage, the fruits may retain their firm, flavorful, juicy characteristics.

Fruits and vegetables are susceptible to cold injury at above freezing temperatures, and there is a wide range in fruits and vegetables in their injury due to freezing. Some foods are injured with a slight exposure to freezing temperatures (tomatoes) and other foods can be frozen and thawed several times without permanent injury (parsnips). In any event, living fresh tissues must be kept alive if their food values are to be maintained by cold storage practices. Most fruits are stored at between 32° and 35°F, and 85 to 90 per cent relative humidity, except bananas, citrus fruits, and pineapples at 55°F. Most vegetables and root crops are stored near 32°F, and with between 90 and 95 per cent relative humidity except for potatoes which are stored at 38°F, tomatoes at 50°F, and sweet potatoes and pumpkins at 55°F. Soft fruits may keep a week, hard fleshed fruits for several months.

Fruits, vegetables, eggs, meats, fish, poultry, and dairy products may be harvested, gathered, or slaughtered some time prior to going into refrigerated storage, and deterioration may have already begun. A food does not generally improve in quality during cold storage. Only sound foods should be given the attention required for successful storage. Even under optimum conditions, storage in cool chambers only retards food deterioration. A number of storage diseases and disorders occur to foods; however, adequate control measures have been found for most of these disorders.

The commercial nut crop is held in unrefrigerated storage if the crop is to be marketed during the winter. If they are to be held in storage for longer periods they are held in cold storage. Pecans are stored immediately after harvest, in any case, to prevent rancidity and staleness from developing. Nut storage temperatures are usually below 40°F. All varieties of nuts retain their quality best when unshelled. Nuts absorb storage odors, and therefore should not be held in chambers with foods having pronounced odors. The relative humidity of a nut storage room is found best between 65 and 75 per cent. Higher humidities encourage mold growth, lower humidities tend to desiccate the nut kernels.

When foods are removed from a refrigeration chamber to a warm humid room, moisture collects on the surfaces of the cool food. Foods with surface moisture decay more quickly than dry foods.

Food Freezing

While ice-salt systems were used to freeze foods in the mid 1800's, and patents for freezing fish for example, were granted in 1861 in Maine, and even earlier in England in 1842, the invention of mechanical refrigeration in the late 1800's provided the base for the subsequent commercial exploitation of the process. Frozen foods have become important items of commerce (90 per cent of Iceland's export trade is frozen fish) and important in food preparation for dinner tables.

Clarence Birdseye fathered this revolution by developing quick freezing processes and equipment, and successfully promoting consumer units of frozen foods. He overcame tremendous obstacles. In the 1920's there were few mechanical refrigerators in homes in the United States. In the 1930's, as facilities for food freezing and retail distribution developed across the United States, frozen foods began to find their place in commerce. Yet it was not until the late 1940's that they became important competitors of other consumer types of preserved foods.

The present day finds competition between all methods of food preservation, and this competition is being resolved by consumers. Those foods best preserved by freezing are generally frozen. Those foods highly acceptable as canned products continue as highly successful consumer goods. The economic struggle for survival between fresh, canned, dried, and frozen foods in a free market evidences itself in better foods at lower prices for consumers.

Living cells contain much water, often two-thirds or more of their weight. Because of this high water content, most foods freeze between the temperatures of 25° and 32°F. The temperature of the food undergoing freezing remains relatively constant at its freezing point until it is almost completely frozen, after which time the temperature begins to approach that of the freezing medium. Quick freezing is described as a process in which this occurs in a food in thirty minutes or less.

The basic principle of all rapid freezing methods is the speedy removal of heat from foods. These methods include freezing in cold air blasts, direct immersion of the foods in a cooling medium, contact with refrigerated plates in a freezing chamber, and freezing with liquid air, nitrogen or carbon dioxide. Freezing in still air is the poorest method of all, due to its inherent slowness. By circulating cold air, the freezing rate can be greatly accelerated.

The rate of freezing is important when considering food quality. If the ice crystals which form are allowed to grow slowly, relatively large crystals develop. If made to occur rapidly, many small, fine crystals are formed. This has important ramifications in terms of the quality of the thawed food. As ice crystals grow they puncture tissue cells. Upon thawing, the foods loose cellular fluid and have a soft texture. In rapidly frozen food, a nearly natural appearance can be maintained in the thawed food.

Frozen foods must be packaged to protect them from dehydration during freezing and subsequent frozen storage. Sublimation of ice occurs in unprotected foods, resulting in a condition called freezerburn. Freezerburn irreversibly alters the color, texture, flavor, and acceptability of many frozen foods. Roast beef acquires the appearance of light brown paper due to freezerburn. Adequate packaging prevents and controls this freezing disorder.

The freezing process itself is not destructive to a nutrient in a food. In fact, the lower the temperature of a food, the better the retention of nutrients. But, involved in the freezing preservation of foods is the preparation and processing of the commodity. During the processing steps quality and nutrient losses occur, for example, during blanching, washing, trimming, and grinding.

Some nutrient losses occur during frozen storage, the higher the storage temperature, the greater the losses. Best results with frozen foods are obtained by quick freezing, and storage of the frozen foods at temperatures below $-10°F$. Commercial frozen food storage warehouses however are usually kept at $0°F$ which is an adequate compromise between economics and technological requirements. Storage at temperature above $10°F$ has significant degradative effects on most frozen foods.

Freezing foods had advantages in destroying certain parasites, the best example being *Trichinella spiralis* destruction in pork. Lowering the temperature of infected or suspect food to $0°F$, or below kills all stages of this parasite. Frozen foods are not suitable for the growth of parasites, micro-organisms, and insects in general, so long as the foods remain frozen.

Refreezing a thawed food may result in important quality changes, and these are measurable. Animal tissues appear less prone to freezing and thawing damage than are fruit and vegetable tissues, and fruits are particularly sensitive.

Fish and poultry are best quick frozen. Thawed frozen fish has more loss of tissue fluids than meat or poultry. This loss in fish can be reduced if it is cooked quickly and before it is completely thawed.

FOOD PRESERVATION BY DRYING

Drying is the most widely used and perhaps the oldest method of food preservation. It is a process copied from nature, certain features having been improved.

All of the cereal grains are preserved by drying, and the natural process is so efficient that it usually requires little added effort by man. However, there have been periods in history when climatic factors were unfavorable and grains failed to dry properly in the fields. In these instances man attempted to assist the natural action by supplying heat to the grains, which otherwise would mold.

Grains, legumes, nuts and certain fruits mature on the plants, and dry in the warm harvest wind. The natural sun drying of foods yields highly concentrated materials of enduring quality, yet a highly complex civilization cannot be so dependent upon the elements which are so unpredictable. Sun drying remains the greatest food preservation action, however. More fruits, for example, are preserved by drying than by any other method of food preservation.

Evaporation and desiccation are terms which note more or less the same action. The term dehydration has taken the meaning of artificial drying; dehydration has assumed the meaning in the food industry as that process of artificial drying.

The use of heat from a fire to dry foods was discovered independently in the Old and New Worlds. Ancient man dried foods in his shelter; pre-Columbus American Indians also used the heat from fire for this purpose. Yet it was not until 1795 that hot air dehydration chambers were invented in France.

Dehydration implies control over climatic conditions within a chamber. Sun drying is at the mercy of the elements. Dried foods from a dehydration unit can be superior in quality to their sun dried counterparts. Furthermore, less land is required for the drying activity. Sun drying for fruit requires approximately one acre of drying surface per 20 acres of crop land. Another consideration is that sanitary conditions are more controllable within a dehydration plant than are possible in open fields contaminated with dust and by insects, birds, and rodents.

Dehydration obviously is a more expensive process than sun drying, yet the dried foods usually have more commercial value due to improved quality. The yield of dried fruit from a dehydrator is also slightly higher because sugar is lost during sun drying due to the continued respiration of tissues and also due to fermentation by yeasts. The color of sun dried fruits may be superior to dehydrated fruit under optimum condition of operation of both. Color development in certain immature fruits continues during slow sun drying, but does not have an opportunity to occur in a dehydrator. In cooking quality, dehydrated foods are usually superior to sun dried counterparts. However, sun dried animal flesh and fish can be highly acceptable. On the basis of cost, sun drying is inexpensive, but on the basis of time to dry, and quality in general, dehydration has distinct advantages. Furthermore, sun drying can not be practiced widely due to unfavorable weather conditions in many areas where agriculture is a rewarding activity.

Dried and dehydrated foods are more concentrated than any other preserved form. They are less costly to produce, there is a minimum of labor required in their production, processing equipment is not elaborate, dried food storage requirements are at a minimum, and distribution costs are reduced (one car load of dried, compressed foods usually equals ten car loads of the fresh commodity).

There are chemical and biological forces operating in foods, as noted earlier. The chemical forces in dehydrated foods are controlled by packaging and employment of certain chemical additives. The biological forces are controlled by reducing the free water content and by heating. To be suitable to support the growth of microorganisms a food must have free water available to the microorganisms. By reducing the water content of a food, which also increases the osmotic pressure, microbial growth can be controlled.

Foodstuffs may be dried in hot air, superheated steam, in vacuum, in inert gas, and by the direct application of heat. Air is generally used as the drying medium because it is convenient, and burning of food can be controlled. Air is used to conduct heat to the food being dried, and to carry away the liberated moisture vapor. No elaborate moisture trapping or recovering system is needed with air, as is required if other gases are used. Drying can be forced gradually, and tendencies to scorch and discolor are within control. In general, more air is required to conduct heat to the food to evaporate the water present than is needed to transport the water vapor from the chamber.

If the temperature of the air is high and the relative humidity low, there is danger that moisture will be removed from the surface of foods being dried more rapidly than it can diffuse to the surface from the moist interior of the food particle. A hardening or casing is formed, and this impervious layer or boundary which forms, retards the free diffusion of water. This is prevented by controlling the relative humidity of the circulating air and its temperature.

There are many types of driers used in the dehydration of foods. The type chosen is governed by the nature of the commodity to be dried, the desired form of the finished product, economics, and operating conditions. Drum driers are used for milk, certain vegetable juices, cranberries, and bananas. Continuous vacuum driers are used for fruits and vegetables. Freeze driers are used for meats and heat-sensitive foods. Spray driers are used for whole eggs, egg yolks, and milk. Rotary driers are used for some meat products. Cabinet driers are used for fruit and vegetables. Kiln driers find applications in drying apples and some vegetables. Tunnel driers are used for fruits and vegetables.

Acceptable dehydrated food should have the taste, odor and appearance of fresh products, reconstitute readily in water, retain nutritive values, and have good storage stability. Many foods, for example, potato chips, are consumed because the removal of water and the heating connected with the drying process give them distinctive and desirable flavors. In other foods, such as starch and spaghetti products, dehydration is a necessary step in their production. However, in many instances, dehydrated foods have not been as acceptable generally in the past as foods processed by other methods, yet the potential remains. Recently, dehydrated, precooked meals have been developed that are very tasteful.

A recent technological development has yielded excellent dried foods which will have an impact on food preservation in the future. This new process is called freeze-dehydration. In a high vacuum, it is possible to establish specific conditions of temperature and pressure whereby the physical state of food can be maintained at a critical point, permitting successful dehydration, with greatly improved results in terms of taste, appearance, and rehydration characteristics. Because of the excellent qualities of these dried foods, widespread commercial application is expected.

In general, fruits to be dried are sorted, washed, peeled, trimmed, and treated with sulfur dioxide. Safe drying temperatures are near 140°F. In the dehydration of fruits, the moisture contents are reduced to 15 to 25 per cent depending upon the fruit. This is achieved by placing fruit on trays and either sun drying, kiln drying, or tunnel drying. Some fruit juice powders are produced by adding corn syrup and vacuum or spray drying. Dehydration affords a means of producing dried fruits in new forms and with better quality than is possible by sun drying. Some of the fruits which are commercially dehydrated are apples, apricots, peaches, nectarines, pears, prunes, grapes, figs, cherries, and berries. Freeze-dried fruits are of exceptionally fine quality, but the process is expensive.

In dehydration of vegetables, enzyme systems must be inactivated, and this is accomplished by a process called blanching—by heating them in boiling water or steam. Many vegetables are more stable if given a sulfur treatment. The moisture content of vegetables should be less than four per cent if satisfactory storage life and quality retention are to occur. Vegetables are usually dried in tunnel driers. For some powdered vegetable products, drum and spray driers are used. The amount of dried vegetables on the market is relatively small and limited in variety. Potatoes are the most important dried vegetable available. Most of the other successful vegetable products are flavoring ingredients such as onion, celery, parsley, and their powders. Some dehydrated vegetables are sold in soup mixes and some are used in remanufacturing canned products. Vegetables to be dried are washed and prepared before blanching. Carrots and potatoes are peeled and sliced or diced, green beans sliced, etc. Blanching times vary for the different vegetables from 3 minutes for leafy vegetable to 20 minutes for corn. The safe drying temperatures for most vegetables are between 140° and 145°F.

Meat is usually cooked before it is dehydrated. The moisture content of meat is then near 50 per cent prior to drying, and is reduced to less than four per cent. Large fish are cleaned and split down the back, salted and dried. Small fish can be salted and dried whole.

Dried milk powders are of two types, either of whole milk or non-fat skim milk. Drying may be accomplished by the use of vacuum drum or spray driers. The general procedure is as follows: milk is preheated, clarified, condensed, standardized, and dried. Milk powder is used in large volumes by bakers and food manufacturers as a raw ingredient. Usually low temperature, spray dried milk is preferred as it has a better flavor and color and its rehydration qualities are very acceptable.

Eggs may be dried as mixed whole eggs or separated into yolks and egg white. Before drying, the glucose content of the eggs should be fermented, or reduced by enzyme treatment, to yield a product with storage stability. Whole eggs and egg whites are usually spray dried.

Eggs, meat, milk, and vegetables are ordinarily packaged in sealed containers. Moisture vaporproof plastic films, metal foils, and metal containers are usually employed. The tin can offers protection against insects, moisture loss or gain, and permits packaging with inert gas. Packaged dehydrated foods to be kept for long periods of time are best stored at cool temperatures.

PRESERVATION OF FOOD BY CANNING

Nicholas Appert, a French confectioner, invented the canning of food. He discovered that food heated in sealed glass containers was preserved so long as the container was not reopened or the seal did not leak. These observations occurred shortly after 1800 and at a time when the cause of spoilage of foods was not known. Nevertheless, for the next 50 years, canning was practiced with rather good success, not knowing why the process worked. The reason remained to be discovered by Pasteur.

Canning has no counterpart in nature, and is a method of preserving foods which has changed the eating habits of hundreds of millions of peoples. Following the discovery of the process, there were a number of complementary discoveries concerning containers to be used, steam processing equipment, and mechanization of the entire process. Cans originally were made by a tinsmith, who was able to make a few dozen a day. Modern, high speed production machines are now capable of forming and fabricating more than 200 cans a minute. The tin coated steel can has become a most successful container for preserved foods, although glass containers have been equally perfected which can be manipulated with mechanical equipment, and are functional in the canned foods market. Certain products are traditionally packed in glass, for example, jams, jellies, and green olives. Cans are traditionally used for meat. Either container is adequate, and current usage finds many foods packed in both types of containers.

Following the discovery of canning, plants appeared across the ocean in the United States, and by 1820 there were plants operating successfully in New York and Boston. In 1830 sweet corn was canned in Maine. By 1840 canneries began appearing in the agricultural belts of the midwestern United States. In recent years the canning industry has made steady progress in the improved mechanical efficiency of processing plants. More production is obtained with fewer people. Some factories produce more than a million cans of food a day.

Perry carried canned foods in his search in 1824 for a Northwest passage to the Orient. Some of these canned foods still remain intact more than 125 years later. A number of these cans were opened and fed to animals and found to be useful in animal metabolism although there had been some chemical changes in the food. At the present time the useful commercial storage life of canned foods is considered to be from 1 to 5 years, depending on the food, its temperature of storage, and the condition of storage. Canned foods stored in the tropics are functional for at least a year; foods stored in the northern temperate zone may be stored successfully for much longer periods.

Success in canning foods depends on the heat sterilization of foods in hermetically sealed containers. Heating destroys the micro-organisms present and inactivates enzymes. Enzymes must be inactivated, otherwise a slow self-decomposition of the foods occurs during storage of the canned food. The hermetically sealed container prevents the reinfection of the food once sterilized, and prevents gaseous exchanges from occurring. The latter is significant in preventing chemical oxidation of the food during subsequent storage.

The general scheme of commercial canning may be depicted as follows: receive raw products; prepare product (wash, sort, peel, trim, chop, bone, etc.); fill food into containers; exhaust filled containers; seal lids to filled containers; heat sterilize; cool; and store canned foods.

Unfortunately, the application of sufficient heat to destroy food spoilage micro-organisms and enzymes also results in some undesirable changes in the foods. There are alterations in the color, flavor, texture, and nutritive value of foods in canning.

The prompt dispatch of raw perishable foods through the processing operations is required if high quality products are to result. Any decomposition in the raw product will be detrimental to the processed foods, and there are losses in quality that may occur throughout the canning process. Proper attention to procedures is required. If allowed to become contaminated and decompose, or if partially prepared foods are exposed to air and high temperatures for long periods of time, it may be expected that the quality of the processed foods will suffer. Under standard operating procedures in commercial canning plants, the alterations in quality of foods may be anticipated in greater or lesser degree, depending upon local plant conditions.

Foods with pH values in the basic range include eggs, some seafoods, and lye hominy. Lye hominy is the only food item canned which is normally basic, the degree of alkalinity being dependent upon manufacturing procedure. If all the lye is washed from the treated kernels of corn, it would be expected that its pH would be slightly less than 7.0, the neutral point. Meat, fish, poultry, dairy products, and vegetables generally fall into a pH range of 5.0 to 7.0. This large group is commonly referred to as the low acid group. Manufactured food items such as soups and spaghetti products, as well as figs and pimientos fall into what is called the medium acid food group. These foods have pH values between 4.5 and 5.0. Foods with pH values greater than 4.5 require relatively severe heat treatment because the lower limit of growth of an important food poisoning organism, *Clostridium botulinum*, is at a pH value of 4.5. Inasmuch as a millionth of a gram of the toxin produced by this organism will kill man, certain precautions are indicated to protect the public health. All foods capable of sustaining the growth of this organism are processed on the assumption that the organism is present and must be destroyed. Foods could be classed then into two groups, depending on whether this organism can grow or not. If the organism can grow, then high temperature steam pressure sterilization of the canned product is required to insure and safeguard the public health. Unfortunately this organism is extremely heat resistant, and heat treatments necessary to kill it also reduce the quality of these foods.

Foods with pH values between 4.5 and 3.7 are called acid foods. Fruits such as peaches, pears, oranges, apricots, and tomatoes fall into this class. Potato salad made with vinegar is also in this group. The main food spoilage organisms with this group are not heat resistant.

Next in order of increasing acidity are the berries, pickle products, and fermented foods. The pH values range from 3.7 down to 2.3. An example of this high acid group is cranberry juice.

Another important group of foods is one termed high acid-high solids. Jams and jellies are in this classification.

Foods of the acid, high acid and high acid-high solids content require mild heat treatments for their preservation by canning. Usually heating the canned food in boiling water for approximately a half an hour is satisfactory to insure sterilization of the container and the food it contains.

It is possible to classify foods then on the basis of acidity and pH value. Plant tissue (except fruits and berries) and animal tissue (including meat, fish, poultry and dairy products) are classed as low acid goods. Manufactured items with several ingredients may fall into the medium acid group. Fruits are in the acid group. Berries, fermented products, and certain citrus products fall into the high acid group as do jams and jellies. Such a classification is useful in indicating the type of heat process required for the successful presentation of the foods by canning.

There are widely held notions concerning the safety of opened canned food containers. One is that opened cans of food rapidly become poisonous. This idea evidently does not include evaporated milk, as it is a common procedure to punch holes in these cans and hold them in the refrigerators without ill effects. In truth, canned foods that are opened should be refrigerated, and should be considered perishable once opened. Canned foods will spoil more rapidly than fresh foods, once an inoculation of micro-organisms has been made by air or dust, in opened canned products. Certain foods should be removed from opened containers not from the aspect of danger to health but from the loss of quality of the foods. Pigmented foods may bleach in opened cans, and corrosion of the tin-plated steel is accelerated in the presence of oxygen from the air. In many circumstances, opened cans are the best container for a food, and may be the most sterile container available in a household. Adequately processed canned foods are not hazards to public health unless recontaminated. A dish or a pan is likely to be a source of bacteria which will find the food placed in it a suitable environment for growth. In any event, opened canned foods should be treated as perishable foods.

Important developments in canning technology have yielded improvements in the quality of canned foods, notably in color, flavor, and texture, as well as improved nutritional value. This new technology permits a wider range in processing, container types, forms, and sizes, and in the future will include foods in heat tolerant plastic films. The future for foods preserved by canning is promising, yet the competition from other means of preserving foods is mounting. Improvements in some canned foods are required if they are to be competitive with other means of preserving foods which are also improving.

FOOD FERMENTATION AND PICKLING

Micro-organisms outnumber other living entities on this planet, and can be found existing actively or passively wherever living organisms occur. While the energy for life on this planet is captured by green plants in the photosynthetic process, micro-organisms are in large part responsible for the final decomposition of the photosynthetic products. Animals play a minor role in the cycle.

Inasmuch as bacteria, yeasts, and molds are to be found throughout the environment of man, it is to be anticipated that these micro-organisms are in direct competition with other living entities for the energy for life. Whenever the conditions of nutrients and environment are favorable for microbial activity, it will normally be found.

Man must compete with all other living entities on earth. In order to retain food supplies for himself, he must interfere with this natural process, and he has evolved a number of techniques. One is the preservation of food by controlling, yet encouraging, the growth of micro-organisms. Some micro-organisms can be employed to create unfavorable conditions for others, yet retain in the foodstuffs the nutrients we desire.

While micro-organisms were not identified as the important agents in food spoilage until a century ago, wine making, bread baking, cheese making, and salting of foods have been practiced for several thousand years. For all those years food preservation was practiced using unknown, invisible, active, living organisms.

While food preservation systems in general inhibit the growth of micro-organisms, all such organisms are not detrimental; in fact, the production of substantial amounts of acid by certain organisms creates unfavorable conditions for others.

In definition, respiration is that process whereby carbohydrates are converted aerobically into carbon dioxide and water with the release of large amounts of energy. Fermentation is a process of anaerobic, or partially anaerobic, oxidation of carbohydrates. Putrefaction is the anaerobic degradation of proteinaceous materials.

Sodium chloride (salt) is useful in a fermentation process for foods by limiting the growth of putrefactive organisms, and inhibiting the growth of large numbers of other organisms. Certain bacteria have been found which can tolerate and grow in substantial amounts of salt in solution.

The word fermentation has undergone evolution itself. The term was employed to describe the bubbling or boiling condition seen in the production of wine, prior to the time that yeasts were discovered. However, after Pasteur's discovery, the word became used with microbial activity, and later with enzyme activity. Currently the term is used even to describe the evolution of carbon dioxide gas during the action of living cells. Neither gas evolution or the presence of living cells is essential to fermentative action however, as seen in lactic acid fermentations, where no gas is liberated, and in fermentations accomplished solely with enzymes. There is a clear difference between fermentation and putrefaction. Fermentation is a decomposition action of carbohydrate materials; putrefaction relates to the general action of micro-organisms on proteinaceous materials. Fermentation processes usually do not evolve putrid odors, and carbon dioxide is usually produced. In putrefaction, the evolved materials may contain carbon dioxide, but the characteristic odors are hydrogen sulfide and sulfur containing protein decomposition products. A putrid fermentation is usually a contaminated fermentation. Putrid kraut or pickles result from microbial growths decomposing protein, rather than the normal fermentation of carbohydrates to acid.

There are three important characteristics micro-organisms should have if they are to be useful in fermentation and pickling:

(a) The micro-organisms must be able to grow rapidly in a suitable substrate and environment, and be easily cultivated in large quantity.

(b) The organism must have the ability to maintain physiological constancy under the above conditions, and yield the essential enzymes easily and abundantly in order that the desired chemical changes can occur.

(c) The environmental conditions required for maximum growth and production should be comparatively simple.

The application of micro-organisms to food preservation practices must be such that a positive protection is available to control contamination.

The micro-organisms used in fermentations are notable in that they produce large amounts of enzymes. Bacteria, yeasts, and molds, being single cells, contain the functional capacities for growth, reproduction, digestion, assimilation, and repairs in the cell which higher forms of life have distributed to tissues. Therefore, it is to be anticipated that single-celled complete living entities, such as bacteria, have a higher enzyme productivity and therefore fermentative capacity than found with other living creatures.

Enzymes are the reactive substances which control chemical reactions in fermentation. The micro-organisms of each genus and species are actually a warehouse of enzymes, with its own special capacity to produce and secrete enzymes. Man has yet to learn to synthesize them.

A gram of dried organism endowed with high activity, lactose-fermenting enzymes, is capable of breaking down 10,000 gm. of lactose per hour. This great chemical activity is associated with the simple life-process requirements of the organisms, the ease with which they obtain energy for life, their great growth capacity and reproduction rate, and their great capacity for maintenance of the living entity. One generation may occur in less than 20 minutes.

But there is a balance in effort. In living, the organisms consume energy. The product of their actions is a substrate of lower energy than that native material upon which they were planted. But, the product of the activity in the instance of wine is one which man generally enjoys more than the native juice, from which the wine was produced.

Micro-organisms have available carbohydrates, proteins, fats, minerals and minor nutrients in native food materials. The micro-organisms first attack carbohydrates, then proteins, then fats. There is an order of attack even with carbohydrates, first the sugars, then alcohols, then acids. Since the first requirement for microbial activity is energy, it appears that the most available forms, in order of preference, are the CH_2, CH, CHOH, and COOH carbon linkages. Some linkages such as CN radicals are useless to micro-organisms, and are actually poisons to them.

Micro-organisms are used to ferment sugar by complete oxidation, partial oxidation, alcoholic fermentation, lactic acid fermentation, butyric fermentation, and other minor fermentative actions.

(a) Bacteria and molds are able to break down sugar (glucose) to carbon dioxide and water. Few yeasts can accomplish this action.

(b) The most common fermentation is one in which a partial oxidation of sugar occurs. In this case, sugar may be converted to an acid. The acid finally may be oxidized to yield carbon dioxide and water, if permitted to occur. For example, some molds are used in the production of citric acid from sugar solutions.

(c) Yeasts are the most efficient converters of aldehydes to alcohols. Many species of bacteria, yeasts, and molds are able to yield alcohol. The yeast, *Saccharomyces ellipsoideus,* is of great industrial importance in alcoholic fermentation. The yeasts yield alcohol in recoverable quantities. While other organisms are able to produce alcohol, it usually occurs in such mixtures of aldehydes, acids, and esters that recovery is difficult. The change from sugar to alcohol has many steps.

(d) The lactic acid fermentations are of great importance in food preservation. The sugar in foodstuff may be converted to lactic acid and other end products and in such amounts that the environment is controlling over other organisms. Lactic acid fermentation is efficient, and the fermenting organisms rapid in growth. Natural inoculations are so widespread that in a suitable environment, the lactic acid bacteria will dominate, i.e., souring of milk.

(e) Butyric fermentations are less useful in food preservation than those above. The organisms are anaerobic, and impart undesirable flavors, and odors to most foods. The anaerobic organisms capable of infecting man, causing disease, are commonly butyric fermenters. Carbon dioxide, hydrogen, acetic acid, and alcohols are some of their fermentation products.

(f) In addition to the above there is a fermentation which involves much gas production. It is useful in food preservation, although gas production has disadvantages. Energy-wise it is less efficient to produce gases (carbon dioxide and hydrogen) which have little or no preserving power in concentrations found in comparison with lactic acid. Too, the important food spoilage organisms are capable of growing in such environments. In gassy fermentations, sugar molecules are altered to form acids, alcohols, and carbon dioxide. It is usually necessary to include some other controlling influence such as adding sodium chloride to a substrate with this form of fermentation.

(g) There are many fermentative actions possible in food which act in detriment to the acceptability of treated foods. Generally the organisms capable of attacking cellulose, hemi-celluloses, pectin, and starch will injure the texture, flavor, and quality of treated foods.

Foods are contaminated naturally with micro-organisms, and will spoil if untended. The type of action which will develop is dependent upon the conditions which are imposed. The most favorable to a given type of fermentation under one condition will be altered by slight changes in a controlling factor. Untended meat will naturally mold and putrefy. If brine or salt is added, entirely different organisms will take over.

Inasmuch as the two important fermentations in foods are oxidative and alcoholic, the growth of organisms can be controlled by the acidity of the food. In fruits and fruit juices, yeasts and molds quickly establish themselves. In meats, yeasts are less active than bacteria and molds. In milk, an acid fermentation is established in a matter of a few hours.

Organisms can be selected on the basis of their salt tolerance. This is a useful procedure in controlling fermentations. Certain lactic acid bacteria, yeasts, and molds either tolerate salt or adapt to moderate quantities of it. Spore-forming bacteria are either not tolerant to salt in solution, or they are sufficiently inhibited by the subsequent growth of salt tolerant organisms producing acid, i.e., lactic acid bacterial growth, which supplements the original inhibition effects of the salt, that they, the spore formers, do not develop. Proteolytic bacteria, unable to tolerate salt, are inhibited from growth. Salt, vinegar, and spices are commonly used in complementary action in many fermented foods. Spices vary in their antibacterial activity, some (mustard oil) being very active, others (black pepper) having little effect.

Wine and beer and similar fermented products yield palatable beverages from natural juices of fruits and carbohydrate substrates. In alcoholic fermentation, the formation of alcohol from sugar is accomplished by yeast enzymes, which are contributed by the growing yeasts. In a suitable growth medium, and in an adequate environment, the amount of alcohol produced depends upon the amount of sugar present and the efficiency of the yeast in converting the sugar to alcohol. Eventually yeasts produce such a quantity of alcohol that they themselves can no longer tolerate it, usually when about 16 per cent alcohol has been developed, although some yeasts can tolerate up to 18 per cent.

Vinegar manufacture requires two distinct fermentation processes. The first transforms the sugar into alcohol by the growth and activity of yeasts. The second change is brought about by vinegar bacteria, and changes the alcohol into acetic acid. One of the chief causes of failure in preparing vinegar, and a factor often not considered, is that the vinegar making process has these two distinct steps, and that one must be completed before the other starts. Further, the alcoholic step requires the presence of very little air, and the acetic acid step requires a large volume of air. Theoretically, for every 100 parts of sugar present in a fruit juice, 51 parts of alcohol and 49 parts of carbon dioxide are produced. In the acetic acid fermentation, 100 parts of alcohol should yield 130 parts of acetic acid. In practice, starting with 100 parts of sugar, approximately 55 parts of acetic acid are obtained under favorable conditions. The legal minimum vinegar standard in the United States is four per cent acid; hence, it is necessary to use a juice that contains at least eight per cent sugar.

Pickled fruits and vegetables are made by fermenting them in high salt solutions. The salt controls the growth of objectionable organisms, and fermentation occurs, stabilizing the tissues by the conversion of the sugar present into acid. Sauerkraut is prepared from shredded cabbage by the same procedure.

Dairy products are fermented successfully in the manufacture of cheeses. The protein in the milk is first coagulated, then the curd which is obtained is converted into cheese due to the growth of selected organisms. By controlling micro-organisms, temperature, and substrate, hundreds of different kinds of cheeses, with distinct flavors, can be prepared. Some have become world famous.

Pickled, cured, and smoked meats are important preserved products. The curing is first accomplished by dry curing or with pickling solution methods. The ingredients used in curing meats are sodium nitrate, sodium nitrite, sodium chloride, sugar, and citric acid (or vinegar). Pickling and curing of meats is best accomplished at cool temperatures. In general curing occurs at the rate of about an inch a week. Curing may be combined with smoking in preserving animal flesh. The smoke acts not only as a dehydrating agent, but deposits a coating on the surface of the meat. Pork and beef tissues are commonly preserved by these methods in the temperate climates even in modern times. This ancient process still finds widespread use due to the palatable nature of the products produced.

PRESERVATION OF FOODS AS SUGAR CONCENTRATES

A food substance which contains 65 per cent or more of soluble solids, which contains substantial acid, may be preserved with mild applications of heat, providing the subsequent product is protected from the air. With 70 per cent soluble solids, high acid is not required to insure success by this method of food preservation.

The manufacture of fruit jellies and preserves is one of the important fruit by-product industries, and is based on this high solids-high acid preservation principle. Not only are such fruit concentrates an important method of preserving fruits, but equally, in modern day commerce, they are an important utilization of fruits which, though otherwise of excellent qualities, do not possess attractiveness in form or color. Such fruits do not usually enter fresh market channels. In addition to the pleasing tastes of such preserved fruits, they possess substantial nutritive values.

Jelly making, once strictly a household process, has taken its place as an important food manufacturing activity. In contrast with most other food industries, this fruit preserving industry is more frequently located near the consumer centers than in the fruit production areas.

Other food products may be concentrated as a means of preservation, including sweetened condensed milk. This product contains more than 70 per cent soluble solids and results in a useful preserved milk product.

Jelly, jam, preserves, marmalades, and fruit butters are products prepared from fruit and/or juices with sugar added and by concentrating by evaporation to a point where microbial spoilage can not occur. Mold growth on the surface of fruit preserves is controlled by the exclusion of oxygen, i.e., covering over with paraffin. Modern practice replaces the paraffin with vacuum sealed containers. Moisture losses, mold growth and oxidation are thus controlled.

Fruits and their extracts obtain their jelly-making characteristics from a substance called pectin. Jelly only forms when a suitable concentration of pectin, sugar, and acid is reached in water. Jelly formation occurs when the pH value is near 3.2, and the sugar concentration is more than 60 per cent. Under practical conditions, a pint of fruit juice, extracted from suitable fruits, to which is added a pound of sugar, and heated to a temperature of 221°F at sea level will normally form a jelly.

Ideally, fruits for jelly making should contain sufficient pectin and acid to yield a good jelly. Such fruits include crab apples, sour apple varieties which are not overmature, sour berries, citrus fruits, grapes, sour cherries, and cranberries. Sweet cherries, quinces, and melons are rich in pectin but low in acid content. Strawberries and apricots contain sufficient acid but are low in pectin. Peaches, figs, and pears are low generally in both acid and pectin. Because pectins are available commercially, and edible acids are plentiful, it is possible to correct defects in acid content or pectin content of fruit in jelly making.

Candied and glacéed fruits essentially involve their slow impregnation with syrup until the sugar concentration in the tissue is sufficiently high that it prevents the growth of spoilage micro-organisms. The candying process is conducted in such a manner that the fruit does not soften and become merely jam, or become tough and leathery. By treating fruits with syrups of progressively increasing sugar concentrations, desired results may be obtained. Following sugar impregnation, the fruits are washed, dried and packaged, or, they may be coated with a thin glazing of sugar. Sugar coated candied fruits are called glacéed fruits.

PRESERVATION WITH CHEMICAL ADDITIVES

Chemical agents can contribute substantially in the preservation of food and can help prevent the loss of seasonal surpluses. In economically underdeveloped countries, lack of functional storage facilities and the inadequacy of transportation and communications systems may increase the necessity of using certain chemical additives for purposes of food preservation. Too, in tropical regions, where high temperatures and humidities favor microbial attack, and increase the rate of development of oxidative rancidity, a wider use of chemical antimicrobial agents and antioxidants may be justified than can be in countries in more temperate climates. It is recognized that the increased risks associated with the increased use of chemical food additives must be weighed against the benefits gained from preventing food losses and making more food available in areas in which it is needed. In such circumstances, chemical food additives might be used to supplement the effectiveness of traditional methods of food preservation rather than to replace these methods.

On the other hand, in countries which are technically and economically highly developed, the availability of adequate facilities for refrigerated transportation and storage greatly reduces, even if it does not eliminate, the need for chemical preservatives. In these countries, however, there is an increasing demand for more attractive foods of uniform quality, and for a wide choice of foods at all seasons of the year. Moreover, large quantities of many of the foods consumed must be transported from distant producing areas, a fact which often creates special transportation and storage problems. For such purposes, a variety of useful food additives is likely to be needed, varying considerably from region to region and even from country to country. In making decisions concerning the use of an additive, attention is given to its technological usefulness, the protection of the consumer against deception and the use of inferior techniques in processing, and to the evidence bearing on the safety of using the additive from a health standpoint.

Food additives have a legitimate use in the food processing and distribution systems of both technologically advanced and of less well developed countries in promoting the utilization of available foods.

The use of food additives to the advantage of the consumer may be technologically justified when it serves the following purposes: the maintenance of the nutritional quality of a food; the enhancement of keeping quality or stability with reductions in food losses; making foods attractive to the consumer in a manner which does not lead to deception; and providing essential aids in food processing.

The use of food additives is not in the best interest of the consumer in the following situations and should not be permitted: to disguise the use of faulty processing and handling techniques; to deceive the consumer; when the result is a substantial reduction of the nutritive value of the food; when the desired effect can be obtained by good manufacturing practices which are economically feasible.

There are two broad categories of chemical preservatives useful in food preservation: inorganic and organic agents. Inorganic agents include sulfur dioxide and chlorine. Organic agents include benzoic acid, certain fatty acids including sorbic acid, fumigants such as eythlene and propylene oxides, and antibiotics. Each has specialized uses which are beneficial in their actions. Sulfur dioxide is widely used in the preservation of fruits. Chlorine compounds are important in the purification of water for drinking and processing purposes. Benzoic acid is useful in preventing the growth of yeasts and molds in fruit products. Sorbic acid has been found useful in preserving packaged cheeses. Ethylene oxide has been used in the sterilization of spices and flavoring compounds. Antibiotics have been used to prolong the fresh storage life of meat, poultry, and fish.

RADIATION PRESEVATION OF FOODS

The discovery of the chain reaction opened a new horizon of scientific endeavor. Nuclear fission has been applied practically in yielding power to do a portion of man's work task. Attempts are now being made to mold the radiations yielded by the fission process into useful applications. One of these applications involves contributions to the solution of that ageless problem of an adequate supply of food for all men.

It is important to recognize not only the potential benefits to be derived from the successful application of radiation in food storage and distribution, but also the limits to such applications due to the alterations which irradiation produces in treated foods. Because of the ability of radiation to initiate chemical and nuclear reactions, questions of the health and safety of treated foods arise. It is imperative that conclusive proof be obtained of the absence of noxious changes in irradiated foods in human diets. Research in this aspect of irradiated foods has been underway in many countries since the middle of the 1950's. These studies in general have not yet been terminated. Preliminary evidence appears encouraging. Furthermore, limited studies with human volunteers so far have yielded no untoward physiological reaction to date due to consuming the irradiated foods covered in the studies.

While at present there is no commercial application of food preservation by irradiation, some applications have been developed to a very advanced stage. The first products which are likely to come into commercial use seem to be those requiring very low dose treatments. The successful application of radiation to the disinfection and stabilization of foods will directly involve not only the economics of food distribution but will also have important repercussions even in food production itself. While radiation can permit a new degree of freedom in distributing perishable fruits, vegetables, meats, poultry, and fish, increasing the useful distribution life of a commodity also extends market opportunities. Areas which could not supply a market in the past due to inherent barriers caused by spoilage and decay may now find great opportunity.

Food Irradiation Applications

There are at least six distinct areas of application of radiation to food distribution (see Table 34). First of all, there is permanent preservation. To qualify, a radiation sterilized food must conform to high standards of consumer appeal, nutritive value, wholesomeness, economy, and storage stability, in competition with other preserved products. Second is the application of limited radiation doses to prolong the storage life of market commodities such as cut meats, fresh fish, fresh fruits and vegetables with or without refrigeration. The satisfactory extension of storage life of natural commodities without losses in market and quality characteristics has yet to be resolved, and radiation may enjoy a special position. Third, destruction of insects in various life cycle stages in food products is successful with radiation. Deinfestation of packaged foods can be accomplished. Fourth, the growth processes of plant tissues are radiation sensitive. Examples of this application are seen in sprout inhibition of potatoes and in onions. Furthermore, the application of low level radiation doses to seeds of some plants prior to planting has been found to increase the yield of edible crops from 10 to 50 per cent. It should be recognized in comparison that hybridization yields some 15 per cent increase in crops. Fifth, radiation has potential value in improving the texture of meat and vegetables. For example, asparagus can be fibrous, and peas become starchy, yet low level irradiation treatments tenderizes the shoots and sweetens the peas. Tenderization of meat is easily accomplished. Sixth, the destruction of parasites in man's food and beverages and the control of food poisoning organisms in foods is within existing technology.

Potential Value of Irradiated Foods

Radiation sterilized chicken has been stored successfully at room temperature for almost three years. Radiation sprout inhibited potatoes have been cold stored at Purdue University for more than two years with less than 15 per cent weight losses and storage for three years has been completed to date. Deterioration is more marked following two years of storage. Examples of useful radiation treatments for foods can be found with all the important food groups.

There are conflicting views and interests in the radiation stabilization of food process. It is obvious that radiation stabilization will not make obsolete the vast refrigeration facilities that are spread over the world; it is obvious that most people on earth, on the other hand, have no refrigeration facilities. There are therefore different needs of people in this regard, and there are radiation applications for both.

With the refrigeration resources in the United States and certain parts of Europe, major industrial interests here have been found in low level irradiation which requires that the food generally be kept in cold storage. This is the so-called pasteurization range of less than a million rads (unit of measure; chest x-ray equals 0.6 rads) for consumer food items. This food is not sterile; cool storage temperatures are needed to retard the surviving organisms from growth. Extension of the useful refrigerated storage and distribution lives by a factor of 5 to 10 for perishable foods may be obtained with this approach over the conventional methods in use today.

Radiation offers a new degree of freedom in distributing perishable fruits, vegetables, meats, poultry, and fish. When the useful distribution life of a commodity is extended by a significant factor, this means that areas which could not supply a market in the past due to inherent barriers because of spoilage and decay, may now find greater opportunity.

Present Outlook—Cautiously Optimistic

In summary, the food irradiation research to date has shown that many foods can be successfully stabilized through irradiation. With the present rate of expanding technology most foods should fall within the successful category. Suitable packages are available for irradiated foods. Functional plastic films are becoming available. The nuclear physics problems relating to the process have been resolved. Radiation stabilized foods are being established as wholesome and useful for mankind to consume. Of the foods tested on consumers, they generally are unable to tell which item in a meal is irradiated, providing all the technology available is applied.

The health and welfare of mankind are intimately interwoven in the fabric called the economics of food distribution. The application of radiation to the disinfection and stabilization of foods directly involves the economics of food distribution. A vast opportunity is available. The present outlook of researchers in this field is cautiously optimistic (Desrosier and Rosenstock 1960).

SUMMARY

In the past 100 years two large bodies of information have become available which are useful in understanding food storage and distribution problems. One deals with chemistry and the chemical composition of plants and animals. The other deals with biology and the organisms associated with plants and animals. As a result, it is now recognized that natural foodstuffs have associated organisms which draw their nutrient requirements from the chemical constituents of foods, which as a consequence decompose and for the most part become lost for human consumption.

Food harvests locally are basically annual affairs and in order to keep food between harvests, or ship foods from one area to another, it is necessary to control the growth of organisms and control chemical reactions in foods. A number of methods have evolved which can more or less control such deteriorations. Included in these methods are drying, salting, pickling, fermenting, the addition of chemical preservatives, cold storage, canning, and freezing.

In spite of the fact that most of these methods have been available to most people for centuries, more than 25 per cent (and perhaps 50 per cent) of the many foods produced are not eaten by people. Why is it that we do not have better methods of storing and distributing foods?

One reason no doubt is that the bulk of the research undertaken in the field of food and agriculture has been concentrated in the area of food production. Food storage and distribution in comparison have received insignificant attention by governments in spite of the fact that the ability to store and distribute food is a critical problem all over the world. Man must learn not only how to produce food; it does him no good until the food is consumed, and he can not eat it all before it spoils.

There is a competition between man and other biological forces on earth as to which will consume the nutrients available first, i.e., in food short India, five billion pounds of grain were consumed this year solely by pests, while people went hungry. There is no way of knowing what the toll is on the grain crop of the world due to molding and insect infestations.

Food production research must go hand in hand with research into how to keep the foods once produced. In analogy, what has happened in food research in the past could be related to the flight of a bird. If one wing represents food production and the other wing represents food distribution, to develop one wing without the other is to have the bird travel in circles of bewilderment rather than to have a useful flight.

The food component not available in sufficient amounts in human diets in the world is high quality protein, which will be discussed in the next chapters. It turns out that high quality protein foods are also the most perishable. The best source is animal flesh and the most widely employed method at present in the world to keep meat edible is to keep the animals alive. This turns out to be a very inefficient system, because the animal continues to consume feed.

There has been no new food found of importance in the past 450 years and modern man has had little better success in food preservation. There has been no major discovery of consequence in food preservation in the past 150 years, which is now widely applied to make more and better food available to people.

Furthermore, present systems of preserving foods in some degree of "fresh" quality have yet to find widespread application in the world. For example, canned and frozen foods do not constitute a significant part of the food supplies available to the world's 3.0 billion human inhabitants of the present day. The people who invented canning barely use it. Further, most people in the world do not have refrigerators.

There is hope that the peaceful uses of atomic energy will hold a special place in the future in food preservation, providing present efforts yield successful processes. However, this method has been known for 15 years, the first commercial application has yet to occur to improve food storage and distribution practices, and during this time the world's population has increased by almost a billion people. It is unfortunate that so little attention has been given to this area, which holds some promise to better the life of mankind on earth.

PART IV

World Starvation and Its Control

CHAPTER 12

World Food Consumption Patterns

INTRODUCTION

We have seen that food production is uneven throughout the world. Some existing extremes in world food supplies per person per year are shown in Table 35. There is also a wide range in food consumption patterns between countries, shown for the United States and India in Table 36.

While the food needs of each person is individual and characteristic, the food consumption patterns of the people in the world are not known for each individual. However, there are average values which can be found which tend to show the food consumption patterns in general (see Fig. 19).

Of the food supply available per person, there is no measure for a whole population of what is actually consumed or what portion of the food that is available is discarded as waste.

Further, the adequacy of food supplies is not dependent solely on being sufficient in quantity and it would be useful in discussing the world food consumption patterns to have some unit of measure of the quality of a diet. Unfortunately, there is no comprehensive unit available. A diet for an adult which contains about 50 gm. of protein per day, of which one-third is from animal sources, has been established by various experts to be a rough minimum standard of quality in a diet. The best we can do is to consider the adequacy

TABLE 35

EXISTING EXTREMES IN WORLD FOOD SUPPLY PER PERSON PER YEAR[1]

	Maximum	Minimum
Cereals and flour in terms of flour and milled rice, lbs. per year...........	425 (Turkey)	165 (United States)
Potatoes and other root crops (including sweet potatoes and cassava flour), lbs. per year......................	528 (Poland)	18 (India)
Sugar (as refined sugar but not including syrup and honey), lbs. per year..	128 (Australia)	2 (China)
Pulses and dry legumes, lbs. per year...	48 (Brazil)	2 (Austria, China, and Denmark)
Meat (including poultry and offal), lbs. per year......................	242 (New Zealand)	2 (India)
Milk (whole milk for consumption as such and as processed-milk products), lbs. per year....................	858 (Iceland)	1 (China)
Fats and oils, lbs. per year...........	57 (Denmark)	2 (Japan)
Calories per day..................	3,380 (New Zealand)	1,590 (India)
Per cent of calories derived from animal products......................	49 (New Zealand)	4 (Japan)
Average total protein intake, gm. per day............................	98 (Oceania)	50 (Far East)
Average animal protein intake, gm. per day............................	67 (Oceania)	8 (Far East)
Per cent of total calories from cereals...	57 (Italy)	27 (Denmark)

[1] From Joslyn and Olcott (1959).

TABLE 36

COMPARISON OF THE YEARLY AVERAGE FOOD CONSUMPTION IN THE UNITED STATES AND INDIA, 1949–1950[1]

Food Product	Consumption, Lbs. United States	India
Cereals and starchy roots.............	279	277
Beans, peas, etc...................	15	44
Fruits and vegetables..............	447	90
Meat, eggs, fish, milk..............	856	110
Fats............................	42	7
Sugar..........................	103	29

[1] From Joslyn and Olcott (1959).

of food consumption patterns in terms of the calorie content of the diets in general. In Table 37, the estimated calorie requirements of people in various countries is compared to the average calorie content of the diets available. The variations from these requirements can then be established in general terms, and are shown in this table.

CALORIC INTAKE IN THE WORLD

It is noted that the caloric requirement of people in various countries varies.

TABLE 37

CALORIE SUPPLIES MEASURED AGAINST REQUIREMENTS[1]

Region and Country	Recent Level	Estimated Requirements	Difference of Requirements
	Calories		Per Cent
Europe			
Belgium-Luxembourg..........	2,770	2,620	+5.7
Denmark....................	3,160	2,750	+14.9
France.....................	2,770	2,550	+8.6
Greece.....................	2,510	2,390	+5.0
Italy.......................	2,340	2,440	−4.1
Netherlands.................	2,960	2,630	+12.5
Norway.....................	3,140	2,850	+10.2
Sweden.....................	3,120	2,840	+9.8
Switzerland.................	3,150	2,720	+15.8
United Kingdom.............	3,100	2,650	+16.9
U.S.S.R.	3,020	2,710	+11.4
North America			
Canada.....................	3,060	2,710	+12.9
United States of America.......	3,130	2,640	+18.5
Latin America			
Argentina...................	3,190	2,600	+22.7
Brazil......................	2,340	2,450	−4.5
Chile......................	2,360	2,640	−10.6
Colombia...................	2,280	2,550	−10.6
Cuba.......................	2,740	2,460	+11.4
Mexico.....................	2,050	2,490	−17.6
Peru.......................	1,920	2,540	−24.4
Uruguay....................	2,580	2,570	+0.4
Venezuela..................	2,160	2,440	−11.5
Near East			
Cyprus.....................	2,470	2,510	−1.6
Egypt......................	2,290	2,390	−4.2
Turkey.....................	2,480	2,440	+1.6
Far East			
Ceylon.....................	1,970	2,270	−13.2
India......................	1,700	2,250	−24.4
Japan......................	2,100	2,330	−9.9
Pakistan....................	2,020	2,300	−12.2
Philippines	1,960	2,230	−12.1
Africa			
French North Africa..........	1,920	2,430	−20.9
Mauritius...................	2,230	2,410	−7.5
Tanganyika.................	1,980	2,420	−13.2
Union of South Africa........	2,520	2,400	+5.0
Oceania			
Australia...................	3,160	2,620	+20.6
New Zealand...............	3,250	2,670	+21.7

[1] From United Nations (1957).

In establishing this requirement for various peoples the method employed by United Nations groups takes into account the environmental temperature in which a population exists, average body weights, age distribution, and sex ratios of the population. It is recognized that the values obtained by this method may not correspond very closely to those reached by national authorities who have fuller experiences with national food situations. All estimates of this type are subject to a considerable margin of error. But, for the purpose of comparing food consumption this data does tend to illustrate the broad aspects of the world food problem. For example, in Table 37, the average calorie supplies in some countries of the world for which adequate data are available can be compared with the average requirement of the populations in these countries.

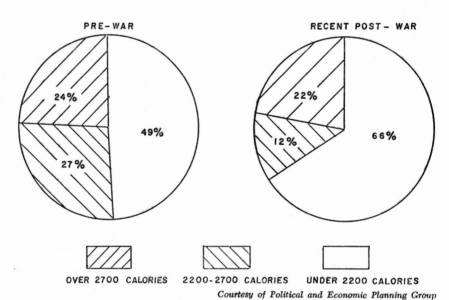

PERCENT OF TOTAL POPULATION

PRE-WAR   RECENT POST- WAR

OVER 2700 CALORIES   2200-2700 CALORIES   UNDER 2200 CALORIES

Courtesy of Political and Economic Planning Group

FIG. 19.   CALORIE LEVEL AVAILABLE IN GENERAL TO THE PEOPLE OF THE WORLD, PREWAR AND RECENT POSTWAR

One fact immediately becomes obvious. The calorie supplies in general are short of needs in most regions except Western Europe, North America, and Oceania.

There are wide variations and even some exceptions to the general patterns given in Table 37 for the different countries in the different regions of the world. The fact that the average calorie supply in one country is smaller than in another country need not necessarily imply that the former is worse fed than the latter, especially if the two countries differ widely in regards to environmental conditions and factors influencing the physiological needs of these

TABLE 38

TRENDS OF AVERAGE PER CAPITA CALORIE SUPPLY IN SELECTED COUNTRIES AND PERCENTAGE
DERIVED FROM CEREALS AND STARCHY FOODS[1]

Country	Average Per Capita Calorie Supply			Per Cent of Calories from Cereals and Starchy Roots		
	Prewar	1948/49– 1950/51	1953/43– 1954/55	Prewar	1948/49– 1950/51	1953/54– 1954/55
	⟵—Per Capita per Day—⟶			⟵——— Per Cent ———⟶		
Europe						
Austria.............	2,930	2,670	2,800	49	54	47
Belgium-Luxembourg......	2,810	3,840	2,960	50	45	43
Denmark...........	3,420	3,170	3,330	33	39	34
Finland............	2,990	3,100	3,140	53	51	45
France.............	2,870	2,790	2,830	51	51	47
Germany, Western...	3,040	2,680	2,930	47	55	43
Greece.............	2,600	2,490	2,540	61	62	58
Ireland, Rep. of......	3,400	3,440	3,610	50	48	45
Italy...............	2,510	2,380	2,570	65	65	60
Netherlands.........	2,840	2,940	2,940	44	43	37
Norway............	3,210	3,110	3,130	44	44	37
Portugal...........	...	2,310	2,500	..	60	59
Sweden............	3,110	3,160	3,030	37	34	32
Switzerland........	3,140	3,170	3,090	39	41	37
United Kingdom.....	3,110	3,080	3,210	35	39	33
Yugoslavia.........	3,020	2,140	2,710	76	80	72
North America						
Canada............	3,010	3,070	3,080	35	28	28
U.S.A.............	3,150	3,160	3,080	32	27	26
Latin America						
Argentina..........	2,730	3,210	2,840	44	45	41
Brazil.............	2,150	2,340	2,350	48	49	52
Chile..............	2,240	2,380	2,490	61	62	59
Cuba..............	2,610	2,730	...	49	48	..
Honduras..........	...	1,990	1,980	..	55	52
Peru..............	1,860	2,070	2,080	64	66	65
Uruguay...........	2,380	2,890	2,810	40	35	40
Venezuela..........	...	2,160	2,270	...	46	48
Far East						
India..............	1,970[2]	1,620	1,850	69[1]	67	69
Pakistan...........	...	2,150	2,130	..	72	79
Japan.............	2,180	2,050	2,200	77	78	71
Philippines.........	1,910	...	1,920	67	..	74
Africa and Near East						
Egypt.............	2,450	2,370	2,480	72	72	72
Israel.............	...	2,680	2,870	..	51	54
Southern Rhodesia...	...	2,280	2,630	..	74	75
Turkey............	2,450	2,490	2,660	76	74	73
Union of South Africa.	2,300	2,600	2,580	67	59	58
Oceania						
Australia..........	3,300	3,320	3,120	34	33	31
New Zealand.......	3,260	3,340	3,400	30	30	28

[1] From United Nations (1957).
[2] Includes Pakistan.
... Data not available.

TABLE 39

CONSUMPTION OF PULSES, FISH, AND MEAT IN SELECTED COUNTRIES[1]

Kilograms per Capita per Year

Country	Pulses and Nuts			Fish			Meat		
	Prewar	1948/49–1950/51	1954/55	Prewar	1948/49–1950/51	1954/55	Prewar	1948/49–1950/51	1954/55
Europe									
Austria	4	3	3	2	2	3	49	30	46
Belgium-Luxembourg	7	4	4	6	7	7	46	44	50
Denmark	1	3	5	15	18	15	75	62	63
Finland	3	2	2	6	8	11	33	28	33
France	8	7	6	6	6	6	61	62	75
Germany, Western	3	4	3	7	8	7	53	29	45
Greece	16	15	17	6	6	6	20	11	16
Ireland, Rep. of	2	2	2	3	3	4	55	53	54
Italy	22	13	12	4	4	5	20	15	19
Netherlands	6	4	4	6	7	6	38	28	38
Norway	3	3	4	21	28	20	38	33	35
Portugal	..	9	7	20	16	18	..	14	15
Sweden	4	4	4	20	20	21	49	49	52
Switzerland	5	5	9	1	2	2	53	44	50
United Kingdom	5	6	6	12	12	10	68	53	66
Yugoslavia	..	4	9	..	1	1	..	15	21
North America									
Canada	6	6	5	5	6	6	62	70	80
U.S.A.	7	7	7	5	5	5	71	84	88
Latin America									
Argentina	2	2	4	2	2	2	107	116	104
Brazil	..	26	25	..	3	2	..	39	27
Chile	10	6	9	7	6	10	38	38	32
Cuba	12	17	..	3	3	..	33	35	..
Honduras	..	12	11	..	2	..	..	..	..
Peru	..	18	9	..	2	2	..	16	20
Uruguay	..	4	2	..	1	2	..	114	96
Venezuela	..	13	16	..	8	7	..	22	18
Far East									
India	22[2]	21	26	1[1]	1	1	13	2	1
Pakistan	..	19	7	..	1	1	..	4	4

Country	Prewar Kilograms per Capita per Year	Prewar Per cent Consumed as Liquid Milk	1949/50 Kilograms per Capita per Year	1949/50 Per cent Consumed as Liquid Milk	1954/55 Kilograms per Capita per Year	1954/55 Per cent Consumed as Liquid Milk
Japan	4	18	2	15	3	19
Philippines	..	..	5	17	9	12
Africa and Near East						
Egypt	7	2	10	2	12	2
Israel	..	..	15	13	11	10
Southern Rhodesia	..	..	32	2	29	2
Turkey	17	1	16	1	16	2
Union of South Africa	38	2	42	3	43	5
Oceania						
Australia	120	5	111	4	108	4
New Zealand	109	6	108	6	103	6

[1] From United Nations (1957).
[2] Includes Pakistan.
.. Data not available.

TABLE 40 (continued)

MILK CONSUMPTION AND PROPORTION AS LIQUID MILK[1]

Country	Prewar Kilograms per Capita per Year[2]	Prewar Per cent Consumed as Liquid Milk	1949/50 Kilograms per Capita per Year[1]	1949/50 Per cent Consumed as Liquid Milk	1954/55 Kilograms per Capita per Year[1]	1954/55 Per cent Consumed as Liquid Milk
Europe						
Austria	208	80	107	93	215	82
Belgium-Luxembourg	136	60	150	65	175	50
Denmark	195	86	210	83	206	57
Finland	276	94	267	97	311	91
France	150	57	150	59	167	53
Germany, Western	160	72	136	71	170	76
Greece	75	56	64	48	86	49
Ireland, Rep. of	150	94	181	88	193	88
Italy	74	49	79	59	106	50
Netherlands	200	62	..	..	220	93
Norway	251	75	342	74	310	63
Portugal	..	..	..	..	26	62
Sweden	302	83	302	81	295	61
Switzerland	328	74	340	70	310	68
United Kingdom	152	65	212	73	206	73
Yugoslavia	..	..	..	..	106	74

TABLE 40 (continued)

MILK CONSUMPTION AND PROPORTION AS LIQUID MILK[1]

Country	Prewar		1949/50		1954/55	
	Kilograms per Capita per Year[2]	Per cent Consumed as Liquid Milk	Kilograms per Capita per Year[1]	Per cent Consumed as Liquid Milk	Kilograms per Capita per Year[1]	Per cent Consumed as Liquid Milk
North America						
Canada	221	73	240	86	240	81
U.S.A.	204	59	249	55	237	58
Latin America						
Argentina	163	71	165	64	155	61
Brazil	...	...	79	84	30	87
Chile	54	56	78	62	100	65
Peru	...	...	40	60	40	63
Uruguay	...	...	183	69	180	86
Venezuela	...	...	107	21	120	19
Far East						
India	65[3]	100[3]	43	100	46	100
Japan	4	100	4	100	10	100
Africa and Near East						
Egypt	40	45	...	...	55	76
Israel	...	...	95	63	120	68
Southern Rhodesia	...	...	33	97	38	92
Turkey	...	...	...	...	32	69
Union of South Africa	76	89	83	86	88	74
Oceania						
Australia	164	67	195	71	180	73
New Zealand	220	86	...	...	270	77

[1] From United Nations (1957).
[2] Total milk consumed including dairy products, in terms of liquid milk.
[3] Includes Pakistan.
... Data not available.

populations. The significance of average figures in Table 37 which exceed the estimated requirements also call for some comment. In the opinion of the experts of the United Nations FAO, such excesses do not necessarily mean that the average person in these countries consumes more food than he or she requires. It is thought that in the well fed prosperous countries a considerable gap exists between the estimated per capita supplies of food available at retail levels and the calories consumed as estimated with the best available systems. There is also a gap between the supplies of food available in stores and the food consumed by people in the population who have been studied individually. The amount of food that is offered for sale need not necessarily all be consumed by people.

Quality of Diets

As was noted above, the adequacy of food supplies does not depend solely on their being sufficient in quantity. The quality of the diet is equally important. The useful measure of the quality of the diet is the proportion of total calories consumed which are supplied by the different food categories. The consumption patterns for pulses, nuts, fish, meat, and milk are shown in Tables 38, 39, and 40.

When populations consume a large part of the diet in terms of staple foods, the staple food item may dictate the value of the whole diet. People who consume diets low in protein (for example, diets containing large amounts of cassava, or highly milled cereals) develop malnutrition. Unfortunately such diets are found in the parts of the world where the total calories available are also inadequate. Three quarters of the world's population is poorly fed because of the poor quality of the diet in terms of protein, and/or from an actual shortage of calories themselves. Unfortunately the diets of people in Asia, Africa, and certain parts of South America are nutritionally inadequate generally.

Surveying the food consumption patterns of people around the world, it is important to recognize that not only are a large number of the world's population undernourished but these undernourished people are concentrated in certain regions. (See Fig. 20, page 215.) Food surpluses in some countries exist alongside with food deficiencies in others.

World food shortages in terms of the number of people divided into the world food production does not yield an adequate impression of the situation. Areas which have a food deficiency at the present time are the areas in which population increases are great, areas with a low level of economic development which cannot afford to import the surplus foods grown or occurring elsewhere. The ability to store and distribute food efficiently is extremely important. In those areas where a high degree of technology can be applied in food storage and distribution, the state of economic development is high. In those countries with lower orders of technology in food storage and distribution the state of economic development is low. There is no simple solution to this dilemma.

Food consumption patterns in terms of calories consumed have been discussed above. The next question concerns the nutritional quality of the diets of people. As we have seen earlier, the quality of the diet depends on the presence of essential nutrients. Unfortunately, as noted earlier, there is no simple unit such as the calorie that can be used to measure the quality of the diet. The protein content of a diet is one of the best available indicators; foods rich in protein are also comparatively good sources of many of the other essential nutrients required by men. This is particularly true for foods of animal origin. Therefore, the animal protein content of diets is a better indicator than the total protein content. According to the United Nations reports, the quality of world food supplies when judged by this criterion has been unsatisfactory for the majority of the world's population, both before and after World War II. Where food supplies are more than sufficient in calories, it is found that in general the diet is composed of a high protein content and a good proportion of it would be from animal products. Where calories supplies are inadequate, the amount of protein in a diet is usually very small and the supply of protein from animal products frequently is less than ten grams per day per person. In this respect, the position of people living in the underdeveloped areas has noticeably worsened. In the Far East for example, animal protein consumption even before World War II was already the lowest level of the world. Yet, a large portion of the world's cattle is there.

Another indicator of the quality of a national food diet is the proportion of the total calories furnished by cereals and starchy foods. When consumption of these is high (for example, supplying two-thirds or more of the total calorie intake), clear evidence is afforded

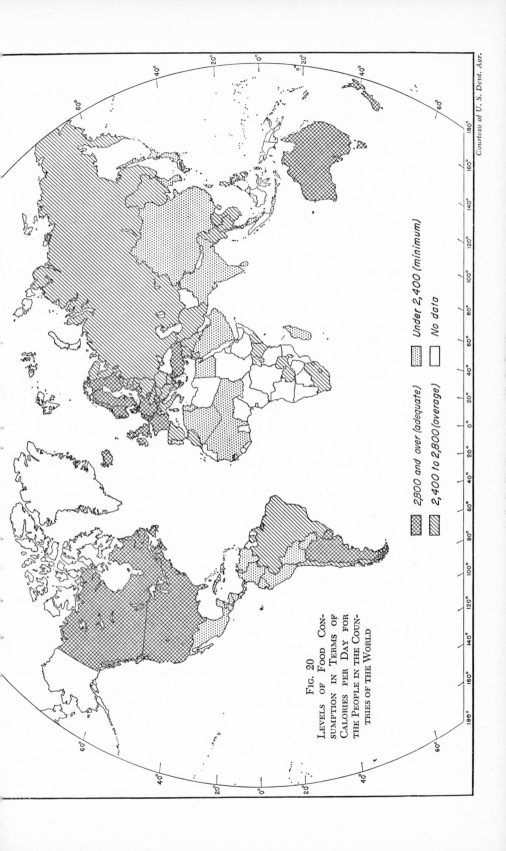

Fig. 20
Levels of Food Con-
sumption in Terms of
Calories per Day for
the People in the Coun-
tries of the World

2,800 and over (adequate)

2,400 to 2,800 (average)

Under 2,400 (minimum)

No data

Courtesy of U. S. Dept. Agr.

of nutritional imbalances. The relevant data reported for the various regions of the world were shown in Table 37.

The tendency to consume less cereals and starchy roots and more nutritionally rich (protective) foods such as meat, milk, eggs, fruits and vegetables usually occurs in countries in which real incomes are rising, especially where the levels were already relatively high. This is significant in North America, Oceania and in Western Europe, and it occurred in almost all countries of the world that emerged from World War II with high real incomes. Impoverishment compelled the other countries to concentrate on producing foods of the highest calorie (or energy) content. While there has been some recent improvement, the prewar pattern has by no means been fully restored and the per capita consumption of protective foods remains below prewar levels in many of the underdeveloped countries of the world.

There has been a special emphasis placed on increasing the consumption of fluid milk. This has been partly due to the growing realization of the important role milk has in safeguarding the health and nutritional status of infants and children and nursing and expectant mothers. During postwar years relief shipments of surplus dried and condensed milks have been made and these products are now familiar to people who were not formerly accustomed to drinking milk in any form. In more recent years the volume of international trade in milk and milk products has more than doubled and these products have in fact established themselves as important items in regular international trade at the present time. An interesting observation made recently indicates that a part of the substantial increases in fluid milk consumption in some countries and the large exports of dried and condensed milks by others has been possible by the division of milk formerly used to make butter. (See Table 40.)

Surveys Meaningful

United Nations' study groups have concluded that the national average food supply data are supported by the results of diet surveys which have recently been made. These surveys have shown that the diets consumed by sample groups in many of the heavily populated regions of the world are quantitatively deficient, and millions upon millions of people are not getting enough food to satisfy their hunger. Such diets have serious effects on the health and well being of these people.

The most serious nutritional deficiency now prevailing in many areas of the world appears to be associated with low protein consumption. This is known to be responsible for high mortality in children from 6 months to 5 years of age in Africa, Central America, and probably in other regions. Other examples could be quoted to indicate the wide prevalance of malnutrition in the world.

FACTORS INFLUENCING THE TRENDS IN FOOD CONSUMPTION

It is important to recognize that there are variations even within a country relative to levels and patterns of food consumption by different population groups within a country. Countries which are underdeveloped at the present time appear to be widening the gap between the diets available for the well-to-do and the poorer members of the population. This situation is being aggravated by population increases. The data which is available at the present time on the differences in food consumption by people is very fragmentary and at best is difficult to assemble and interpret wisely. However, with a broad view there are broad categories into which men clearly fall. Most of the world's people are undernourished.

The emergence of nutritional sciences has caused the realization that human health requires not only a diet which satisfies hunger but also a diet balanced to yield the essential nutrients required from a biological sense. There is also a growing interest in the factors which influence consumption of foods. One factor which has evolved during the past few decades has been the growth of large scale enterprises for food storage and distribution. These enterprises influence food consumption by offering goods for sale; some foods are promoted more than others.

In underdeveloped countries some degree of planning for economic development is most important. It is necessary to be able to foresee changing food consumption patterns with some accuracy and to make provisions for the increased demand of foodstuffs which accompanies economic development. Policies can be designed to avoid, on the one hand, the inflationary strains which demands have on supplies and, on the other hand, the surpluses which develop when demands change. This is particularly important in countries where food commonly accounts for more than half of a consumer's expenditures of income.

The principal factors which are thought to determine the pattern or level of food consumption in any one group are perhaps known in a general way. Tradition is one of the important factors. Most people tend to be conservative in what they will eat and their preferences for foods are dictated by customs. This means, from a practical viewpoint, foods which are readily produced in an area will constitute a major portion of the diet. Examples of this may be found in rice eating populations in tropical river valleys, barley, wheat, and oat eating in cooler climates, meat and milk consumptions in areas suited for pasture and crop production, and fish near the seacoasts and oceans.

When domestic production of food becomes inadequate, the tendency is to import supplies from other areas and to import the same foods which are traditionally consumed. Furthermore, when people migrate, they take with them their concepts of diet and tend to prefer the familiar crops and domesticated animals. People from northwestern Europe, for example, who have migrated still eat much the same foods as their forefathers did centuries ago, even though they now inhabit different parts of the world (or have been subjected to the strong influences of foreign cultures in their own home land). Food traditions are reinforced by religious customs and laws, especially when it comes to eating or not eating certain types of foods, for example pork.

The forces of tradition need not be an overpowering factor since historical and recent events have shown that changes in dietary patterns can be made. One of the most striking changes in dietary patterns occurred following the discovery of America. Corn, potatoes, tomatoes and a number of food items which were unknown to the Old World became basic components of the diets in the Old World cultures. In recent years there have been changes in traditional diets, for example, the substitution of vegetable fats for butter, the acceptance of processed and preserved foods for fresh.

Perhaps the most important factor influencing food consumption by people is their income. While the first essential is to satisfy hunger, at low levels of income this can only be done by consuming a diet consisting mainly of inexpensive foods including cereals and starchy roots. In most of the low income countries in the Near East, Africa, and the Far East such foods may equal more than three-fourths of the total food intake.

Once hunger can be satisfied and an increase in income occurs, a person tends to consume more of the expensive foods which add variety and pleasure to eating. These more expensive but protective foods at the same time improve health.

United Nations experts report that the increasing consumption of sugar and various sweetened beverages is becoming of such importance in the Near East, for example, that it has been called a major tragedy. The poorer working people of towns often spend much of their income on such material and little money is left for essential foods. This seems to be a phase often associated with the beginning of a rising income level in communities. It is thought that this can be overcome by education, and higher incomes.

Real income has an immense importance in determining the level and pattern of food consumption. In general, and within limits, as the per capita income rises, so, too, does the amount and quality of food eaten. However, the rate of increase varies considerably for different foods and for different levels of income (United Nations 1960).

The relationship between food prices and food consumption levels can be viewed in two ways. In the first place, there is an influence of price on the quantity of food consumed. In the second place, the quantity of food produced depends on the price the food can bring.

In general, it is found that the pattern of diets in most countries has a base of cereals and starchy foods supplemented by the more expensive (and attractive) foods, to the extent that a person can afford. When incomes first begin to rise above subsistence levels, the more expensive foods are largely additions to the basic diet. At higher income levels the consumption of the staple foods begins to decline and to be replaced by a larger intake of meat, fruit, vegetables, and milk, which ultimately make up a larger and larger part of a diet. These considerations in themselves point to the predominant importance of income in determining both the level and pattern of food consumption (United Nations 1959, 1960).

There is a basic connection between economic development and nutritional improvement. Until productivity is raised and large segments of the people in a country can earn higher incomes, substantial improvements in nutrition are unlikely. At low levels of income, a rise of ten per cent in income can be expected to lead to an increase of more than ten per cent in food expenditures for more attractive foods. For these reasons, the process of urbanization is thought to be a major factor in the influencing of food consumption patterns (United Nations 1960).

In the world food surveys conducted by the United Nations (1953, 1957) one of the conclusions reached is that although there are probably few communities in the world whose daily minimum requirements are less than 2,200 calories per day, recent average supplies for two-thirds of the world's population fall below this level. It should also be noted that in many of the countries where daily supplies exceed 2,200 calories per day per person, this still falls short of the requirements of these people.

It is estimated that approximately 3 out of 4 people in the world do not have enough to eat. Furthermore, the food consumption patterns must be considered not only in terms of average daily supply available for a year but also the all too frequently occurring hungry periods must not be forgotten.

Of the underfed people in the world about 70 per cent are concentrated in Asia, and another 18 per cent live in Africa and Latin America. The distribution of world population according to the average daily supplies of calories is shown schematically in Fig. 20.

CHAPTER 13

Closed Cycle Food Factory—Technological Breakthroughs

ENERGY FROM THE SUN

Life is an energy demanding system and this energy comes originally from the sun in the form of radiation. One part of the energy is captured by the planet and its atmosphere. The other part is captured by a component of this planet—the green plants. It is now recognized that a small fraction of the energy that reaches the earth is captured by the plants.

The energy capturing process of plants is photosynthesis, through which light energy is converted into simple carbohydrates. It is expected then that these compounds would be found present in the largest amounts on earth, and it turns out to be the case.

Energy in the form of heat is absorbed by the earth, the air and the water associated with this planet; this heat is obviously sufficient to maintain the degree of warmth necessary for life and the rate of chemical reactions as we know them on this planet.

The basic problem which confronts mankind is that the energy capturing system via plants does not yield the food needs of the men who presently inhabit this earth. Man might perhaps solve his present dilemma by more efficiently using the photosynthetic process to provide more good food (hence better living for man) than is generated with present practices.

THE FOOD NEEDS OF LIVING ORGANISMS

All living creatures and plants are made up of organic units called cells. Every living thing begins life as a single cell and all cells are derived by the process of division from some preceding cell. Each cell is a dynamic system of molecules which are grouped into intricate complexes, which interact with each other and with molecules beyond the cell border. This system is called protoplasm and is life itself. Life is demonstrated solely by protoplasm and all growth occurs only under the guidance of the already existing protoplasm.

Protoplasm requires energy to function. This energy basically comes from that captured in the form of chemical compounds in photosynthesis. The breakdown of these compounds releases the stored energy which protoplasm manipulates within certain given limits.

While all living cells generally require much the same chemical elements, and in rather similar proportions, the form in which a specific chemical element must be provided may vary substantially. Green plants require only carbon dioxide, water and simple inorganic elements found in soil, and the presence of radiant energy of visible wave lengths. Animals do not have photosynthetic capabilities, so, in order to experience life, they must draw their nutrient needs from plants, or other animals.

Proteins Are Critical for Life Processes

Cells contain enzymes, those catalysts of life which are manufactured by the cell itself. These catalysts are essential for life and chemically are proteins. Enzymes apparently guide and achieve the whole series of chemical reactions called the life process, from signals received from the nucleus or nuclear material, the information and control center of a cell.

Limiting Chemical Compounds on Earth

A cell can do no better in its biosynthetic role than perform its work on the chemical compounds available to it. Each species of organism has evolved its own peculiar organization, arrangement and demand for chemical compounds and has its own particular assortment of enzymes.

Enzymes are the keys which lock or unlock energy. Each kind of enzyme is capable of unlocking or locking only one kind of lock or kind of compound. Therefore, the nature of the compounds a cell has available is very important because a cell has only a limited number and kind of enzymes or keys.

Proteins vary in kinds and quantities, in plants, animals and man. Man requires proteins which are "complete" or contain a certain type and arrangement of amino acids. There are some 20 odd amino acids widespread in nature, ten of which are essential to the growth and development of man. *Proteins in general are not plentiful in plants, and complete proteins, as required by man, exist in no one plant but are present in most animals.* Animal protein is then the chemical compound or biological polymer in limited supply insofar as man is concerned. On the other hand, complete proteins are useless to plants until broken down by other organisms into simple chemical compounds such as urea, nitrates or ammonia, sulfates, carbon dioxide, and water. Hence, there is a cycle of activity on earth, and for organisms at each stage in the cycle there are specific requirements for chemical compounds.

Important Differences in Life Processes

While throughout the plant and animal kingdoms there is an overriding similarity of metabolic mechanisms (synthesis of genetical units are much the same in a virus and a man), there are occasionally some very subtle differences in organisms for performing similar tasks. These are a part of the subtle but significant variations found in the various kinds of living entities on earth. These perhaps represent alternate solutions to a common problem, yet functional in the life scheme for the particular organism. Some of these variations are most important to mankind and he has attempted to select those with particular uses to him.

For example, consider the legume crops; they have a peculiar ability to take nitrogen from the air and convert it into nitrates which then are usable to the plant, and thereafter to almost any plant which follows it in growth in the soil site. This discovery was the basis for the legume rotation which helped to supply man's needs for foods for several centuries. It is now known to be a symbiotic process of bacteria and the plant. The critical factor about nitrates is that they eventually become a part of the protein in plants, which eventually may yield this protein to animals who, by living, convert the plant protein to complete protein, which man then consumes, to be used in becoming his living substance—protoplasm. Legumes were useful plants for man to collect and perpetuate.

What Is High Quality Protein?

High quality protein is the result of a fantastically complex series of biochemical syntheses. This effort is the key to all human life on earth. This syntheses has not been achieved by science to this date without the use of some components of living cells.

High quality protein for a man is protein which contains as its components the kinds and the quantities of building blocks (amino acids) in usable form and as required by man for growth and maintenance of his cells and his organizational structure.

Test of Protein Need

The rate of growth is perhaps the best test of a protein's value to the young. A test of the protein requirements of an adult is found by measuring the balance between the amount of nitrogen taken into the body as protein, and the amount of nitrogen lost as urea and other minor nitrogenous waste products. Such a state of equilibrium is called a nitrogen balance and is required for good health, to the best of present knowledge. Yet, more than half of the world's population operates with a negative balance. High quality protein is a limiting factor to the growth and development of man (Table 41) just as much as a supply of nitrogen limits the growth of plants.

Nature's Various Protein Factors

Photosynthetic plants are the prime producers of the energy rich chemical compounds for the other life on earth. Man is not capable of such a synthesis and neither are the other animals. Man and animals require chemical compounds in the form of carbohydrates, fats, and proteins as building blocks for life. Animals vary more than men in their demands. Some animals can digest certain plants such as grasses, deriving energy from them, which man cannot. Some animals refine and condense grass into meat and milk which man can use for human consumption. While cattle and sheep can thrive on coarse bulky foods, hogs and hens require cereal grains and supplements to achieve rapid growth. In the process they convert the grain into pork or poultry and eggs which are more digestible and nutritious to man. They "upgrade" the grain.

Growth is the building process of our meat animals. This building process is important to us. With dairy cows, the adult must be produced before the productive function (milk) begins. Most of the beef cattle we eat are young adults. Chickens rapidly convert grain to flesh, for the first ten weeks.

An insight into animal metabolism may lead to a better understanding of this conversion.

ANIMAL METABOLISM

The metabolism of many animals is in the same order of magnitude as man's. It is related to the surface area of the body. Animal temperatures in general are maintained within narrow limits, as is

TABLE 41

CALCULATED MINIMAL PROTEIN REQUIREMENTS OF HUMANS AS GRAMS PER KILOGRAM OF BODY WEIGHT[1,2]

	1	2	3	4	5	6	7	8
	Age Yrs.	Wt. Kg.	Basal Req.	Growth Req.	10% of (3+4) as Fecal Loss	Total Min Req.[3]	Cow's Milk BV=74[4] (Factor =1.266)	Limiting Diet BV=60[4] (Factor =1.667)
Men	25	70	0.28	0.01	0.03	0.32	0.41	0.53
	45	70	0.28	0.01	0.03	0.31	0.39	0.52
	65	70	0.28	0.01	0.03	0.31	0.39	0.52
Women	25	58	0.30	0.01	0.03	0.34	0.43	0.57
	45	58	0.30	0.01	0.03	0.33	0.42	0.55
	65	58	0.30	0.01	0.03	0.33	0.42	0.55
Pregnant (2nd half)			0.30	0.10	0.04	0.44	0.56	0.73
Lactating (850 ml. daily)			0.30	0.21	0.05	0.56	0.71	0.93
Infants	Birth to 3/12	4.55	0.59	1.01	0.16	1.76	2.23	2.93
	3/12 to 6/12	6.65	0.53	0.57	0.11	1.21	1.53	2.02
	6/12 to 9/12	8.35	0.50	0.36	0.09	0.95	1.20	1.58
	9/12 to 12/12	9.60	0.48	0.21	0.07	0.77	0.97	1.28
Children	1–3	12	0.45	0.04	0.04	0.54	0.68	0.90
	4–6	18	0.41	0.08	0.05	0.54	0.68	0.90
	7–9	27	0.37	0.08	0.05	0.50	0.63	0.83
Boys	10–12	36	0.34	0.06	0.04	0.44	0.56	0.73
	13–15	49	0.31	0.07	0.04	0.42	0.53	0.70
	16–19	63	0.29	0.04	0.03	0.36	0.46	0.60
Girls	13–15	49	0.31	0.07	0.04	0.42	0.53	0.70
	16–19	54	0.30	0.02	0.03	0.35	0.44	0.58

[1] National Research Council (1959).

[2] The groupings used in formulating the table, except for infants, were those used by the Food and Nutrition Board, National Research Council, Recommended Daily Dietary Allowances, Revised 1958. For infants, the age and weight values were taken from Table 7 of the 5th edition of the Mitchell-Nelson Textbook of Pediatrics. The 50th percentiles for boys were used throughout. The weight value for birth to three months (4.55 kg.) is an average of the birth weight (3.4 kg.) and the weight at 3 months (5.7 kg.), etc.

[3] The values in Column 6 represent calculated minimal requirements of a provisional protein with a Biological Value of 100, or an amino acid proportionality pattern comparable to that.

[4] *These are calculated minimum values and not recommended allowances.* Any recommended allowance should consider individual variability and allow for the specific needs of a particular population under varying conditions.

our own. Their energy comes from carbohydrates, fats, and proteins, as does ours.

Carbohydrates are the energy source for animals, yet, relatively
little is found in an animal body. The fat stored in an animal results
from eating excess feed. Carbohydrates and proteins may be converted to body fat. The animal body contains two carbohydrates,
one a simple sugar, glucose, the other a starch-like compound called
glycogen. Glycogen is readily converted in the liver to sugar, to
be burned for energy or for use by the body.

There is very little sugar in any of the tissues; the most is found
in the liver (six per cent) and the least in the brain (one-tenth per
cent). Most other tissues have a half of one per cent or less. The
free sugar in blood and body fluids is usually less than one-tenth of
one per cent. The values for animals are generally similar to
those found in man.

The stored sugar in the animal is used in less than ten hours. At
the end of this time the fasting animal must either burn fat or use
protein for energy. In fact the body does both almost at the onset
of fasting. The starch-like glycogen is stored in muscles for use in
muscular activity. When waste products of this activity accumulate,
the animal is fatigued, and must rest. Eating sugar will raise the
level in the blood, hence is a quick energy source. Sugar alone is
not sustaining because it is a simple carbohydrate and does not
contain the useful chemical bondings with minerals.

Because high quality protein is the expensive nutrient (they are
complex molecules in short supply) it is fed at a minimum level to
animals consistent with good health and production.

The protein the animal eats is broken down in digestion to the
amino acids, which then pass into the blood stream, and then on
to the animal's tissues. Body tissues are constantly being renewed
since movement slowly destroys them. In the young, there is also
the growth process to feed. Protein is required by animals, just as
it is required by man.

Tissue protein in animals is thought to be formed by the reverse
of the digestive process of a protein, building protein from the
amino acids liberated in digestion. We know that animals as well
as humans manufacture proteins because they are present in all
organs of the body. The exact mechanism is not known, although
great strides in understanding are now being made.

Blood proteins have received major attention of scientists. Liver, bone marrow, spleen, and the intestines are all involved in the building of blood proteins. The liver plays a dominant role in this activity. Much of blood proteins are antibodies, those chemical entities which give us protection from disease.

As far as is known, the flesh proteins of chickens, hogs, cattle, and fish are approximately of equal biological value as food for man.

The metabolism of plants, animals, and men have much in common. Vitamin B_1 is a part of the enzyme systems of plants, animals, and humans, used to burn sugar to obtain energy. But the rate of metabolism of sugar in the human body and in animals is controlled by complex hormone systems. The surplus energy stored in the human and animal body is in the form of fat. These fats are ready sources of energy, being constantly broken down and rebuilt. Fat is stored under the skin and between muscles and in body cavities. The amount of fat in the liver depends upon the amount obtained from the diet, the amount transported from the liver to fat storage tissue, and the amount burned for energy. Normally the liver will have about five per cent fat. Vitamin B_6 is essential to plants, animals, and humans in fat metabolism. This vitamin is required to build fat from sugar and to convert protein to fat (Sherman 1952).

Feed and food are digested in the animal and man in much the same manner yielding simple sugars, fats, and amino acids. These pass through the intestinal walls into the blood and go to the liver. The feed or food residue not digested is evacuated from the body. Feces consist of metabolic waste products, governed by the quality and amount of feed consumed by the animal.

Water is produced when sugar is burned in the body. This water and some of that present in food is excreted from the kidneys, keeping our systems operative. Urine is not a loss of the digestive process, but an excretion from the kidneys. Usually, urine is sterile from healthy animals, as is the milk of the cow and even flesh.

The intestinal tract is the passage through the animal. The liver is the store house, manufacturer and distributor of chemical compounds in the animal body.

Variation Between Animals

There are great variations in the efficiency of converting grain, for example, to high grade protein for human food. A chicken during its first ten weeks effects a maximum conversion of grain to flesh. A hog is half as efficient. A beef steer is half again as efficient as a hog, or one-fourth that of a young chicken.

Chicken Broilers

The most integrated animal refinery presently operating is the broiler industry. More than a billion broilers are produced and consumed annually in the United States at present (Desrosier 1959).

The broiler meat business started in the late 1930's in the United States. It is an example of the efficiency possible in producing flesh for our diets. Two and a half pounds of feed yield one pound of chicken flesh, which is the average commercial yield (Table 42).

TABLE 42

COMPARISON OF UNIVERSITY OF MARYLAND BROILER RESULTS DURING THE LAST 8 YEARS[1]

Year	Age	Av. Body Wt.	Feed Cons/ Unit Live Wt.	Est. % of Metabolizable Energy Retained in Carcass[2]
	Wk.	Lbs.		
Practical broiler feeds, both sexes				
1952	10	3.08	2.81	21.0
1955	9	3.03	2.37	22.2
1956	8	3.05	1.96	24.4
1960	8	3.51	1.96	26.4
1960	7[2]	3.09	1.90	
Experimental broiler feeds, males				
1955	$7\frac{1}{2}$	3.01	1.60	27.5
1958	$6\frac{1}{2}$	3.02	1.19	31.8
1958	7	3.04	1.04	

[1] From Combs (1961).
[2] 750 calories of gross energy per pound assumed.

Chicken feed is made from ground corn and oats with vitamins A, D, and B complex added to enrich the meal. Mineral supplements of calcium and phosphorus are added to complete the ration for young chicks (Table 43). The feed may be delivered to the broiler farm in truck load quantities. The young chicks are confined, hence require only one man to tend between 15,000 and 25,000. One man can tend four broods per year—60,000 to 100,000 per year. Special strains of chickens have been developed which have a high conversion ratio of feed to flesh. In eight to ten weeks, broilers reach the $2\frac{1}{2}$ to 3-lb. weight class, during which each will have eaten about ten pounds of feed on the average. The broiler farm has about a ten week cycle. At the close of every cycle the buildings and areas

TABLE 43

NUTRIENT REQUIREMENTS OF CHICKENS[1] (IN PERCENTAGE OR AMOUNT PER POUND OF FEED)[2]

	Starting Chickens 0–8 Weeks	Growing Chickens 8–18 Weeks	Laying Hens	Breeding Hens
Total protein, per cent	20	16	15	15
Vitamins				
Vitamin A activ. (U.S.P. Units)[3]	1,200	1,200	2,000	2,000
Vitamin D_3 (I.C.U.)	90	90	225	225
Vitamin K_1, mg.	0.24	?	?	?
Thiamine, mg.	0.8	?	?	?
Riboflavin, mg.	1.3	0.8	1.0	1.7
Pantothenic acid, mg.	4.2	4.2	2.1	4.2
Niacin, mg.	12	5.0	?	?
Pyridoxine, mg.	1.3	?	1.3	1.2
Biotin, mg.	0.04	?	?	?
Choline, mg.	600	?	?	?
Folacin, mg.	0.25	?	0.11	0.16
Vitamin B_{12}, mg.	0.004	?	?	0.002
Minerals				
Calcium, per cent	1.0	1.0	2.25[4]	2.25[4]
Phosphorus, per cent[5]	0.6	0.6	0.6	0.16
Sodium, per cent[6]	0.15	0.15	0.15	0.15
Potassium, per cent	0.2	0.16	?	?
Manganese, mg.	25	?	?	15
Iodine, mg.	0.5	0.2	0.2	0.5
Magnesium, mg.	220	?	?	?
Zinc, mg.	20			
Iron, mg.	9.0	?	?	?
Copper, mg.	0.9	?	?	?

[1] From Combs (1961).
[2] These figures are estimates of requirements and include no margins of safety. *Underlined* figures are tentative. The protein requirements apply to rations containing 900 calories of productive energy per pound for starting and growing chickens, and 920 calories of productive energy per pound for layers. These values are equivalent to approximately 1,285 and 1,310 calories of metabolizable energy, respectively.
[3] May be vitamin A or provitamin A.
[4] The amount of calcium need not be incorporated in the mixed feed, inasmuch as calcium supplements fed free choice are considered as part of the ration.
[5] At least 0.45 per cent of the total feed of starting chickens should be inorganic phosphorus. All of the phosphorus of nonplant feed ingredients is considered to be inorganic. Approximately 30 per cent of the phosphorus of plant products is non-phytin phosphorus and may be considered as part of the inorganic phosphorus required. A portion of the phosphorus requirement of growing chickens and laying and breeding hens must also be supplied in inorganic form. For birds in these categories the requirement for inorganic phosphorus is lower and not as well defined as for starting chickens.
[6] Equivalent to 0.37 per cent of sodium chloride.

are cleaned, repaired, and disinfected. Breaking the cycle also disrupts the cycle of disease organisms and parasites.

Fish

Variations in fish also occur. Fish can be efficient food producers, although they are variable and man has less control over them. Just to maintain 100 lbs. of 10-inch bass in a pond, we must add about one pound of minnows a day. Any less than this amount and the bass will burn their own substance to keep alive. The bass collectively will lose a pound a day. If we want to show a maximum gain, we must feed about four pounds of minnows a day (Allen 1954).

The bass food chain is long, progressing from plankton to insects to small fish to bass. In general terms, it might take about five pounds of plankton to feed a pound of insects, five pounds of insects to feed a pound of small fish, and five pounds of small fish to make one pound of bass, or about 125 lbs. of plankton to make a pound of bass. On the other hand, it takes just five pounds of plankton to make a pound of carp. Plankton are the critical part in this chain in natural waters (Allen 1954). But, the bass can not exist solely on plankton. Neither could man.

Feeding Higher Animals on Single Cells

Since single-celled photosynthetic microscopic plants contain most of the nutrient needs of some animals, it might be possible to grow them under controlled conditions to feed animals rather than grow higher plants in soil. Algal growth would be far more efficient per unit of land in the sun than higher plants. Man cannot exist mainly on an algae (plant) diet due to his specialized nutrient demand, but he can do very well on animal flesh. If it were possible to by-pass the complex chain of events now required for plant cultivation in soils, subject to the unpredictable weather, it might be possible to generate all the high quality protein requirements of man, in a form he would accept (i.e., chicken, pork, fish, beef).

Efficiency of Light Utilization of Algae vs. Higher Plants

In the following, the term "photosynthesis" is used in its broadest sense, as described by Went (1957), to mean the total dry weight increase of a plant as a result of the conversion of light energy into chemical energy, or the sum total of all the plant's energy storing processes best measured as total increases in dry matter in the plant.

Went has found that algae are approximately five times as efficient in conversion of light energy to plant cell products than higher plants. Algae conversion over-all is about ten per cent of the incident light energy into chemical compounds while higher plants convert about two per cent.

The difference according to Went appears to be explainable as follows: The major processes in plant metabolism are: (A) photosynthesis, (B) translocation of carbohydrates, (C) transformation of these into plant body products, and (D) respiration. Algae can transform at their maximum about 30 per cent of the incident light in step A, while higher plants achieve ten per cent.

In this scheme, although A is 30 per cent efficient in algae, A plus B plus C minus D results in a net conversion of ten per cent of the incident light energy into useful chemical compounds. For higher plants, A is about 10 per cent, and A plus B plus C minus D turns out to be a two per cent conversion.

It is because of this high efficiency that the belief exists that algae are the best plant material available for transformation of light energy into animal feed products.

CLOSED CYCLE SYSTEM FOR FEEDING ANIMALS

The scientific literature of the present day contains references to the ability of chickens, hogs, and beef cattle to grow on a diet of microscopic photosynthetic plants, supplemented with minor nutrients, most of which are ground rocks of special kinds (Burlew 1953).

The most recent scientific literature has included increasingly more information concerning the growth of algae, a microscopic photosynthetic plant, the nutrient requirements of algae, and the environmental requirements of algae (Meyer *et al.* 1951; Allen and Ornon 1955; Tischer 1958; Guame 1958). In fact, the literature contains many references to algae as a human food (Tamura *et al.* 1958). Algae are eaten at present as a constituent in the diets of many millions of people in the world (Jensen 1953; Orr 1943; Oser 1958; Russell 1953; Sax 1955; Tischer 1958; Phillips 1959; Huntington 1945).

Recognizing that these two (one, the efficiencies of algal growth, and two, the ability to feed animals on modified algae diets) might be combined to generate high quality protein, it appears that a possibility exists to generate an important component of good food for people which would meet man's biological and cultural requirements.

Regarding the human requirement for good meat to eat, more men accept chicken as an item in the diet throughout the world than any other species in the animal kingdom (Jensen 1953; Huntington 1945). In fact, chicken is one of man's most prized foods. Less men will eat beef and less still accept pork. For this reason, it might be useful to consider what we could do with the feeding of algae to chickens rather than going through the soil-plant-grain cycle as is presently done.

Recent research with emphasis on closed cycle feeding systems for space travel (of more than a few months in duration) have developed data in a form which suggests a useful application to life on earth (Tischer 1958; Gaume 1958).

Needs of Algae

Algae are photosynthetic organisms. They inhabit water naturally, and require for optimum growth a source of light in the visible range, mineral sources (ground rock), a nitrogen source, and carbon dioxide (Meyer *et al.* 1951). Live and healthy algae reassemble these ingredients into useful compounds as do the other photosynthetic plants.

Composition of Algae

Wet living algae are three-fourths water; when dried such that they have but five per cent water remaining, the other 95 per cent is distributed as follows: protein, 45 per cent; fat, 3 per cent; ash (mineral), 7 per cent; carbohydrates, 35 per cent, and other organic compounds about five per cent (Tischer 1958). One pound of wet growing algae contains about one-fourth of a pound of useful organic compounds, which in fact, are nearly ideal for the growth of certain animals (Howe 1950). In fact, many animals grow in nature on algae diets, undisturbed by man (Allen 1953).

Algae Fed Directly to Chicks

The chick is efficient as a converter of grain into flesh (Table 42). Knowing the composition of certain useful algae (Tables 44, 45, 46), and averaging what the chick eats to become the broiler from birth to ten weeks of age, it can be calculated that one-half pound of algae would be required as an average to be generated per chicken per day, from hatching to ten weeks of age.

Chick Needs in Terms of Algae

If we fed chickens on algae, how much volume would be required to sustain one chicken through such a cycle? *Under optimum con-*

TABLE 44

PROTEIN CONTENT OF CHLORELLA COMPARED WITH THAT OF TYPICAL ANIMAL FEEDS[1]

Product	Av. Protein Content
	Per Cent
Fish meal	60
Chlorella	50
Brewers' yeast (U.S.P.)	48
Torula yeast (fodder grade)	48
Soybean meal (typical seed meal)	44
Dried skim milk	36
Brewers' dried grains	25
Wheat (typical grain)	12

[1] From Burlew (1953).

TABLE 45

AMINO ACID ASSAY OF DRIED CHLORELLA[1]

Nutrient	Pilot-Plant Sample	Torula yeast
	Per Cent	Per Cent
Crude protein	44.0	48.0
Arginine	2.06	3.61
Histidine	0.62	1.31
Isoleucine	1.75	3.75
Leucine	3.79	3.57
Lysine	2.06	4.14
Methionine	0.36	0.84
Phenylalanine	1.81	2.41
Threonine	2.12	2.58
Tryptophane	0.80	0.66
Valine	2.47	2.98
Glycine	2.20	0.22

[1] From Burlew (1953).

TABLE 46

VITAMIN ASSAY OF DRIED CHLORELLA[1]

Vitamin	Pilot-plant Sample	Laboratory Sample
Carotene (mg./lb.)	. . .[2]	218.0
Thiamin (mg./lb.)	11.0	4.5
Riboflavin (mg./lb.)	26.2	16.3
Niacin (mg./lb.)	54.0	109.0
Pyridoxine (mg./lb.)	. . .	10.4
Pantothenic acid (mg./lb.)	3.6	9.1
Choline (mg./lb.)	. . .	1,370.0
Biotin (mcg./lb.)	. . .	67.0
Vitamin B12 (mcg./lb.)	45.0	10.0

[1] From Burlew (1953).
[2] Data not available.

ditions with present knowledge five gallons of actively growing algae will sustain growth, and permit a harvest from their numbers to feed one chicken through the 10 week period. Less than five gallons is actually required.

Need for 10,000 Chicks

What would the requirement be for 10,000 chickens? A generator to yield the feed for 10,000 chickens in 10 weeks, or about 50,000 chickens per year once the cycle is started, would amount to 50,000 gallons of algae, or a tank about 10 x 20 x 30 feet.

Light a Limiting Factor

But this tank (or pool) alone would not fulfill the needs of algae in any location on earth. The limit to such a system first would be the amount of light available for photosynthesis. In a deep tank this would be grossly inadequate and it would be necessary to supply light artificially (Burlew 1953).

Hanrahan and Bushnell (1960) reviewed the work at the National Institute of Health and the General Dynamics Corporation on the use of fast-growing algae discovered by Sorokin at the University of Texas. Whereas algae in suitable environments in daylight multiply every few hours, the fast-growing selection of Sorokin multiplies several times an hour. To achieve this rate of growth a dense algae slurry containing the required nutrients is pumped past extremely intense light sources. The cells respond favorably to the intermittent exposure to light, as might be anticipated. In a sense, each pass through the light amounts to a "day" and each dark period following the exposure amounts to a "night." Green plants in nature use the night period to consolidate the energy made during the day. The efficiency of this new system of algae culturing, using fast-generating algae selections, a suitable nutrient solution, and intermittent lighting of extreme intensities, is such that cell production can be achieved with $1/20$th the volume required with earlier techniques. This new technology and algae strain make obsolete much of the early algae work.

Further, some algae can tolerate extremes in environmental conditions. One type of algae is found thriving in the Yellowstone National Park geyser pools at temperatures of 180°F. The new strain of algae which has such high yield (15 grams per quart per day) grows best at 104°F.

Equivalent Farm Land for Algae Tank Production of Animal Feed

Suppose we could develop a generator of this size, supply the light artificially 24 hours a day and supply the minerals needed along with carbon dioxide. What would be its equivalent in terms of land area to yield the grain with present practices to feed 50,000 chickens a year (the time required to elapse between grain harvests during which five cycles would pass through the algae sytem).

A young chicken converts about two and a half pounds of grain into one pound of body weight. Assume that an efficient stage to develop the chick, in terms of optimum conversion, is two and a half pounds of body weights. Each chicken then eats through more than six and a half pounds of grain in passing from egg to broiler. Then, 10,000 chickens would need at least 65,000 lbs. of grain, and 50,000 chickens would need five times this amount, or 330,000 lbs. of grain (Desrosier 1959).

Using corn as an example, harvests of 60 bushels to the acre are about average in the United States for good farm land. Corn weighs about 56 lbs. per bushel, so the harvest is about 3,300 lbs. of grain per acre per year, and about 100 acres of good land would be needed to yield the same nutrients for growth of these chicks as could be harvested from a tank 10 x 20 x 30 feet. *Or, the algae culture could be allowed to occupy one acre of ground; the yield might still be many times the capacity of good farm land.*

Exaggerated Comparison

Algae do not have all the nutrients known to be required by the growing chicks (Table 42). So, a portion of the algae yield would be used to serve as a nutrient base upon which to culture yeasts (Prescott and Dunn 1940). These yeasts would convert algae into more yeasts which are recognized as excellent sources for protein and the vitamins of the B complex (Table 47). In addition, growing yeasts produce carbon dioxide gas, and this gas could be collected and fed back to the algae. Carbon dioxide can be a limiting factor in the growth of algae; they need a ten per cent CO_2 atmosphere.

It is also possible to convert algae "bodies" into other nutrients,

TABLE 47

VITAMIN CONTENT OF YEASTS (MCG./GM. DRY MATTER)[1],[2]

Yeast	Thiamin	Ribo-flavin	Niacin	Panto-thenic Acid	Vitamin B6 (pyri-doxine)	PABA	Folic Acid	Biotin
I. Commercial Samples								
Bakers', compressed	11–60	25–80	293–482	150–280	25–39	24–167	23–54	0.8–2.4
Bakers', foil	88–139	57–59	256–336	131–157	...	28–39	...	0.56–1.47
Bakers', active dry	7–29	31–70	180–351	100–150	...	35–67	...	0.43–1.52
Brewers', undebittered	110	38	400	80	31	...	30	1.1
Brewers', debittered	104–250	25–80	300–627	72–86	23–40	15–40	19–30	1.1
Primary Grown	120–205	40–80	250–700	112–150	32–40	10–16	...	2.5
T. utilis, grown on molasses	22	54	440–490	...	...	...	...	...
T. utilis, grown on sulfite waste	5–14	33–70	153–467	40–123	...	...	...	2.5
II. Experimental yeasts, grown aerobically								
S. cerevisiae	28–41	39–62	277–568	...	...	11–62	19–36	0.45–3.6
T. utilis	6–42	26–68	213–690	106–180	28–47	15–40	7–15	1.1–3.6
C. arborea	13–33	46–70	301–580	...	...	11–21	12–26	0.24–3.2
O. lactis	12–29	40–55	186–248	...	...	...	6–15	1.3–2.1

[1] From Peterson (1948).
[2] The data in this table represents, presumably, unfortified yeasts, i.e., yeasts to which the vitamin has not been added or yeasts that have not been grown with the object of producing a yeast of high vitamin content. However, one cannot be sure that the sample is an unfortified product, as authors do not always give this information.

using selected micro-organisms to develop fat soluble vitamins and other minor nutrients. However, a small part of the total algae produced would have to be diverted to these uses.

Another problem involves the freshening of the algae culture by dialysis after prolonged growth. Anti-metabolites slow growth eventually, but these can be removed with presently available techniques (Burlew 1953).

Pork Production

Trials have been undertaken with hogs, cattle, and chickens on algae diets supplemented with vitamins and minerals in Israel, in the Orient, the United States and other countries.

The algae can be served to the chick or the hog in the form of a thick "soup," rather than as a dried feed. Such a "soup" also provides a built-in water supply for the animals.

The hog is a rather good converter of feed into flesh (about 5 to 1) and should be also considered in such a scheme. Some fish have a 5 or 6 to 1 ratio, too. Beef cattle may be too inefficient to operate effectively with much a system, based on their 10 to 1 ratio of conversion of feed to flesh. There may be some application for milk production, however.

Speculations on Economics of System

To return to the 100-acre good farm land equivalent of the algae tank, we might investigate the economics of the situation.

One hundred acres of good farm land applied to grain production is not sufficient to yield an adequate living for a farmer in the United States today. An economic unit for this purpose may be a 500-acre farm of which about 400 acres is tillable land, with another 100 acres of land not used for crops, but for house, barns, sheds, yard, ponds, woods, and roads. Such a farm with good soil and buildings might sell in this day's market for 400 dollars an acre. This would be an investment of about $200,000 in land. It is presently considered that the equipment necessary to operate such a grain farm efficiently would amount to about $20,000. There is then an investment of about 220,000 United States dollars in capital required for such an operation. If the tillable land were all planted to corn, all productive, and the price of corn were one dollar a bushel, then the farm would yield about 60 dollars an acre, or about $24,000 a year.

Of this amount, about one third could be estimated as the return to the farmer as compensation for his work including return on his investment. With such a $220,000 investment, he would yield perhaps $8,000 a year, and this would include both his own labor and the return on his investment. He might earn less money from his labor and the risk of his investment than he could earn at four per cent interest in a bank.

Considering solely the amount of animal feed yielded from such a 500-acre farm unit, it would be equivalent to the animal feed yield of 4 or 5 algae generators 10 x 20 x 30 feet, and these 4 or 5 could cost up to $220,000 to build and equip.

If we are attempting to yield meat for our tables with our grain production, it might seem reasonable to direct our energy to the generation of meat by growing microscopic photosynthetic plants under intensive systems rather than go through the farming cycle, which at best is limited by the ever changing weather, plant diseases and insect problems.

It is possible to have algae serve as a base for feeding animals rather than grain production. It also seems economically worthy of exploration.

Non-Farmland Farming

Some countries in Asia, Southern Europe, and the Near East, for example, long ago depleted their soils of fertility. It would seem nearly an impossible task to attempt to regenerate the soils to the level that an adequate food supply could be generated in the near future with the resources they have available. Furthermore, in areas near the equator which have intense sunlight, shallow algae generators using solar energy alone might be worthwhile.

If we added one-half pound of chicken a day to a man's diet, each generator could supplement the diets of about 1,000 people. They might become rather tired of chicken after a while, but this is not nearly as bad as lack of food, and shifts might be made eventually to pork or fish or beef.

Major Obstacle—Light Sources

There are some important further considerations. Sunlight alone is not sufficient to operate such an algae generator at a satisfactory rate. Sunlight intensity too is variable. Energy must be available to be converted into a constant light source to illuminate the algae to permit photosynthesis to occur at a maximum rate (Burlew 1953). At one time it was thought that algae would not respond to constant lighting. By pumping the algae slurry through an intense light source or completely bathing algae in light, *it has been found that continuous algae production can be obtained with the yields for algae stated earlier* (Tischer, 1958; Hanrahan and Bushnell, 1960). Therefore, the major obstacle to this system is the need for a suitable light source—24 hours a day, or, an equivalent focused sunlight.

Power from Atomic Energy?

Sunlight is available for less than half a day and it varies by the month in intensity and in effectiveness. As a result, the generators presently must have a very large surface area exposed to the sun, and the generator must be shallow in depth to allow adequate photosynthetic action to occur in the algae due to the poor penetrating power of light. Using shallow ponds would require substantial amounts of land to be turned to this use. Even at that, a gain might conceivably be realized over grain production for the area of the world near the equator. However, such attempts have not been successful at present in northern latitudes.

The solution is to apply artificial light to the algae generator. In the past this meant producing artificial light from electricity, which was generated from energy released by burning fossil fuels or using falling water. The use of electricity in the past for this purpose was not considered economically justifiable. Furthermore, the places where men live which need this help may not have good power sources or energy sources available. What is required is a small, self-contained, almost portable power source. This has not been available. *But, there has been an important discovery which has drastically altered this situation.*

Atomic energy has been applied successfully in producing electricity. As mentioned earlier, several entire cities now have light (day and night) from atomic energy power stations. Ships have also been powered around the world by it.

With power available from atomic energy, a most exciting situation develops; some form of closed cycle food generating system may well come into being. And, power sources similar to those which now service a city of 100,000 people with electricity might provide the light needed to generate part of the food for a large group of people.

We can estimate the upper limit that such a system could cost from the fact that on the average, a man exchanges one-fourth of his life's work for food, and a good share of this cost is for animal protein.

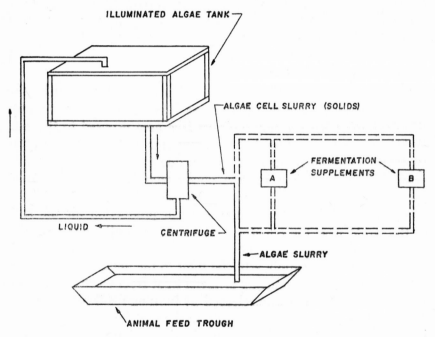

FIG. 21. CLOSED CYCLE ALGAE–ANIMAL FEEDING SYSTEM

Closed Cycle Food Factory

We could speculate as to what such a factory might look like. First, there would be two components: One, the algae generator and associated equipment, and two, the chicken processing plant (Fig. 21).

The algae generator could be a unit which discharged a steady stream of algae by centrifugal means (something like a cream separator in dairy plants) from the water system they occur in. This stream of algae would be a thick "soup" and would be piped to feed preparation tanks then to chicken feeding houses. Chicks would eat down a system of feeding troughs, then to the end of the growth chamber. The trip would take about ten weeks, and cover perhaps a distance of a few hundred yards. At the end of the growth chamber would be the chicken processing plant.

We could speculate one step further. Atomic energy power plants must be cooled on the one hand, and on the other, the release of atomic energy also produces intense radiation as a by-product. If the coolant is liquid sodium, it becomes radioactive. A loop taken externally from the core of the reactor can be engineered to be used as a radiation source (Desrosier and Rosenstock 1960). Animal flesh, being highly perishable, must be preserved if it is to be stored and distributed. Radiation has been proved capable of sterilizing chicken and pork with good results (Desrosier 1959). Hence, the animal flesh generated by the closed cycle system could be preserved by radiation produced as a by-product of releasing atomic energy, the power from which would supply the illumination for the system.

Hence, from the start to the finish, the animal protein generating plant would be a closed system. Into one end would come the electrical power lines, the mineral supplements and the baby chicks. From the other end would come a steady stream of sterile packaged chicken.

Furthermore, if we envision peoples around the world leading civilized lives in association with one and another in towns and cities, which are being serviced with electrical power generated by atomic energy systems, we can envision the production of power locally in slightly surplus quantities, and this amount of power could be applied to the lighting of closed cycle food factories, eliminating the limiting feature of closed cycle systems at present. Together, they might allow man to live on earth in good health.

Focused Sunlight and Wind for Power

A simple "early stage" closed cycle system might look something like that in Fig. 22. The algae tank would be filled by means of a pump with power from a windmill, and the algae suspension would be forced under pressure into a high lux illuminator. Here sunlight could be focused with reflectors or lenses onto the algae suspension, which then would present a surface a few inches thick. A thin water filtering system to capture infrared radiation could be placed between the solar reflector and the algae, to reduce heat intensity. The algae would pass through the illuminator, experience a "day" and be pumped in "night" back to the algae surge tank. The power for the pumping action would come from a small windmill, very much like those now used in Holland in moving irrigation water. A daily harvest of algae would be made, and this could be accomplished by pumping the algae slurry through a powdered leaf filter. Leaves are widely available, are good sources of carotenes, and, in addition to acting as a filter in powdered form, would be a useful supplement to the animal feed. The filter with entrapped

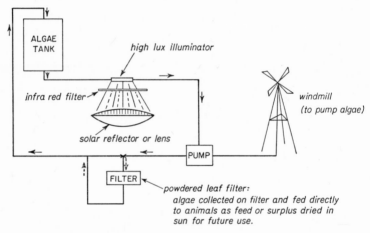

FIG. 22. EARLY CLOSED CYCLE ALGAE SYSTEM

algae would be removed from the system, and fed directly to chickens or other animals as their feed, or dried in the sun and stored if in surplus. Another powdered leaf filter would be inserted in place for the next harvest.

Such a system would not require a large land area to operate, and it could use natural resources that are available. Some areas have good sunlight intensities for more than 300 days a year, and wind is hardly ever calm, or less than two miles per hour, anywhere on the globe for any appreciable length of time.

Closed Cycle Fish Culturing

In the Far East, fish is the main animal protein in diets and several methods of producing fish are widely employed. In some areas, ponds for fish culturing are plowed, tilled, limed, fertilized, weeded, cultivated, and harvested. Like chickens, fish can be produced in cages. One pound of fish can be obtained from five pounds of vegetable matter. Highly intensive fish culturing is possible and occurs in unindustrialized countries of Asia (Meyer 1961).

One of the newer developments is the cultivation of fish in rice fields. Nearly 200 million acres of rice land occur in Asia and in wet rice cultivation, the fields remain flooded for 3 to 8 months a year. At the end of the season these fields are yielding a small harvest of naturally stocked fish. The Japanese have shown that the culture of fish can be greatly increased.

The application of present fish cultural practices to rice fields could yield about a half billion pounds of fish a year, even with present knowledge (Meyer 1961).

Using plants to feed animals is a natural phenomena. The use of algae directly as animal food also appears in nature. The application of the system has not been very great to date yet the potential appears worthy of trial, especially with the new algae strains and technologies.

SUMMARY

The food needs of men, animals, and plants are adequately recognized. Insofar as man is concerned, the limiting nutrient is high quality protein, which occurs in no one plant but is an inherent component of most animals.

High quality protein can be produced by feeding microscopic photosynthetic plants directly to animals, by-passing the seed-plant-grain cycle presently used in agriculture.

A closed cycle system of producing animal protein operates in the oceans. A simple system can also be developed on land which could increase the animal protein supplies in the world by a factor of 1 to 10.

For maximum efficiency, artificial illumination is required, and with this, perhaps the meat and fish supplies of the world could be expanded very greatly.

A closed cycle system for producing meat is described which could yield a half pound of chicken daily to the diets of 1,000 people, be equal to 100 acres of good farm land, and occupy a space equal to one large living room in a house.

Since men in industrial nations now exchange about 25 per cent of their energies for food, and a large part of it for animal protein, the closed cycle system for producing meat falls within the realm of economic feasibility.

With the advent of atomic energy, it is now possible to develop power supplies for communities and at the same time supply closed cycle food systems with electric power to use to illuminate algae.

Furthermore, from 0° to 25° North and South of the equator, photosynthesis occurs at high rates but so, too, does respiration. As a result, there is a low net accumulation of photosynthetic products. In this area there are no large effective animal populations. This is the region in the world where a large part of the world's people live, and where widespread protein shortage exists.

The successful agriculture of the world has been largely located in the cooler climates. Attempts to transpose this technology to hot tropical and subtropical areas have not been successful. Closed cycle systems of animal production appear to have immediate application in this troubled zone of the world. In fact, the closed cycle system should function more effectively for algae near the equator due to its favorable light intensity and temperature.

It would seem appropriate also to explore the uses of modified sea water as a suitable nutrient source for the new algae strains.

It has become clear in recent years that our potential to produce good food is enormous and that food production at present is in its infancy. It is hoped that some indication of this potential has been adequately described herein.

CHAPTER 1

Minimum Adequate Foods for man

THE NEED FOR MORE FOOD

From the information available in Chapter 12, it is clear that the daily intake of foods by the 3.0 billion people of the world is inadequate, and an especially critical shortage exists in the consumption of high quality protein. In Chapter 9 it was concluded that food production techniques must be improved greatly. It was also shown in Chapter 9 that the critical component to produce is high quality protein. But, solutions to this problem are available, and some were presented in Chapter 13.

Assuming some solution can be brought about, we could take another step toward conquering starvation. This step would be to develop a minimum adequate food supply for all men. The information required is available, and no new technological breakthroughs are required. This is the subject of this chapter.

In Part I we discussed the impact of food supplies on man and of man on food supplies. We saw that the full potential of a man cannot be achieved if he is inadequately supplied with his biological demand for nutrients. If he does not consume the needed nutrients, he exists in some degree of starvation. This condition has been clearly demonstrated to influence man's health, vigor, abilities, personality, and his contributions to society. Biologically, man's diet must supply him daily with the 50 odd specific chemical compounds known to be required in human nutrition if he is to have good health. Also, as noted earlier, the form in which these nutrients are taken is a cultural problem, which also must be considered lest the nutrient source be completely rejected by him.

Biological Demand Fixed

Once the nutrient needs of a man are known, there is no minimum or optimum where these needs are concerned. His biological demand is fixed by his genetical heritage, influenced by the state of his health, and modified in terms of the quantity needed by his subsequent actions.

245

How Many People in the World Can be Helped

As noted in Chapter 2, if we are to consider helping the people of the world, it would be useful to have some index of how many of the 3.0 billion people present can be helped. As indicated earlier, an estimated 95 per cent of the human population on earth can be classified as "normal" relative to their mental abilities. The remaining five per cent are considered to be abnormal and only one-twentieth of these appear to fail to be able to achieve self independence in society under the best of circumstances. Under present circumstances, a large percentage of the human population on earth falls into this category although they need not.

Man Requires All Nutrients Regularly

It is worth while to repeat the following at this time. In beginning stages, nutrition studies are conducted with small animals. If their life spans are short and their metabolisms like our own, under certain conditions we can interpret results in terms of our own, providing the factor being measured is significant to both man and the animals. With two groups of white rats, for instance, one fed an adequate diet, mostly of plant foods, and the other a well-balanced diet with added animal protein, we find that animals eating the diet made generous with the added animal food make distinct gains over the others (which are considered normal). The high animal protein diet yields animals with earlier maturity, longer lives, greater success in rearing young, and increased vigor over the life span. In free competition this group dominates, other things being equal.

On the other hand, suppose we take a group of animals, and on one day give them one half the known essential nutrients, the next day give them the other half, and continue such a diet. They show distress conditions in a very short time. A diet containing all essential nutrients must be given daily and regularly if optimum performance is to be obtained. Every nutrient should be present, in balance, at each meal. The balance is most easily obtained from both plant and animal sources, with emphasis on animal.

DEVELOPMENT OF MODERN MAN AND HIS FOOD SUPPLY

With the above in mind, it is useful to look at some of the men who have gone before us. In the first place, there are no records of humans on this earth prior to their use of fire. Cooking tenderizes foods, as we know. If we had to design a jaw and skull capable of tearing raw flesh from a bone, perhaps we would decide on a protruding jaw and strong skeletal features. Primitive man got by with a smaller skull case, too.

Peking Man and Diet

The earliest form of man found on earth complete with indications of the foods he ate was uncovered in a cave near Peking, China in 1923. Ashes in this cave indicate that fire was used. The remains of 38 human forms were found. Skulls have protruding jaws, receding foreheads, and brows with ridges. Males were about five feet tall; women were half a foot shorter. Fifteen were teenagers when they died; the oldest form was about 50. Life expectancy was in the 20-year class. Animal remains reveal that this Peking chap was a meat eater and he lived in that cave half a million years ago. Charred bones indicate that he ate bison, deer, rhinoceros, mammoth, sheep, camel, baboon, wolf, and other animals. He split bones and skulls and ate marrow and brain. No doubt he ate to capacity when food was plentiful and probably tried even the roots of grass when food was scarce. Unearthings in this cave reveal that this Peking man ate berries at least (Jensen 1953).

Neanderthal Man and Diet

In 1857 an important man-type was found who apparently is an intermediate between the Peking man and early modern man. This Neanderthal man buried his dead. Findings indicate that the men were about five and a half feet tall, and the females a foot shorter. From skulls, jaws, teeth, and other bones, the Peking man was indeed followed by the Neanderthal man in order of human form on earth. He too used fire, was a meat eater, and a cannibal. He ate berries and nuts, supplemented with roots, shoots, and other plant foods when meat was scarce, which was regularly. Life expectancy was in the twenties. The Neanderthal man ruled the roost for the next 400,000 years, more or less.

Stone Age Eskimo and Diet

The Eskimo is a descendant of that age from Asian stock. Early Arctic explorers tell us that the Eskimo of that day looked upon vegetable foods as a substitute, not to be eaten with pleasure. The present Eskimo diet tends to be low in vitamin C, obtained in generous amounts in fruits, in fresh blood, and just-killed flesh. In the vigorous Arctic climate, a fresh food supply is only available a few months a year (Jensen 1953).

Food a Sorting Agent of Man

In every group of men all through time there has been variation between individuals. There have been thousands of generations of man, enough to explain many changes. Superior hereditary traits showed results in time. Certainly survival was contingent on a food supply. Food had its impact on evolutionary changes. All the food needs of man must be present in plant and animal tissues. Human beings with food needs different from that found in plants and animals never survive long. Food acts as a sorting agent.

Cro-Magnon Man and Diet

In 1940, a group of boys discovered a cave in France and revealed remains of the Cro-Magnons. They replaced the Neanderthal man in Europe. The Cro-Magnon ate flesh, drank blood of animals, and ate his neighbor or those he found in his path. His cave drawings are revealing. Using radioactivity dating techniques, scientists have established some of the paintings to be 30,000 years old, others as new as 15,000. The Cro-Magnon disappears then from our view, at the beginning of the last warming trend, which ended the last glacial advance in Europe. The land to which life had become acclimated changed drastically. There were major shifts in the earth's rain belts; moist areas turned arid. Man, animals, plants, and lakes and streams were forced to adjust. While evidence indicates that food supplies were plentiful during the Cro-Magnon's best days, he now found life difficult. Meat animals had moved north out of Europe and the meat eating Cro-Magnon tightened his belt, a notch at a time. He did not learn food production; he was the last of the important food gatherers. In the end, he did not make the nutritional grade, being unable to free himself from the ever present struggle for food.

Discovery of Plant Culturing

It wasn't until our ancestors learned about plant and animal culture that they showed many qualities we recognize as human. This occurred about 8,000 years ago in the Tigris-Euphrates valleys. First man learned to domesticate wild animals. Next he discovered that if seeds are nursed in soil, a new plant arises, giving more seed to eat and also seed to plant next year. It was no doubt as exciting a discovery to them as it is exciting to us to learn of atomic energy.

The discovery of agriculture freed man from that full-time task of collecting food to eat. A by-product of this freedom we call civilization. The energy for societies of man to form on earth came from this new food supply. But, in the matter of a few thousand years, the average man on earth was in worse state nutritionally than he had been as a hunter. The discovery and practice of agriculture yielded great grain harvests. A king and his court had a full diet but less fortunate men became solely grain eaters. Man had learned to domesticate animals. Some men extended this process to include fellowman and called it serfdom.

The Invention of Bread

These less fortunate men became the grain eaters. They managed to keep alive but never were able to utilize their inheritance as "man" to its full extent. But, some progress was made. For instance, they invented breadmaking from wheat grains at least 6,000 years ago— no small achievement. At the present time think of the hundreds of foods we prepare from flour. Go into a French restaurant and be tempted by the array of pastries—these are inventions of man. Pass a bakery and be tantalized by the odors from a hot baking oven. Without grain culture and flour, man did not know bread. Bread was an ingenious invention. No counterpart occurs anywhere in nature. But, bread and water are not enough for mankind. Bread and butter is better. Add meat and fruit and it is better still.

American Indians and Food

There have been very few foods invented which alone are sustaining for man. Two of these were found by native American Indians. One (pinole) has received widespread use, the other (pemmican) has vanished.

Many Indian discoveries in agriculture enrich our lives presently; some were reviewed earlier in this book.

The American Indians also learned some important lessons in human nutrition. They knew that the best food for a warrior came from a combination of plant and animal foods. They knew that corn itself could not sustain man in good health. Corn was eaten with meat, fish or game, but never alone. Let us consider two foods the American Indian concocted. In the Southwest the natives made pinole. In the Great Plains the Indians made pemmican.

Pinole

Pinole was a dried flour made from corn and dried beans. A pouch of pinole was carried by a traveling native. A mouthful now and then sustained him in his journey. In Central America we find corn-bean foods are well established in the dietary. Tortillas (made from a corn flour base) are eaten with beans, or with some meat. Beans are a meat substitute. Corn-bean concoctions are considered a low grade diet; but when eaten with fresh meats and fruits the diet can be very nourishing. But, fresh fruits and meats alone nourish man. Eating corn alone results in a nutritional disorder known as pellagra in man and black tongue in dogs.

Pemmican

When the Southwest Indians obtained horses from the gold-hungry Spaniards in the early 1500's, farming was abandoned, and hunting became the way of life again. On horseback these Indians followed herds of buffalo in the Great Plains. They killed enough buffalo to satisfy their hunger, and stored a modified meat for the future, for travel, and for war. Thin strips of flesh were sun-dried, then pounded to a fine powder. The resulting animal-flesh flour contained no gristle, and was simply powdered, lean animal flesh cells. Next, fat from the buffalo was heated to drive off moisture. This rendered fat was mixed with an equal volume of the dried flesh cells in a pouch of animal skin. A thousand pounds of buffalo yielded 90 lbs. of dried meat and fat and was called pemmican. The pouch of pemmican was tied and sealed with a hard fat; it was then weatherproof (Stefansson 1956).

Pemmican was known to be edible after 30 years of storage. One pound of pemmican was equal to six pounds of raw meat with its fat. Six pounds of meat with its fat is all an average man will eat a day even under most rigorous conditions. He knows when to stop; he becomes sick.

Pemmican and Salt Pork Eating Explorers

Pemmican was an important item of trade in the Hudson Bay Company. The ration was purchased from Indians during periods of surplus and sold back to them when food was scarce. Another food used by North American pioneers was salt pork. Salt pork contains mostly fatty tissue with layers of lean. There were two types of early explorers in America—pork eaters and pemmican eaters. Surprisingly, each yields about 80 per cent of the calories in terms of fat and 20 per cent in terms of lean flesh. But, pemmican was superior due to its lack of bulk and non-perishable nature.

Early pioneers were robust adventurers exploring the hinterland. They apparently accepted pemmican; it would allow a man to eat a handful three times a day, and march 30 miles with a hundred pound pack on his back, in addition to his weapon, bedding, and food ration.

Pilgrims Reject Pemmican from Cultural Consideration

When the Pilgrims came to America, they settled on the East Coast. They nearly starved until aided by Indians. What evolved was a combination of the best of native Indian and European agriculture. We accepted a number of Indian customs, but strangely, we never took one of their best discoveries. We took their tobacco habits, their crops and agriculture, but not pemmican.

When our frontier families finally crossed the Eastern United States coastal mountain ranges, and headed west, settlers saw pemmican as a beastly native food, and associated it with most of the undesirable traits of these noble savages. So, while modern man took from the native Indian most of his secrets, one of his best was omitted.

A little less than one pound of pemmican is reported to give a man all the nutrients he requires. It is the only such food ever made by man which is not perishable, and which totally satisfies his hunger, nourishes him, and maintains him in good spirits.

The Indians knew that there was good pemmican and ordinary pemmican. To such rigorous folks, a little human hair or other miscellaneous matter in food was of no consequence. To modern man, the aesthetic nature of food is important.

But, good pemmican has been attested by thousands of adventurers, even up to the present day. And this food has a background of nourishing man which cannot be disputed. Pemmican has passed all tests—it can sustain man.

As the Indians were pressed by pioneers and the buffalo herds shrank in numbers, pemmican, too, slowly disappeared. However, there remain some foods which are related to pemmican. For instance, minced meat pie is a lean meat-suet-fruit concoction. Other pemmican type foods contain meat, fruits, and nuts. But this merely dilutes the food value of pemmican and makes it more bulky. It is not possible to concoct a more concentrated food for man than one with powdered animal flesh cells and rendered fat. These two items are the most potent sources of nourishment for man. One third of a water glass full of pemmican is a full satisfying meal—equal in food value to a very large thick steak.

Admiral Peary and Pemmican

Admiral Robert Peary is considered by many to be our greatest modern explorer. He wrote in 1917 that of all the foods he knew, pemmican was the only one a man could eat every meal of a day, 365 days a year, and have the last mouthful taste as good as the first. It was the most satisfying food he knew. After finishing the last morsel of pemmican in a meal, Admiral Peary wrote that he "would not have walked a step for anything in food the best restaurant in the world could place before me."

Army Trials with Pemmican Ration

At the close of World War II pemmican was studied by military forces as a possible ration for troops in the frozen areas on earth. Teams of men were fed a modern pemmican under carefully supervised tests. After three days the tests had to be terminated. The men were unable to accept the new diet, became ill, and were unable to protect themselves in the cold. As a result there are reasons to believe that a single food ration for a large number of people leaves much to be desired. Good food for modern man must not only meet the biological needs but also the cultural requirements.

Single Food Supply for Man Inadequate

Attempts to feed large numbers of people on a pemmican or similar type product have not been too successful. Furthermore, economic considerations indicate also that such a diet could not be seriously considered as a single food source for men. Such diets are the equivalent of five or six pounds of fresh meat a day per person!

Therefore, from the past experiences of men, the evidence tends to dispute the idea of a single minimum adequate food for man. The use that might be put for such a food would be in emergency or disaster feeding situations. Even under such situations, the need would not be for complete protein so much as adequate calories.

This being the situation, what is and what might be done to improve present man's food intake in the world? Some solutions must be found. Fortunately a large groups of scientists have been working for some time in this area. Some of the results of this work are reviewed below.

Artificial Synthesis of Nutrients Not A Solution

It is important also to dispel at once the notion that giant food pills which contain all the known nutrients for man might be consumed. To attempt to provide the 50 odd nutrients needed in a biological sense by a man by synthesis in laboratories would be unrealistic and a fantastically inefficient approach. Furthermore, the syntheses required are not fully known. This then is obviously not an adequate solution to the problem of developing the food needs of mankind.

Limiting Component of Human Diets at Present

The critical need for high quality protein in human diets has been quite clearly described by Sebrell (1961).

"Man's need for protein is not felt and goes unrecognized unless the deficiency is severe enough to bring him to famine edema and to the edge of the grave while his children die of kwasiorkor or remain 'underdeveloped.' The man does not see the reason why herdsmen and the hunters (who are meat eaters) have always been parts of the most vigorous tribes and civilizations. It is no coincidence that the underdeveloped people of the world today are those on poor protein diets."

Protein shortages are widespread in the world. To counter these shortages, two steps might be taken. One, the concoction of vegetable protein supplements to human diets which could serve as a temporary measure. Second, the development of adequate animal-plant food supplies so that the least a human being would consume would be his minimum nutrient requirements.

VEGETABLE PROTEIN SUPPLEMENTS FOR HUMAN DIETS

An immediate step forward for most areas of the world where protein deficiencies are widespread is to judiciously mix vegetable proteins to form a supplement for human diets.

Individual plant proteins are relatively poor because their amino acid content does not suit man's needs. Plant proteins must either be supplemented with animal protein or mixed with other plant proteins which have the missing amino acids. The other alternative of supplementing with synthetic amino acids may some day be practicable, but costs are still prohibitive.

When adding protein-rich foods of vegetable origin to a diet, however, there is an optimum proportion above or below which its biological value is decreased. For this reason, the combination of proteins of vegetable origin for child feeding, where protein quality may be critical, requires a degree of precision to yield adequate protein sources comparable in quality to protein-rich foods of animal origin (Scrimshaw and Bressani 1961).

INGREDIENTS FOR PROTEIN ENRICHED PLANT FOODS

Due to the nature of present food production, cereal grains form the staple food item in most areas of the world. Hence the bulk of such "protein enriched foods" must be carried by these grains. All cereal grains have the double disadvantage of a relatively low protein content (which often decreases further with processing and a poor protein quality due to shortages of one or more of the essential amino acids. These disadvantages can be corrected in part by combining cereal grains with foods of higher protein concentration which supply essential amino acids in such proportions as to correct the major deficiencies of the cereal grains.

There are five large groups of plant products used for this purpose: (1) legume seeds, (2) oil seed cakes, (3) nuts, (4) palm kernels, and (5) leaf proteins. Some of these have received attention as protein supplements, but many have been neglected or require further study. Although algae and yeast have frequently been suggested as protein sources, thus far they have not proved sufficiently palatable to constitute more than a small percentage of the total diet (Scrimshaw and Bressani 1961).

The legume seeds in general are not much better than the cereal grains although they are relatively good sources of lysine (the first limiting amino acid in cereal grain protein), but are limiting in methionine, which is adequate in cereal grains. Furthermore, legume seeds must be cooked for maximum utilization, and improper processing will decrease their protein value. The actual protein values vary widely within the group which includes the peanut (*Arachis hypogaea*), the soybean (*Glycine max*), the common bean (*Phaseolus vulgaris*), the cow pea (*Vigna sinensis*), the chick pea (Bengal gram), *Cicer arientinum,* and beans of the genera *Vicia Pisum, Lens, Dolichos* and *Canavalia.*

Since the soybean has been a human food for centuries, and because it is now an important commercial source of oil and of press cake for animal feeding, this legume has received the greatest attention. It can be prepared in a variety of forms for human consumption and the literature is voluminous on this subject. Cooked soybean meal contains approximately 44 per cent protein, with a quality superior to most vegetable proteins although inferior to proteins of animal origin. Soybeans have a strong, slightly bitter flavor which limits their acceptability for many people.

A major current interest is to develop concentrated protein fractions from soybeans and to adapt fermentation procedures used on a home-scale in the Far East to commercial production.

The peanut or groundnut has been widely investigated because of the value of its oil which yields the meal as a by-product. Like other legume seeds, peanuts are short in methionine and relatively low in arginine, lysine, and isoleucine when compared to animal protein.

Another group of important protein sources includes the seeds of cotton, sesame, sunflower, rape, mustard, poppy, linseed, safflower, and hemp. Many of these have specific disadvantages of flavors or toxic substances which limit their usefulness. Cotton is produced extensively for fiber and cottonseed presscake is a by-product of oil extraction. The presscake is produced at low cost in such large quantities that it is of major importance as a protein concentrate in animal feeds. It contains gossypol which is toxic to some animals, by reason of making lysine unavailable to the animal organism. At present, good cottonseed flours for human consumption are available which are low in gossypol, have a protein content in excess of 50 per cent, and a biological value of about 65 per cent. Furthermore, they have amino acid patterns which are complementary to cereal proteins.

Sesame has a nutritive value similar to cottonseed, but no known toxic principle. The removal of the hard hull is necessary to reduce the crude fiber content and to eliminate a slight bitter aftertaste. Sesame is not too popular because the seed pod of most varieties shatter readily. New varieties are being developed to overcome this difficulty.

Sunflower seed is another good source of (oil and) protein concentrate, but so far its large-scale production is limited to Argentina, Chile, and Russia.

The nuts are not sufficiently plentiful to offer important practical advantages for large scale protein supplementation of cereal diets. Of the palm kernel proteins, only copra has been studied. A review on copra protein by Curtin (1950) discusses production, composition, processing, and properties. Copra protein has been used in low cost protein foods in combinations with peanut flour and chick peas. A disadvantage of copra protein is its high fiber content. Little is known of the other palm nut meals, but their crude fiber content is unfavorable.

Methods for the separation and concentration of leaf protein have been receiving considerable attention. The quality of the protein is no better than that of the legumes, and leaf proteins are not as effective as legumes in improving the protein quality of cereal diets because of a relative deficiency in methionine and cystine. Studies with poultry have shown that the gross protein values of leaf protein are generally lower than expected from their amino acid composition, probably due to low digestibility. It is noteworthy that the nutritive value of rice can be improved by adding a cooked leaf meal.

Soybean Food Mixtures

One of the first supplements proposed for treatment of severe protein deficiency was a soybean-banana mixture. This was abandoned in favor of more concentrated and better balanced supplements.

Soybeans must be soaked, skinned, minced, and cooked before being fed, which limits their use in the home. It is necessary to neutralize the trypsin inhibitor present and, further, several of the preparations cause gastrointestinal disorders. Work with a fungus treated soybean product "tempeh," preparations such as the Indonesian "saridele" and American "soy milks," hold promise that the problems inherent in the use of soybean for infant feeding may eventually be solved.

For countries with a large soybean production, soybean protein can be a valuable addition to the diet.

India: Chick Pea, Cow Pea, Bean, Peanut Flour, and Sesame Mixtures

India has developed several formulas for multipurpose foods. Two of these, known as Mysore Food A and B, have undergone extensive biological trials in the Nutrition Research Laboratories in Hyderabad, India. Mysore Food A contains about 25 per cent Bengal gram (chick pea) "dhal" and 75 per cent peanut meal, and Mysore Food B, 25 per cent Bengal gram, 65 per cent peanut flour, and 10 per cent sesame meal. Bengal gram has given good results in the treatment of cases of kwasiorkor when compared with skim milk.

Mexico: Corn-Beans

Mexican research into corn-bean mixture have had some success. Studies have been reported by Altschul (1958) of the nutritive value of a mixture of lime-treated maize (as tortillas) and black beans in the 4:5 proportions by weight common in some Mexican diets. The slope of the curve showing weight gain of rats fed this mixture was only 0.93 ± 0.037 as compared with 1.84 ± 0.040 when 22 per cent of the protein came from milk. Similarly, the absorption and retention of nitrogen by malnourished children is reported variable from child to child and much lower than with isocaloric diets containing isonitrogenous quantities of milk. The addition of tryptophan and lysine to the maize-bean diet greatly improved nitrogen absorption.

Incaparina

The Institute of Nutrition for Central America and Panama (INCAP) located in Guatemala has had notable success in recent years with vegetable protein mixtures and supplements. Two useful formulations have been reported by this organization by Scrimshaw and Bressani (1961) along with data on growth experiments with animals (Table 48) and people (Table 49).

INCAP Vegetable Mixture No. 8, made up of 50 per cent lime-treated maize (masa) flour, 35 per cent sesame flour, 9 per cent cottonseed flour, 3 per cent Torula yeast, and 3 per cent Kikuyu leaf

TABLE 48

REPRESENTATIVE RAT GROWTH EXPERIMENT WITH INCAP VEGETABLE MIXTURE 9' (21 DAYS—
5 RATS/GROUP)[1]

Protein in Diet	Average Weight Gain, Gm.		Protein Efficiency[2]	
Per cent	V.M. 9'	Casein	V.M. 9'	Casein
5	22	22	1.88	2.14
10	66	67	2.30	2.38
15	104	105	2.11	2.31
20	114	117	1.75	2.00
25	115	121	1.47	1.65

[1] From Scrimshaw and Bressani (1961).
[2] Av. wt. gain/av. protein consumed.

TABLE 49

COMPARISON OF NITROGEN BALANCE IN PRESCHOOL CHILDREN[1]

	Milk	INCAP VM-9
No. of children........................	9	9
Balance periods........................	48	48
Average protein intake, gm./kg./day........	2.3	2.3
Average per cent absorbed.................	82.6	68.9
Average per cent retained[2].................	16.3	17.8

[1] From Scrimshaw and Bressani (1961).
[2] Difference in retention is not significant.

meal, has a protein content of 25.1 per cent which in growth experiments in rats and chicks, and metabolic balance trials in children recovering from protein malnutrition, closely approximates the quality of milk protein. INCAP Vegetable Mixture 9B, containing 29 per cent whole ground maize, 29 per cent whole ground sorghum grain, 38 per cent cottonseed flour, 3 per cent Torula yeast, 1 per cent calcium carbonate, and 4,500 units of added vitamin A/100 gm., has a protein content of 27.5 per cent and is similar in protein quality to Mixture 8 and milk. It can be produced at very low cost, and in the form of a thin gruel (atole), is highly acceptable in Central America.

The thin gruel is made by adding 1 glass of water for each 25 gm. of the mixture and cooking for 15 minutes. It is flavored to taste with sugar and cinnamon, vanilla, anise, or chocolate and served either hot or cold. Incaparina can also be substituted for two-thirds of the flour in most non-bread recipes calling for wheat flour and can be made into puddings as well as used for enriching soups. It has a high acceptability for mass feeding, according to Scrimshaw. Its favorable initial commercial acceptance under the name "Incaparina" suggests that it will make a useful contribution to the problem of preventing protein malnutrition in this area.

Processed plant protein foodstuffs useful in human diets have been developed and can be important supplements to diets in protein starved areas. However, it is most important in devising protein-rich vegetable mixtures to specify the objective and form of use. For example, protein malnutrition is acute in children 1 to 5 years of age who, after weaning, are not given a diet with adequate protein (see Frontispiece). This age group needs a supplement to their diets which will make up the protein deficit and also correct other nutrient deficiencies which occur. This means that for most areas, the mixture should be a good source of vitamin A, riboflavin and calcium, niacin, and iron. The desirable calorie content of the supplementary food depends upon the adequacy of the habitual diet, and is usually of minor concern.

It must be recognized that a vegetable mixture may be entirely satisfactory for the prevention of protein malnutrition in older children and quite unsatisfactory as basis for the formula feeding of young infants. The suitability of a vegetable mixture for feeding premature infants has still less practical importance if its primary purpose is the prevention of protein malnutrition in preschool children. The use of vegetable mixtures as supplementary sources of protein is, of course, not limited to children. It is also beneficial for pregnant and lactating women, and acceptable as a staple in the diet of all members of the family, increasing the probability that the mixture will be made available to the family members who need it most.

As shown in Table 48 and 49 the best of such vegetable protein mixtures fall close to the mark provided by good animal protein.

Plant protein mixtures are adequate substitutes for high quality protein, and good health requires that high quality protein be an integral part of human diets. Not only must the required amino acids be present, but they must be present in the required amounts and proportions of one to another. Furthermore, a minimum adequate human food must contain more than high quality protein.

ANIMAL PROTEIN DIET SUPPLEMENTS

The problem with supplying animal protein in sufficient quantities to satisfy human protein needs is that up to the present time circumstances have not permitted it. There are just a very large number of people on earth, and the conversion of plants to animals is slow and not always efficient.

However, when man's technology of food production has yielded huge surpluses of food or feed in one area, and men in other areas are suffering from protein deficiency diseases, it would seem that the grain surpluses in one area might be used to "prime the pump" to generate animal protein supplements. In the concentrated form, the protein supplements would not be as difficult to transport, and in a dry form, these might be simply preserved and distributed and consumed as additions to diets. In a sense, those that can not help themselves must be given a helping hand from those who can.

To attempt to introduce animal protein supplement systems in critical areas of the world may offer some chances for success providing that some local means develop to continue the supplementation. If non-agricultural methods can be developed to produce animal feed (algae?), and this is not eaten itself by humans in unrefined form, then there might well be some hope in improving the situation. It would appear that there are methods available to produce such animal protein supplements using closed cycle food systems. Recent studies indicate that a two liter tank of algae can yield 35 gm. of algae cells a day. If the algae slurry could be fed directly to animals, as a main source of nutrients, then immense gains in animal protein production might be possible.

The need for some such adjunct to the present methods of food production in the world is clearly implied in the statement by King (1961): "Roughly half of the world's population still contends with recurrent episodes of *severe* starvation. They face a steadily more tragic situation (due to rate of population increases in world). The penalty is heaviest on infants, mothers and small children. For them the sickness and death rates are astoundingly high."

It would seem that a minimum adequate food supply can be developed, and also made available to the world, by judiciously supplementing the diets currently consumed in the world with the components that were found to be missing or in short supply. Adequate solutions are available to meet present crises. But, in the future, world population pressures could well force the development of a standardized minimum human food which would meet solely man's biological needs. When this occurs, and if it occurs, man's cultural existence on earth including his ideas of "good food" will undergo some changes. Most men might then achieve good health, but they would perhaps lose culturally the pleasure of good eating.

CHAPTER 15

World's Population and Its Control

THE PROBLEM

Since I started writing this book there has been an increase in the world's population equal to the population of the United States. After reviewing food production and food consumption data in previous chapters, it becomes clear that the human population for the most part has outrun the ability of the systems which operate in the world to supply people with their minimum needs. The present rate of increase in human numbers must be brought into line with the ability of the world's societies to cope with more people.

It should be clearly stated that up to this point in this book we have addressed ourselves to the starvation problems in the world with its present population of 3.0 billion. Any realistic study of the rate of increase in human numbers on earth clearly reveals that our numbers could double again in the next 40 years! Hence, any discussion of world starvation which fails to take into account the problems brought about by the increasing world population falls short of the mark. World starvation, already to a degree so widespread that it touches most people in one form or another, will increase both in intensity for individuals and in frequency of occurrence in the population as a whole unless remedial action is taken immediately.

This chapter deals with the population problem and its control. There are courses of action which appear required; several should be made operative simultaneously to be effective. The sole addition of food to the system would alone not solve the problems that exist. There appears a need for cultural progress to control our numbers within the limits of our capabilities to supply the people with their minimum essentials for a decent life.

There are at least three courses of action seen working. One, there is a biological control present and found widespread in the world in biological systems. There is no reason to suppose these do not also apply to man. Two, there is an economic factor at work, for certainly the standard of living influences population growth.

And third, there are cultural factors at work which permit or resist the gains that must be made.

THE HUMAN POPULATION CYCLE

Between 1956 and 1961 a population of human beings has been added to the world equal to the present population of the United States. Growth of human numbers on planet earth is at an unprecedented rate. Approximately 100,000 human beings are now being added to the world's population each day. The distribution of the present world population is shown in a general way in Fig. 23.

A man will eat approximately ten times his body weight a year. Present human populations can be estimated to require approximately 3.5 trillion lbs. of food annually. The production of food at the present time is not equal to this quantity, and is poorly distributed. We face a serious dilemma, therefore, not only today but in the future. To realize the full significance of these trends, it is useful to explore the nature of human populations on earth and factors which tend to control our numbers.

World Population Projections

During the last 2,000 years, and in particular during the last 300 years, not only has the world population increased but also the rate at which the increase has occurred has also increased. The number of people who inhabit the earth has doubled in the last 100 years. With the present rate of increase, the number could double again in just 40 years. Staggering problems of how to feed, house and clothe nearly twice our number are now confronting us.

Population projections made by the United Nations for the years up to 2000 A.D. for the world by continents and regions is shown in Table 50. Although populations are increasing in almost every country of the world, the rate at which these increases are occurring are far from uniform. Several important factors have contributed to the large and rapid population growth on earth. Three of these factors are in the fields of public health, food production, and industrialization.

In the last 200 years infant mortality has dropped from 200 per thousand to 30 per thousand. In the industrialized nations, six children out of seven born who would have died two centuries ago now survive. Death rates have fallen from about 40 per thousand to

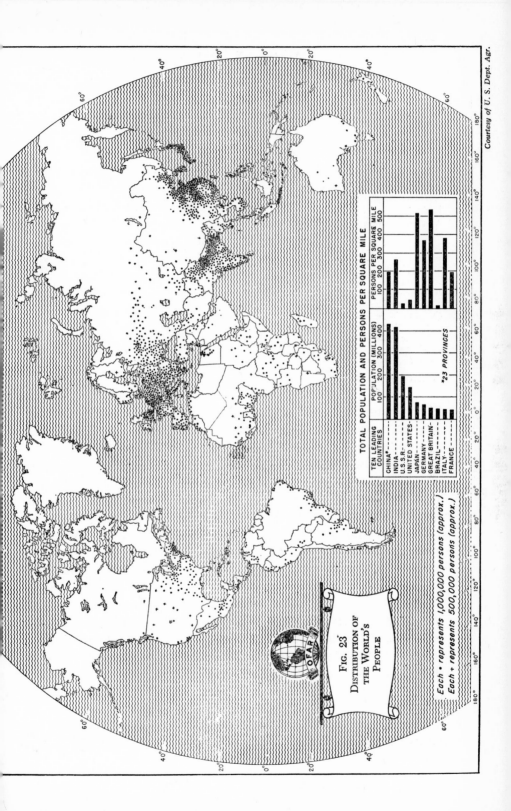

TOTAL POPULATION AND PERSONS PER SQUARE MILE

TEN LEADING COUNTRIES	POPULATION (MILLIONS)	PERSONS PER SQUARE MILE
	100 200 300 400	100 200 300 400 500
CHINA*		
INDIA		
U.S.S.R.		
UNITED STATES		
JAPAN		
GERMANY		
GREAT BRITAIN		
BRAZIL		
ITALY		
FRANCE		

*23 PROVINCES

FIG. 23
DISTRIBUTION OF
THE WORLD'S
PEOPLE

~~~ Each • represents 1,000,000 persons (approx.)
~~~ Each + represents 500,000 persons (approx.)

TABLE 50

POPULATION PROJECTIONS TO THE YEAR 2000 FOR THE WORLD, CONTINENTS AND REGIONS[1]
In Millions

	1950	1960	1970	1975	2000
World Total	2,500	2,920	3,500	3,860	6,280
Africa	199	237	294	331	517
Northern Africa	43	53	67	76	147
Middle and Southern Africa	156	185	227	254	370
Northern America	168	197	225	240	312
Latin America	163	206	265	303	592
Asia (excluding the Asian part of the Soviet Union and Japan)	1,296	1,524	1,870	2,093	3,717
Japan and Ryukyu Islands	84	96	110	117	153
Europe (excluding the European part of the Soviet Union)	393	424	457	476	568
Northern and Western Europe	133	140	148	154	180
Central Europe	128	140	151	156	183
Southern Europe	132	144	158	166	206
Oceania	13.2	16.3	19.4	21.0	29.3
Australia and New Zealand	10.2	12.7	14.9	16.0	20.8
Pacific Islands	2.9	3.6	4.5	5.0	8.6
Soviet Union (Asian and European parts combined)	181	215	254	275	379

[1] From Cook (1959).

12 per thousand. Life expectancy at birth has increased from about 30 years to 65 years. The most important factor which has made this improvement possible has been in the field of public health. Many diseases have been totally eliminated from human populations or reduced to the incidence of minor diseases (P.E.P. 1955).

At the same time food supplies increased, food production improved steadily due to the success of modern agriculture.

The Industrial Revolution was important because it also helped to increase the food supply per person. The Industrial Revolution provided a system for the transportation of the food from areas where it could be produced to the areas in which people lived. People could migrate to areas where employment possibilities existed. The Industrial Revolution also made it possible to mechanize agriculture, and enabled countries which were developing an industrial economy to buy food in exchange for manufactured goods. People shifted from rural to urban areas.

Population Cycle

The Political and Economic Planning Organization of London has described the population cycles in Western Europe as follows (see

Fig. 24). The cycle has four stages which are illustrated by examples in England (P.E.P. 1955).

In stage one, a highly fluctuating population condition existed 200 years ago in England; it is still occurring in other areas. Dur-this stage there is a high birth and high death rate, both greater than

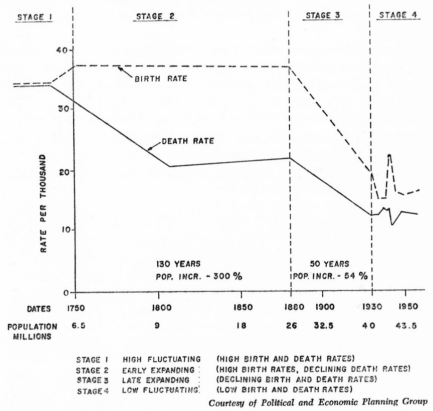

STAGE I	STAGE 2	STAGE 3	STAGE 4

BIRTH RATE

DEATH RATE

RATE PER THOUSAND

130 YEARS
POP. INCR. - 300 %

50 YEARS
POP. INCR. - 54 %

DATES	1750	1800	1850	1880	1900	1930	1950
POPULATION MILLIONS	6.5	9	18	26	32.5	40	43.5

STAGE I	HIGH FLUCTUATING	(HIGH BIRTH AND DEATH RATES)
STAGE 2	EARLY EXPANDING	(HIGH BIRTH RATES, DECLINING DEATH RATES)
STAGE 3	LATE EXPANDING	(DECLINING BIRTH AND DEATH RATES)
STAGE 4	LOW FLUCTUATING	(LOW BIRTH AND DEATH RATES)

Courtesy of Political and Economic Planning Group

FIG. 24. STAGES IN POPULATION CYCLE IN WESTERN EUROPE: INCLUDING ENGLAND

35 per thousand. This is accompained by a slow and irregular increase in population.

The second stage is called the early expanding state. For example, in England 200 years ago, the death rate began to fall rapidly while the birth rate remained rather constant for another 100 years. During the end of that period, births were about 34 thousand and deaths about 21. This gave an annual natural increase of about 13 people per thousand. During the last 130 year period the population trebled.

The third stage is the late expanding stage. In England this began about 1880 when the birth rate in England began to fall rapidly. After 50 more years the rate had dropped to 16 per thousand while the death rate, continuing its decline, had dropped to 12 per thousand. During this 50 year period the population increased by more than half.

The fourth stage is called the low fluctuating stage. In England and in the western European countries, while there was a sharp rise in the number of births immediately following World War II, birth and death rates soon became stable again at about 16 and 12 per thousand respectively, yielding a rather steady but small growth in populations. It should be recalled that in the 1930's the falling birth rate condition which existed in many industrial countries was thought to indicate a declining population in certain countries. This condition was reversed in the late 1940's.

However, it is useful to recall that the trends are generally similar in Europe to those found in England and are spread over about the same amount of time. This cycle has been followed in general throughout the West. In Western Europe the cycle brought about a sixfold growth in population in 300 years. It is important to note also that the Industrial Revolution and the developments in science have permitted a comparable rise in the standards of living. In the last 200 years the western industrial nations have enjoyed an economic growth unknown in the previous history of mankind. The future prospects are equally bright.

Population growths in Western Europe at the present time are at a rate of about seven per thousand per year. Between 1944 and 1949, there was a sharp rise in the number of children born; birth rates in England increased from about 15 to 20 per thousand for a few years. In England this increase lasted for a short time and has now been reported to have disappeared. Similar increases have occurred in most of the countries in Europe and some have already ended. In North America there is still a natural increase of about 16 per thousand in population which is actually greater than the rate of population growth in India. The growth rate in the United States shows no signs of slowing, although great increases in populations following wars have been a naturally occurring phenomenon in the past history of mankind.

It is reported that nearly two-thirds of the world's population (most underdeveloped nations) have reached only the first or second stage in the population cycle (shown in Fig. 24). Death rates are often still high. It is thought that in these areas rapid population growths can occur in the near future.

It is significant to note that the public health improvements which have occurred have raised the general level of health, strength, energy and well-being of people in the industrialized nations of the world.

The concepts of the human population cycle are useful in understanding the current trends in population growth. There is reason to believe that the population cycle followed in the industrialized nations will eventually occur in the now underdeveloped areas. It is, therefore, clear that these areas face problems of great magnitude.

The Future Growth of World Population

The United Nations reports that if plans for social and economic development of impoverished areas are to have any chance of realistic implementation, such plans require a parallel assessment of the dynamics of population growth. Population growths have practical and direct consequences in the economic and social spheres. Within the next 25 years the process which started mankind on its path (perhaps 20 thousand years ago) will culminate in man's full possession of the earth. The growth of human populations is a problem which involves the very nature of the existence of mankind on earth.

The World's Economic, Political and Social Characteristics

The world's social situation has improved significantly since the end of World War II. There have been some substantial improvements in food consumption, health, education, and in income. These improvements reflect in part the efforts of the various governments and voluntary organizations in the world.

Food consumption and food production have improved on a world-wide basis although there is much yet to be done in both fields. Several of the highly industrialized nations are constantly faced with increasing food surpluses.

The United Nations reports that in the field of health, mortality rates have continued their decline particularly in the economically less-developed countries. Epidemic diseases which in the past periodically took their toll in human populations are now being brought under increasing control. Health problems are now becoming more and more those of social industrial nations—those of human degenerative diseases.

The number of children and young people in the world attending school has significantly increased. Literacy is advancing as it never has in the past. Yet, only approximately one-half of the children of the world who are of school age are in school. The national needs for specialized personnel in developing countries are now increasing more rapidly than the capacity of the educational systems in these countries to produce them.

National incomes are rising to new heights and industrial production is growing faster than at anytime in the previous history of the world. But, the general picture of optimism which this suggests should be greatly qualified.

The progress which has been made is small when compared to the extent of poverty and the needs of the people of the world today. We have achieved but a fraction of the potential for human progress.

The progress achieved in the recent past has been uneven in the different fields of endeavor, as well as in different countries and population groups. There is a growth in social stress found in many sections of the world. Housing has not improved much, according to United Nations (1958) reports. Part of our difficulty is due to the rapid urbanization which is occurring and the desire to urbanize is everywhere.

United Nations reports state that the drop in death rates in Africa, Asia and Latin America is due largely to the penetration of modern methods of controlling communicable diseases including the extension of health services that have sharply reduced infant mortality. The use of available resources in these regions has not been kept in balance with needs (United Nations 1958).

Average population increases of about three per cent per year are currently underway in the world. Population growths at this rate cannot fail to have important economic social and political consequences.

Urbanization is proceeding more rapidly in the underdeveloped regions of the world than in the industrialized areas of the world. In industrialized nations the large metropolitan centers are growing at the expense of the smaller towns.

Agrarian economies have often been unable to meet the increased food requirements of enlarging urban areas. Urbanization, when it occurs in underdeveloped areas and unmatched with improved agricultural activities, results merely in a transfer of poverty and underemployment from the country to the city. The social gains that have been made possible by industrialization result instead in an overflow of rural distress conditions. Urbanization also brings new problems arising from conflicts of culture, interactions of old and new customs and patterns of life, difficulties in personal adjustments to the reorganization of social structures. A family in particular undergoes changes in its size, its function, and in the status and role of its different members. Children caught between the new and the old cultures are apt to be victims of the change. The increases in juvenile delinquency in urban areas is a matter of widespread world concern. The very process of industrial development brings with it new problems and inherits old ones. United Nations reports indicate that there is a need for much closer integration of social and economic objectives than has been yet achieved so far in many countries. There is a need for better understanding of the complex problem of development upon which so many people are now basing their hopes for the future (United Nations 1958, 1960).

The rapid growth of population in underdeveloped areas becomes complicated in three ways. **First,** it increases the pressure of populations on land that is already densely settled and retards increases in productivity of agricultural labor. This effect is seen not only in a country where nearly all the cultivable land is now occupied but also in many underdeveloped countries where the density of agricultural populations in the cultivated areas is already high. Here large amounts of potentially productive land is unused because of land ownership systems, lack of capital or techniques to exploit the available land, or for other reasons (P.E.P. 1955).

Second, increases in populations aggravate the problem of capital resource shortages. This is one of the most important obstacles in the economic development of underdeveloped countries. Increasing populations then aggravate this problem.

Third, high birth rates in underdeveloped countries create a heavy load of dependent children upon the sector of the population which is working. United Nations reports that the percentage of children under 15 years of age in the less developed countries of Asia, Africa, and Latin America make up perhaps 40 per cent or more of the total population. European countries, for example, have a value nearer to 20 per cent. Large families inflict a further difficulty upon the worker in the underdeveloped country because he is usually unable to save and invest for economic development. This is then aggravated by the complications of providing the children with adequate education. The resource of educated people is essential if a foundation for social and economic advancement in the long term is to be established (United Nations 1958).

The over-all seriousness of the situation can be clearly recognized. In the next 25 years if present trends continue, a population will be added to the world equal to all the people who were living just 100 years ago.

POPULATION CONTROLS

As Hertzler (1958) has pointed out, we must reassess our views of human destiny and of human demands. He asks, "Are great quantities of persons and things our main goals? Or, is the quality of human life—the good life for each individual and for mankind as a whole—the ultimate objective?" If the major objective, according to Hertzler, is to fully develop the personalities of human beings, this in turn means that the fullest and most harmonious exercise of human facilities and powers, . . . the fullest utilization of the richness of human culture. It would imply the achievement of an ascending scale of values from material and biological to the intellectual and the spiritual. It would imply a richer and wider flowering of the higher qualities that make up man's uniqueness, his intelligence, his creative powers, his moral sense.

We, in general, desire to promote the good life for all races, creeds, classes, and climes. As Hertzler indicates, such a quality of living cannot be achieved in a beehive. Human life can be vastly more than breeding, grubbing and feeding. The world must be looked upon as a good place for human beings also for the ages to come. To achieve this goodness the world requires surpluses instead of shortages. Hence, there is much to be said in favor of policies which tend to stabilize the world population as a guide for the immediate future. This would enable the peoples of the earth not only to move toward the universalized physical optimum, but also to realize and enjoy the highest known reaches of social well-being and opportunity, and of intellectual and spiritual development. This is the kind of society young and old are thought to desire for the future.

Because of the interdependence and interlocking between nations and peoples, population problems anywhere are world problems. The present crisis in human reproduction rates in relation to existing resources involves all the people of the world.

There appears to be a widely held idea concerning the necessity for a world-wide limitation in human populations. The peoples of the world differ in the means of achieving such a stability in the population. While it is beyond the scope of this writing to undertake an investigation of the pros and cons of the various systems of limiting human numbers, adequate coverage of this area of information is to be found in the literature (P.E.P. 1955; Cook 1959; United Nations 1958).

Biological Control of Populations

All living entities have certain features in common. One of the features relates to the growth of a population in a suitable environment. If a suitable environment is inoculated with a population of organisms, a distinct growth pattern develops. Growth curves are of interest because in general they are representative of many populations—plant, animal, and human. The same general principles may underlie the form in which growth in numbers occurs for plants, animals, or humans. Will the laws of biology which apply to plant and animal populations also govern human populations? They have not failed to do so. We do not know for certain where we are on the growth curve, yet it would be a distinct advantage to know. Therefore, it may be useful to explore briefly the nature of population growth curves.

The growth curve shown in Fig. 25 has several portions which deserve some discussion. Portion A is called the *initial stationary phase* of growth and represents a period during which the initial numbers of organisms present become adjusted to the new environment. The increase in numbers is not great at this point. In fact, the number may decrease and this could be shown by a dotted line beneath A on the curve. Only the more vigorous members of the population apparently survive and begin to multiply. Soon this shows itself by an upswing (in the portion of the curve labeled B) which is usually called the phase of accelerated growth. During the phase of accelerated growth the time required for a rapid increase in numbers is dependent upon having suitable environmental conditions and suitable food available. Eventually the organism proceeds to grow in numbers. In fact, a plot of the increase in the

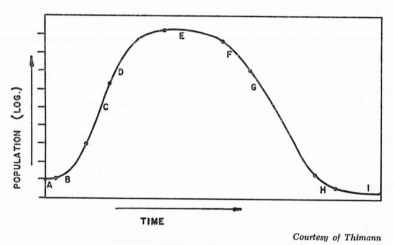

Courtesy of Thimann

Fig. 25. General Biological Growth Curve

number of living organisms plotted against the time shows a straight line relationship. This period is spoken of as a phase of *logarithmic increase*. If this were to continue uninterrupted, the organisms would completely cover the environment in a short time. There is little doubt that at the present time the human populations on earth are in the phase of logarithmic increase. In general, in a biological system this phase does not continue indefinitely because it is limited by the resources available and the uses to which they may be put. Furthermore, the organisms present begin to encounter difficulties. Food begins to run out, organisms become crowded together and this interferes with their proliferation. The rate of increase then begins to decline. This is labeled section D on the curve and is called the phase of *negative growth acceleration*. Eventually the biological system of organisms reaches the point where the total population remains unchanged for a period of time. This phase is called the *maximum stationary phase* and is shown as section E on the growth curve. As conditions become more and more difficult for the organisms, due to the pressures they exert on each other, they begin to grow more slowly. The population then enters a phase of accelerated decrease shown as zone F on the curve. This yields to the condition of a logarithmic death phase G during which the decrease in numbers occurs at a regular and unchanging rate. Finally a condition is reached where an equilibrium between death and birth rates tends to balance each other again, and in a very low population level, called the *phase of readjustment,* labeled H. This yields to the final *dormant phase* I.

Many factors can influence the various growth phases. The form of the growth curve may be affected by changes in environmental conditions, increasing or decreasing the resources or nutrients available, and the competition for resources between different kinds of organisms.

An interesting question arises as to whether the human population on earth will follow this general scheme of growth curves which are found to be valid for many biological systems and populations. There is some evidence that in certain countries the rate of increase in populations has in fact been drastically curtailed. There are several areas in the United States, for example, in which there are declining population numbers (a part of which is due to migration). In some countries this is a serious problem, and population increases are encouraged by giving financial assistance to families (France, Italy).

It is recognized that wars dent the curve but do not change the general course of the growth curve. Diseases may also make their mark.

Interesting studies have been undertaken with rabbits which may be pertinent to this discussion (Allen 1954, 1961). Suppose we have an island which is well isolated from other islands. Let us give this island adequate to excellent environmental conditions and food supplies for rabbits. Assume that there are no predatory animals to harrass the rabbit population. If we inoculate a small rabbit population on this isolated island, the rabbits begin to multiply and follow the growth curve depicted in general in Fig. 26. They go through phase A, and phase B, and phase C, and phase D.   In fact, the rabbits do a little bit more.   They reach a population level which is greater than the ability of the soil to carry such numbers, due to limitations in food production and, equally important, in their desired environmental conditions for growth.   Something peculiar then begins to happen in the rabbit population.   A slight decrease in

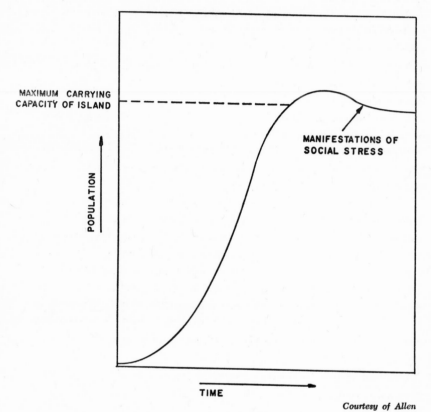

MAXIMUM CARRYING
CAPACITY OF ISLAND

MANIFESTATIONS OF
SOCIAL STRESS

POPULATION

TIME

Courtesy of Allen

Fig. 26.   Growth Curve for Rabbit Population in Isolated Area

numbers begins to occur, and the animals level off in population numbers at a point lower than that which the environment could sustain.   In other words, less rabbits eventually will inhabit the island than the island is capable of supporting!   A striking feature results—a condition thought to be social stress amongst rabbits occurs, and various physiological manifestations of social stress are found.   There are changes in gland size and in hormone activity. There are changes in the appearance in the coat of the animals.

The adreno-pituitary system of mammals is influenced by social pressures. Christian (1950) reports that exhaustion of the adreno-pituitary system results from increased stresses inherent in high populations, especially in wintertime.   In some mammals there is a population-wide death with symptoms of adrenal insufficiency resulting in hypoglycemic convulsions.   Christian has made the following report relating to the ability of rabbits and the influence of stress on rabbit numbers: rabbits became tense from the stress of crowded existences, during which there is a poorer food supply and an insufficiency of food plus an increased demand for exertion.   Such animals, having struggled through a winter, are in no condition physically or physiologically to stand such social stress.   The endocrine glands, which make up the hormones, call for more sugar from the reservoir of the animal, draining the liver, creating a condition called cirrhosis, which yields to death from hypertension.

Although the how and why of psychosomatic ailments in wild rodents are undeniably important to civilized men, the real attraction of stress consists of the way in which it works on organisms.   More recently veterinarians have noticed that neurotic pets tend to have neurotic owners (Deevey 1960).   There has been a report from the Philadelphia zoo blaming social pressures on the rise during the last two decades in which a tenfold increase in arteriosclerosis has occurred in the inmates of the zoo.   Recent studies by Christian and Deevey and others have yielded direct evidence of the impact of stress on mammals.   For a fascinating story concerning the possible impact of stress on human populations, the reader is referred to a recent writing by Deevey, given in reference.   A condition known as pathological togetherness in certain animals, in which sociability is manifested in terms of lower fertility and shortened lives is perhaps noteworthy.

It is recognized that man, being a political and social creature, is subject to the social stresses created by population pressures.   That social stresses are mounting throughout the urban regions of the world is unquestionable.   Juvenile delinquency is but one of the manifestations of social stress.   It would seem that a host of manifestations of "pathological togetherness" are being demonstrated already by humans on earth.   If this is true, then perhaps we as human occupants of planet Earth are entering phase E on the biological growth curve.

WORLD POPULATION GROWTH CURVES

The increases in human numbers on earth since 1 A.D. are shown in Fig. 27. A portion of this curve has been selected for further study (in Fig. 28) beginning about 300 years ago. This portion of the curve is found to have the characteristics of growth curves for biological systems in general.

The key question we must face at present is where on the growth curve is the human population on earth—phase "C," "D," or "E" in Fig. 25, page 272. Unfortunately the answer will only be available in time.

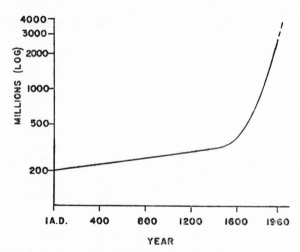

FIG. 27. GROWTH CURVE FOR HUMAN POPULATION ON EARTH SINCE 1 A.D.

We appear to have approached the condition shown in Fig. 26, page 274, where social stresses begin to have physiological manifestations on the members of a population because they have increased in numbers beyond the carrying capacity of their environment.

Certainly we have increased in numbers beyond the capacity of our resources, the way we have been applying them!

Remedial activity is demanded, no matter what the explanation. Some obvious solutions exist.

There are proponents for control of world populations by withholding public health and medical benefits, which tend to keep death rates low. Such a means of control is totally unacceptable; such ideas fall short of an acceptable mark of one man's care for his fellow men.

Acceptable solutions are available without depreciation of moral values. Such solutions will not come about by hope alone.

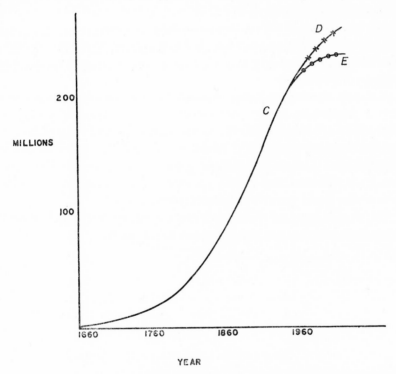

FIG. 28. GROWTH CURVE FOR HUMAN POPULATION IN NORTH AMERICA SINCE 1660

ECONOMIC CONTROL OF POPULATIONS

If we accept the general idea that the standard of living of a family is equal to the resources it has multiplied by what use it makes of these resources and divided by the number of people in the family unit, we could write this in the form of an equation:

$$\text{Standard of living} = \frac{\text{resources} \times \text{use} \times \text{level of technology}}{\text{number of people in family}}$$

While this is not an absolutely balanced equation, most people accept the general idea presented. If we accept this equation, we could write it in another way:

$$\text{Number of people} = \frac{\text{resources} \times \text{use} \times \text{level of technology}}{\text{standard of living}}$$

In other words, one control of populations is the standard of living of the people who make up the population. For most of the population, a higher standard of living permits greater sociability, and large family units tend to restrict social men and women.

There can be little doubt that the standard of living and economic conditions influence the size of populations, be they family units, nations, or continents.

A steady rise in the living standards of the underdeveloped countries is important to the whole world. All underdeveloped countries today are making efforts to increase their food supplies. Few are making any organized effort to control the growth of their populations. Unless population growth can be controlled, living standards will continue to fall. A serious effort must be undertaken to slow the rapid growth in human populations.

The choice appears to be between a great quantity of human life on earth or a higher quality of human life on earth.

Feasts, Famines, and the Future

INTRODUCTION

Estimates of the world's population which is starving depend upon the definition of the word. To some, starvation means people dying from lack of food. To others, it means death from causes indirectly associated with a food deficiency. Does it include all persons suffering from malnutrition? Does it include as starving all those with diets reduced from a usual level? Some may include those who are frequently hungry, though not in distress. Some may include all the above plus those who suffer from over-consumption of food.

Malnutrition may be due to shortages of food, lack of means to obtain food, lack of knowledge as to adequate food selection, inadequate preparation and consumption patterns, or even personal difficulties in metabolism. In the best of environs, nutritionists find that the number of people suffering from malnutrition because of financial reasons is far less than the number suffering from malnutrition for other reasons.

There are approximately 3.0 billion people on earth. If one were to make an estimate, those people with diets inferior to those of the United States perhaps number more than two billion. Those with a nutritional problem number perhaps 1.5 billion. Those hungry but not in distress would be much less than a billion. Those suffering from all forms of malnutrition that can be remedied probably include all of us at one time or another. Those with an acute food shortage would perhaps number in the hundreds of millions. So, the incidents of starvation on earth depend upon the meaning of the term we apply. If one includes sub-optimal nutrition, it is perhaps to be found everywhere (United Nations 1960).

Starvation is known to occur much less severely on farms than in population centers. It has been estimated that more than half of the world's population lives on farms or adjacent thereto; the remainder live in cities. Not all are starving, certainly.

However, the conclusion that must be reached is that there are feasts and famines and the later predominate.

279

FOOD SUPPLIES AND POPULATIONS

We have two problems in this regard. One is the adjustment of the food supply to the population; the other is the adjustment of the population to the food supply.

Consider the farmer and his livestock population. He adjusts the feed supply to the number of animals, and the number of animals to the amount of feed. He tries to raise enough feed to care for his livestock. If an abundant harvest is had, the animals are fed better and their numbers are increased. Following a poor harvest, the feed has to cover the farm's population, and the individual animal's food supply is decreased. The farmer tries to avert liquidation so he buys feed, draws on reserves, and uses feed not ordinarily considered the best for animals.

We have similar problems with human numbers. It has been said that whether the population on a piece of land consists of people or animals, the growing pressure of numbers on land resources results in lower levels of living to the population. High birth rates and modern medicine adjust the human population upward. Famine, war, and disease adjust it downward. Migration usually balances or redistributes existing populations.

Population Pressures on Food Supplies

There is continual pressure of population on the food supply in the United States, in Europe, and in Asia, although the pressures are not alike. In the United States more than one-fourth of our diet comes from expensive, high quality animal foods (meat, milk, eggs). Diets in Asia contain three per cent of animal foods. Europe has an intermediate position, with about 15 per cent of the diet from animal products. In the United States the pressure is for high quality food diets. In certain other areas, the pressure is for sufficient food to satisfy hunger.

Adjustments

Migration, war, famine, and diseases have adjusted our populations to limited food supplies. These forces operate when those that adjust our food supplies upward have been employed to the maximum and have failed.

The world production of food involves huge investments of capital (land and equipment) and labor. The amount of land in cultivation is reasonably stable.   The equipment used is more variable. Even labor in the world is reasonably constant.   Although the aggregate of the amount of capital and labor used in world food production is somewhat regular, there is a wide range in the manner in which they are combined.   In the United States, labor is scarce, relative to land, so equipment is a large proportion of the capital investment.   In Asia, land is scarce, labor plentiful, and machinery represents a small proportion of the capital investment.   In Asia, little change has occurred in the relative importance of land, labor, and equipment.   In the United States, a revolution has taken place in the mechanization of agriculture for food production.

Available Farm Land

Our earth divided by its population yields about 60 acres per person.   Since $3/4$ is covered with water, there remains about 15 acres of land for each man.   Most of this land will not produce enough food to maintain us.   There is about one acre of crop land per person. The really productive areas of the earth actually amount to 0.2 acre for each mouth to be fed.   The reason why such a small portion of the earth's surface is productive is that only about seven per cent of earth has the environmental factors (adequate sunlight, favorable temperatures, favorable topography, adequate and reliable rainfall, fertile soil) satisfactory for the production of food.   Few areas are blessed by having all the factors, necessary for crop production, in the proper combinations.   There are three large areas.   Although these areas are small in proportion to the earth's surface, they support most of us.   These large areas are southeastern Asia, central North America and Western Europe (north of the Alps).   Europe is half the size of North America but has 50 per cent more land capable and adapted to food production.   In yield per acre, care of soil and number of people supported per acre, European agriculture outranks the United States in all phases, other than production per man.

Location of Populated Centers

Like food production, the great centers of population are located in limited areas.   They are in or adjacent to the highly productive areas where food is produced.   A map of the world's food production areas is a good map of where the world's population resides.

This relation of population to food supply is true for all forms of life.   The earth's food production is generally located at low altitudes near large bodies of water.   Most men and animals live at low altitudes near large bodies of water; most fish live in shallow water near land.   It is important to remember that unused land is not an index of how much the population can develop; most unused land will not sustain a population.

Varying Farming Systems

The productive areas of the earth have different positions in the supply of food.   Southeastern Asia produces rice and feeds little to livestock.   Exports are not important, and the area is somewhat self-sufficient.   Europe is a grain producer; some is used to feed livestock, the remainder used for human consumption.   About half of the European grain and potato crop goes to livestock.   The largest portion of the United States grain crop goes to livestock.

Challenge of High Quality Diet

It should be remembered that man has had a higher standard of living, lived longer, and has been most productive when he has had high quality foods.   One challenge in the United States is to continue to improve the quality of its food supply.   At present, few people in the United States purchase grains in their native state.   We buy them in products.   While it takes about five pounds of grain to return a pound of lean pork, and ten for a pound of beef, it appears to be a choice practice, nutritionally, for man where possible.

Good Land Already Settled

Most of our good agricultural land on earth has been settled. Increased food supplies will come probably by more intensive use of our good land than from the expansion of agriculture to our poor land.   About one per cent of the earth's surface is irrigated, either naturally or artificially, but this area supplies between one-third and one-half of the earth's population with food.

Impact of Technology

Occasionally a phenomenal change takes place in agriculture with spectacular results.   In the three centuries that the potato has grown in Europe, the potato helped provide the increased food needs as the population increased fivefold.   Hybrid corn expanded the yield per acre of corn in the United States by about 15 per cent. Such spectacular increases in food production may be only temporary reliefs from the pressure on our food supplies by our populations. One substantial change in food production has been the substitution of the tractor and auto for the horse and buggy. The land necessary for maintenance of work animals is used for food production. This change in the United States contributed more to our food supply than hybrid corn. The use of chemical rather than natural fibers could release even more land. Now atomic energy promises to make a contribution greater than even the above.

Food Production During Disasters

War causes changes in the production of crops. Crops production in a war area declines. Other areas increase crop production by intensive use of land. In the United States, the large livestock populations give us flexibility in our food supplies. Asia, with little or no pasture lands, is already near a maximum intensity with cropping systems. Changing to more productive crops is more effective in increasing our food supply than attempting to increase production of a crop. This shift to intensive agriculture produces more food per acre, but not necessarily more food per worker.

Return of Food for Labor

Relative to food production per acre, field crops average high, livestock low in returns of food for labor. Vegetables occupy an intermediate position. Potatoes, rice, and corn produce almost twice as much food per acre as wheat, while rye produces one-half as much.

Tomatoes, peas, lettuce, lima beans, and asparagus yield one-fifth to one-third that of wheat. Beef and sheep yield only about $1/25$ as much as wheat, and are the lowest yielding food producers. But, they may be grown where other crops may grow poorly or land use is better with grazing rather than cropping.

Vegetables and livestock require that we work ten times as long as we need to for field crops per unit of food produced. We have to work as long for a unit of food from livestock as for vegetables, to obtain $1/25$ as much food as could be obtained from wheat. Highest returns from meat and animals per man hour are obtained from pork, lowest form beef and sheep. It takes 5–10 pounds of feed to produce a pound of meat. When food is scarce, we do not feed animals, we eat them and their feed. Countries with large livestock populations seldom suffer from lack of food. Our livestock refine, condense, and store bulky inexpensive foods for us into smaller quantities of concentrated, expensive foods.

Animals Useful

Livestock serve as a temporary storage place for flesh foods for us. Hogs, cattle, poultry, and sheep are relatively inefficient methods for storing our foods, however. Continued feeding of hogs older than nine months of age is an expensive way to store our food. We obtain best meat yield from chickens in the broiler stage of growth.

Livestock also refine inedible crops into food fit for man. Inedible grasses, cornstalks, hay, etc., are changed into nutritious but expensive foods by animals (beef, milk) for us. The animals also gather and use food otherwise wasted in the fields after harvests, thereby adding to the food of man. Mechanical corn and grain harvesting machines leave and waste food in the field. Animals seek these grains out, patiently, one grain at a time.

Livestock also serve as a condenser of food, condensing grains into nutritious, high quality animal flesh (meat protein).

Buffer Against Famine

In North America, grain fed to livestock is our major buffer against human hunger. In Europe, they use grain and potatoes. In Asia, hunger has no real foe or buffer.

An example of the amount of food made available by shifting livestock feed to human consumption was shown in Germany in World War II with potatoes. They diverted 15 million tons of potatoes from the feed bins to their tables. These potatoes had a food value equal to about 100 million bushels of grain. The amount of wheat shipped by the United States to the whole of Europe in the year ending June 1946, following the war, totaled 270 million bushels. By consuming potatoes directly, Germany increased her annual food supply by 75 lbs. per capita. The grain and potatoes taken away from livestock together amounted to a food supply of 180 lbs. for each person. Furthermore, the food was at hand, and some at least ate the animals. Potatoes are an excellent "famine fighter." In the United States grain (fed to livestock) is our "famine fighter."

It has taken man most of his civilized life to develop methods of producing foods. Adjustments must be worked out to equate food supplies and population needs, otherwise wars, disease and famines will perform the adjustment almost automatically. Food is man's oldest problem. To predict an early or easy solution to the problem would be contrary to fact and history.

Famines have occurred all through history. Scientific agriculture has done much to prevent starvation on regional and national scales. Well-balanced, concerted organization of the elements of land, labor, capital, and management promises even more. The ability to increase the yield of the soil is a striking local success. Yet, it appears inadequate when faced with the problem of feeding the ever increasing human population on earth.

Malthus' Failure

At the end of the 18th century, Thomas R. Malthus of England observed the human race between food supply and numbers, and developed the principle which is known as the Malthusian Theory. In general terms the law states that man tends to multiply more rapidly than his food supply. North America provides an illustration.

When the New World opened, food production increased rapidly, and the population increased explosively. Huge immigrations and increased birth rates resulted in a situation from 1800 to 1900 in which the population increased tenfold. The population along the eastern seaboard soon felt the pressure of numbers. There was a movement westward across the fertile plains. Even with the production of food in new areas, by 1900 the United States food exports began to decline. In the 1920's the United States was an importer of food, eating more than was produced locally. In accordance with Malthus's theory, the population should have multiplied up to the food supply, and it did.

But Malthus did not predict correctly that the United States, for example, would have a food surplus and change from an agricultural to an industrial nation.

He failed in predicting the evolution that occurred in food production and the ramifications that this could have. Malthus's theory appears to be inadequate to be applied to human beings because we have the ability to explore natural phenomena and apply our findings to the improvement of our lot in the world. However, in tradition oriented countries where new technology is not readily applied, conditions postulated by Malthus continue to prevail.

Standard of Living

The term "standard of living" has many meanings to different people. Our standard of living is a function of our resources, our use of them, and our numbers.

Because natural resources are measurable, little change can occur in this regard. Our technical use of these resources, however, appears immeasurable. It is obvious too that there is a level of sustenance for life required by a man before he experiences good health and demonstrates those qualities we recognize as human. This is the power of good food. This is the problem which has not been resolved by present technology.

Significance of Population Densities

According to current population reports, Norway has about 30 people per square mile, England about 500, Belgium about 700, and the state of Missouri about 20 per square mile, and the people in these areas are all on about the same level of well-being. All are infinitely better off than the inhabitants of the continent of North America prior to the discovery of Columbus. Overpopulation is not solely a matter of the man to area ratio or the standing room available, but a situation at a given time and in a given area during which the number of people is too large in proportion to the technological application of the available resources. Whenever the number of people increases beyond an optimum point, various penalties in well-being arise; social stress becomes one of the manifestations (Cook 1959).

Intermittent Starvation and Population Explosion

Starving people have a diminished sex drive. When their strength is revived with adequate food, there appears to be a substantial rise in this interest. In areas of the world where food supplies are very limited except during harvest times, when adequate food supplies become temporarily available, there may be some explanation for tremendous populations which develop, a possible factor in India or China (Huntington 1945).

An inadequate diet even if of high quality not only weakens the majority of mental powers but may lead to an unfavorable reaction when food is once more abundant (Keys *et al.* 1950). The crux of the matter is that the degree, the frequency, and the intensity of human starvation increases with increasing populations, and the world for the most part contains people who are hungry and who are unable to help themselves escape from the downward cycle. The cultural systems of impoverished areas have been unable to find acceptable solutions to starvation, and the inherent slowness with which cultural changes occur holds no promise of being able to solve the problems facing the world's people.

ATTACK ON STARVATION

The existing extremes in food supplies per person per year and the countries in which these maxima and minima occur were presented in Table 35, p. 206. At first glance the conclusion which might be reached is that all that is needed is to have better food distribution. Let us look into this matter of the international movement of selected foods.

International Trade

There are great variations of food production from one area to another (see Table 31, p. 150).

Could international trade eventually provide adequate food for everyone? The answer is—not by itself. World trade in food stuffs in the 1950's was about two per cent below the 1930 levels (Table 51). At the present time, less than ten per cent of the cereals and meat enter international trade. About 30 per cent of the sugar and vegetable oils produced in the world enter international trade.

In general it is the consensus that people over the world do and must live mainly on home produced food. Each continent in general must be basically self-sufficient in food production (United Nations 1959).

Food surplus areas of North America and Oceania could increase food production measurably, but no economic stimulus is available. Increasing the international movement of food supplies not only requires more food to be produced in surplus areas but the ability of poorer countries to import food and pay for the food with a currency which is acceptable to the exporting nations.

It is reported that there is a wide difference between the nutritional need of people and demand for food as measured by the price of foods in the world markets. The production of more food in the well-developed countries is limited by an effective economic demand. More production would not necessarily yield greater income. In Table 51 it is seen that Europe is a main food importer and not Africa and Asia. Europe through its industrial productivity can gain the income to pay for the food which is imported, while Asia and Africa have not exploited resources to the degree which would allow massive food imports in general. A substantial growth in world

TABLE 51

SUMMARY OF INTERREGIONAL TRADE IN SELECTED IMPORTANT FOODSTUFFS, 1949–51[1]

| Region | Net Exports (+) or Imports (−) | | | |
	Cereals[4]	Sugar	Major Vegetable Oils[5]	Meat[6]
	(Million Metric Tons)			
North America[2]	+20.9	+2.5	−0.3	−0.04
South America[2]	+2.3	+0.2	+0.4	+0.5
Oceania	+3.6	+0.4	+0.1	+0.6
Africa	−0.2	+0.1	+1.1	−0.01
Asia	−6.2	−0.4	+1.2	−0.05
U.S.S.R.	+1.7	−0.3	−	−
Europe[3]	−21.0	−2.3	−2.5	−1.0

[1] From P.E.P. (1955).
[2] Central America is included here in North America.
[3] Excluding U.S.S.R.
[4] Wheat, rye, barley, oats, maize, millet, sorghum, and rice.
[5] Groundnut, copra, palm, palm kernel, soya bean, cotton seed, rape seed, sesame seed, sunflower seed, linseed, olive, and castor. Figures give oil equivalent of total production.
[6] Total trade in meat, including fresh, chilled, frozen, prepared, and canned; also poultry and offal.

trade in agricultural food products must await the rise in the purchasing power of underdeveloped nations, and this in turn depends on the capacity of these nations for industrial development. The fact that most of the underdeveloped countries requiring more food cannot afford to buy the food makes it improbable that movement of surpluses from one area to another in the normal course of international trade could be an important factor in alleviating the food supply shortages of various parts of the world.

The United Nations reports that world food production is slightly exceeding the expectations. Present indications are that world agricultural production will continue to increase at approximately the same rate as it has in the past. The volume of world trade in agricultural products reported has seen a slight upward movement.

Nearly half of the increase in the volume of world trade is accounted for by grains and more than 80 per cent by grains, cotton, and coffee.

The United Nations reports that since the 1940's the average unit value of agricultural products in world trade has declined; the eight per cent increase in the volume of trade brought an increase of only four per cent in total value. It is to be noted, however, that the rate of growth of the world's food stocks has slowed considerably since 1954.

Much could be done to increase the effectiveness of the world's food which is distributed, including:

(1) Reducing losses during production of food by plant pests and diseases; (2) reducing losses through infestation of stored products by insects, fungi, and rodents; (3) improved distribution and utilization by advances in food preservation methods; (4) increasing the yield of the soil from areas already under cultivation; and (5) developing new production areas (Joslyn and Olcott 1959).

Improved Productivity

An example of some of the present day dilemmas is seen in agricultural production systems in India. It has approximately one-fourth of the total cattle population in the world. India has the largest cattle density of any area of similar size in the world, and three times the cattle population that occurs in the United States. Yet, less than one-fourth of the population in India will eat meat at all; beef is consumed by some Moslems and not by Hindus. The cattle add a little to the diets available to the Indian people as milk. The use of these animals in work tasks is inefficient because of the diseased and malnourished condition of the animals. Although the dung collected from the animals is needed in replenishing soil nutrients, the dung is used for fuel or for other household uses. Cattle overrun the land and prevent the growth and use of other vegetation essential to the well-being of the population. It has been calculated that these cattle consume three times as many calories as are consumed by the Indian human population. The overgrazing which animals inflict upon the land worsens soil stability, which is further degraded by wind and water erosion.

Efficiency of livestock production is low in underdeveloped countries. In the United States and Europe improved breeds of animals and improved feeding methods have markedly increased the efficiency of conversion of feed to flesh. For example, the time to raise a broiler to three pounds in body weight has been cut from 14 weeks to 9 weeks and feed consumption from 12 lbs. to 8 lbs. Similar improvements in animal production have been recorded with swine; to reach market weight in 1910 required about 150 days whereas at present it requires a little over two months. The egg laying capacity of hens can be over 300 eggs per year per hen.

The method of use of food produced from the land is also important. If a bushel of grain is consumed it might yield enough food for 23 people for one day. Fed to a cow and converted into milk it may yield the requirement for five persons in energy and twelve persons in protein. Fed to a pig, it may yield the energy for seven persons and proteins for five. In the form of eggs it would supply the energy for two people and the protein for eight per day.

MacQillivray (1953) has stressed the importance of considering food production from the standpoint of the amount of nutrients yielded per acre instead of pounds of crop per acre. On this basis, maximum food supplies could be assured by (1) selecting crops or animals that can produce the greatest amount of nutrients per acre; (2) selecting crops or animals that will mature in a shorter growing season; (3) growing plants where possible for human consumption rather than for livestock feed. It is important that the most functional concepts fully impregnate future plans.

There are a number of factors which are interrelated when considering actual changes in food production. Some of the factors are under control by humans and others are not. It was stated earlier that four-fifths of the agricultural land suitable for food production is already under cultivation. What can be done with the remaining uncultivated one-fifth of the available land? The United Nations (1959) reports that one-third of this land lies in Asia, one-fourth in North and Central America largely in Canada and Brazil, and one-fourth in Africa and little elsewhere. It is pointed out clearly that the land which can be cultivated now requires special exertion for its productive uses.

If all the tillable land on earth could be momentarily made available for the production of food crops, with the average yields of the present day, food production could be increased to the point where diets of present undernourished world populations could be raised to adequate levels. Yields of food from land vary *widely* in the different countries. The highest yielding are found in Northwestern Europe and the lowest in the underdeveloped countries of Asia and Africa (see Table 31, p. 150).

If the food production in the less developed countries could be raised to yield that of the higher yielding countries, substantial changes in food harvests could be achieved. India's total output could be quadrupled and India's food problem could be (at least temporarily) solved. Few would dissent from the conclusion that there could, in theory, be adequate provision for a larger population than exists today. Two particular aspects of increasing yields from tillable land are noteworthy.

First, by using better seed and better stock a greater food production can be achieved. Second, there are numerous technical advances which can be made under already available agricultural technology. This would include more widespread and efficient use of fertilizer, better systems of cultivation and irrigation and mechanization. Important problems at present are: (1) fertilizers must be imported into countries needing it the most; (2) improving cultivation practices include changing hallowed traditions of the past; (3) irrigation and drainage of land to improve its agricultural production which involve large capital resources now mostly lacking in underdeveloped countries; and (4) mechanization to obtain large gains in food production otherwise consumed by work animals. Another necessity is the control of the immense losses due to soil erosion, which can be accomplished if sufficient care is given. Such care is largely absent in many areas of the world.

The production of grain has been found to vary by a factor of two, depending on the degree of agricultural technology applied. This usually implies large scale farming rather than small area cultivation. The applications of labor in food production and consolidation of land into economic units for large scale farming could increase the yield of food. Hovever, there are social and cultural problems are not easily resolved, which impede progress at present.

Further, one of the important methods of increasing the amount of food available is to use more adequately that which is produced. There must be a reduction in the waste which currently exists. There is tremendous toll by crop pests and plant diseases at all stages. There is a large loss of food, sometimes estimated to be one-half of the food production, in storage, distribution, handling, and transportation. Insecticides have been developed which are functional and adequate yet so far have had very little influence in areas where they are capable of making immense changes. The damage done by rodents in stored grain in undeveloped areas is an example of a situation that could be controlled almost immediately.

It is to be recognized that in underdeveloped areas of the world peasant cultivation of the land is widespread, and the majority of persons in fact who fall into this catagory are conservative, traditional, and want social stability. Resistance to change is one of the important problems which must be confronted in attempting to increase food production.

Traditional methods which yield below subsistence farming and living are not compatible with the needs and desires of these people for a higher standard of living. Conservatism becomes, according to P.E.P. (1955), "a lethal factor once a population starts to increase substantially. A change to the new in the cultivation of crops and in much else besides can be brought about by a triple agency of education, leadership and demonstration, or, in contrast, by the spur and whip of control. Change by persuasion is slow. Change under compulsion and control may be swift though unstable. Between the two lies the crux of the present world dilemma."

Reports indicate a desperate shortage of scientific and technological manpower and this is remedied only over a large number of years. The rate at which technically qualified people become available determine to a large degree the rate of agricultural development in an underdeveloped area. The supply of experts from the more developed countries to these areas can temporarily achieve some growth. However, an important obstacle exists, even when expert advice is available, in persuading farmers to take advantage of the technology which is available.

There is hope that the ever increasing agricultural technology will somehow be able to achieve a balance between the capacity of the soils of the world and the food needs of people. Hertzler (1955) has written that there is every reason to believe that it will be able to increase the world's food supply greatly.

Yet all carefully reckoned estimates recognize that there are many variables and unknown factors involved. If it were solely a matter of agricultural food technology, then we might assume that all other factors would be neutral; it would be possible to make some predictions with confidence relative to being able to produce the food supplies required by the people of the earth. But the factors which are required to remain neutral are not. The earth's surface is relatively fixed and the agricultural land that is available is limited both in quality and quantity.

Attempts to extend agriculture at the present time will be toward poorer land. The activities required to bring poorer land into production will be *more* expensive than farming the land already under cultivation. Unfortunately the people on earth who have the greatest need are least able to carry out the steps which are required. It should be noted that technology can modify our ideas of "poor" land, i.e., drained swamps, and irrigated deserts.

Impact of Technology on Economics of Food Production

What has technology contributed to the economics of food production? An answer is available from United States data developed by Ruttan and Stout (1957). The relative contribution of land, labor, capital, and operating expenses per $100.00 of products produced on a farm is shown in Table 52.

TABLE 52

ECONOMIC FACTORS IN UNITED STATES FOOD PRODUCTION, 1925–1957[1]

| Factor | Relative Contribution of Factor (Value in U. S. Dollars) | | |
	Year 1925–1928	Year 1951–1957	Per Cent Change[2]
Land	19	12	−37
Labor	32	25	−22
Capital (buildings, equipment, etc.)	18	22	+22
Operating expenses (fertilizer, seed, pesticides, gasoline, etc.)	31	41	+32
Total	100	100	

[1] From Ruttan and Stout (1957).
[2] Percentage changes do not completely cancel each other due to the variations in the magnitude of the base levels from which the per cent change is calculated.

We see that, contrary to what Malthus predicted, land's relative economic contribution has decreased in the United States over a 32 year period by about 37 per cent. Technology has had two notable effects by (1) the invention of some needed inputs (i.e., high analysis synthetic nitrogen fertilizer vs. mined nitrate of soda), and (2) by cost-reducing or output-increasing improvements in existing inputs (i.e., hybrid corn vs. open pollinated corn).

In Table 52, while the relative contribution of land has decreased by some 37 per cent, the operating expenses have increased by about 32 per cent, the capital requirement has increased by some 22 per cent, and the labor requirement has decreased by an estimated 22 per cent, relative to their earlier levels.

From this information, we can estimate what will be required to use poorer land for food production, as discussed earlier. Assume we use land which is one-third less productive than the average presently being used. What adjustment will be required in the factors shown in Table 52? Such an analysis is shown in Table 53.

TABLE 53

ESTIMATE OF THE INFLUENCE OF USING ONE-THIRD LESS PRODUCTIVE LAND ON ECONOMIC FACTORS IMPORTANT IN FOOD PRODUCTION AS PERMITTED BY TECHNOLOGICAL CHANGES IN THE UNITED STATES[1]

Factor	Contribution of Factors (Value in U. S. Dollars)		Per Cent Change[2]
	Good Land	1/3 Poorer Land	
Land	12	8	−33
Labor	25	25	0
Capital	22	22	0
Operating expenses	41	45	+10
Total	100	100	

[1] From Ruttan (1961).
[2] See footnote, Table 52.

Under Malthusian conditions, when an economy shifts to using poorer land, the land claims a larger share of the total product. When the shift is the result of technological changes which reduce the costs of products or raise the productivity of the formerly "poor" land, this increases the supply of land and it therefore claims a smaller share of the total product. Except for Western Europe, North America, and Oceania, Malthusian conditions prevail.

It is seen from Table 53 that, using the agricultural technology available, the utilization of one-third less productive land for the most part increases the operating expenses (fertilizer, etc.) by only ten per cent.

Land becomes a less important factor with increasing technology which is a hopeful situation. Labor requirements also become less restrictive. But, the capital resources needed to equip, operate, and succesfully farm such lands are large. This is the serious limiting factor in the world. Where land and labor are abundant, capital resources are currently in short supply. This is the world dilemma relative to food production for all.

It is very easy for a capital rich nation to take advantage of available technology by shifting capital. In a less wealthy country, Malthusian conditions remain in force.

Plight of Underdeveloped Countries

Considering the above, what can be done in nations who must use more of their less productive land? First, they can convert resources that are available into capital. This new capital could then be used to take advantage of present technologies which could be brought to bear on the land available; for example, the conversion of iron ore into capital, which is then applied to making farm land more productive.

Second, these nations can encourage foreign investments of capital, or gifts from capital rich countries (trade and/or aid). This too could permit a nation to gain the technology it requires, providing the aid were directed toward this end.

Labor, when plentiful, has been employed as a resource. Cheap labor can be exploited, and its products converted into capital. This is being done and has been done in Eastern Europe and China in recent years. But such methods hardly belong to this age on earth.

Contribution of Technology

A third step is also available, one which could solve the food problems in underdeveloped countries. This step involves putting into practice a new technology. Significant improvements could allow increased food production without the large capital investments currently demanded for such purposes. Such technology already appears to be available.

Efforts to speed the rate of technological change deserve major emphasis in development programs of all nations. A basic ingredient in this process is an educated citizenry. A nation needs educated people to take advantage of technologies that are already available. Education is one process through which it is possible to speed the rate of technological change in a nation, and educational processes work to advantage both in food production and food consumption.

Barriers Which Must be Penetrated

There are two major barriers at the present time which restrict attempts to greatly expand food supplies in the world. There are cultural barriers and technological barriers which must be penetrated.

An example of cultural barriers is found in India, for example, where most people lack adequate supplies of animal protein in diets while cattle continue to consume the vegetation of the earth at the expense of the human inhabitants of that nation. Another example is found in the expanding human population on earth without concurrent expansion in the ability to produce food. Insufficient good food exists to nourish even those people already alive. The cultural barrier includes population control.

The technological barrier is often described in terms of our apparent inability to yield more good food for people to eat. The situation indeed would be hopeless if present means of producing good food were efficient. But, this is not the case. The possibilities can be vividly emphasized by the circumstances that we find ourselves in at present:

(1) Less than ten per cent of the earth's land surface is used for food production.

(2) About one-tenth to one-half of one per cent of the sun's radiation received at the earth's surface is fixed as organic material.

(3) Taking the earth's suface as a whole, for each million calories of energy received from the sun only one calorie is converted into human food (Russell 1954).

(4) About half of the food material ultimately produced reaches the human stomachs of the world.

In the past, population pressures forced man to improve on his food supplies. It now appears that these same old pressures are still operative and probably will have the same effects on modern man as they did on his ancestors. As in the past, a number of avenues are open.

The technological barriers have been penetrated. The cultural barriers are under surveillance. There is cautious optimism.

It is for these reasons that a successful attack can now be launched against human starvation.

Bibliography

ADELSON, S. F., *et al.* 1959. Youth learns about food. U. S. Dept Agr. Yearbook of Agriculture, pp. 647–753.

ALBANESE, A. A. 1950. Protein and Amino Acid Requirements of Mammals. Academic Press, New York.

ALBERTY, R. A. 1959. Modern theory of enzyme action. Rev. Mod. Physics *31*, No. 1, 177–185.

ALLEN, D. L. 1954. Our Wildlife Legacy. Funk and Wagnalls, New York.

ALLEN, D. L. 1961. Personal Communication. Population growths in isolated areas. West Lafayette, Ind.

ALLEN, M. B., and ARNON, D. L. 1955. Studies on the nitrogen fixing blue green algae. Plant Physl. *26*, 366–372.

ANDERSON, A. W. 1959. Fish and the fishing industry. Food. U. S. Dept. Agr. Yearbook of Agriculture, pp. 353–370.

ANDREWS, J. S. 1953. Nutritional aspects of cereal proteins. Bakers Digest *27*, 30–33.

ANON. 1948. Yeasts in feeding. Symposium Proc., R. and D. Associates Food and Container Institute Inc. November 8–10. Milwaukee, Wis.

ANON. 1958. Recommended Dietary Allowances. Pub. *302*. National Academy of Sciences-National Research Council, Washington, D. C.

ANON. 1960. Agricultural Outlook. Dept. of Agricultural Economics, Purdue University, Lafayette, Ind.

ANON. 1960. Annual report. World Health Organization, Geneva, Switzerland.

BAILEY, S. F. 1951. Handbook of Agricultural Pest Control. Industrial Publ., New York.

BAXTER, L. D. 1948. The Citrus Industry. Univ. of California Press, Berkeley, Calif.

BEAR, F. E. 1953. Soils and Fertilizer. Fourth Ed. John Wiley and Sons, New York.

BENEDICT, F. G. 1919. Human Vitality and Efficiency under Prolonged Restricted Diet. Carnegie Institute, Washington, D. C.

BLANCK, F. C. 1955. Handbook of Food and Agriculture. Reinhold Publ. Co., New York.

BLAXTER, K. L. 1961. Efficiency of food conversion by different classes of livestock in relation to food production. Federation Proc. *20*, No. 1, Part III, Suppl. No. 7, 263–274.

BONNER, J. 1961. The World's Increasing Population. Federation Proc. *20*, No. 1, Part III, Suppl. No. 7, 369–372.

BONNER, J., and GALSTON, A. W. 1952. Principles of Plant Physiology. W. Freeman and Co., San Francisco, Calif.

BOGGS, M. M., and RASMUSSEN, C. L. 1959. Modern Food Procesing. Food. U. S. Dept. Agr. Yearbook of Agriculture, pp. 418–433.

BOSWELL, V. R. 1959. What makes fruit and vegetables good? Food. U. S. Dept. Agr. Yearbook of Agriculture, pp. 371–377.

BRIGGS, G. M. 1959. Unidentified substances. Food. U. S. Dept. Agr. Yearbook of Agriculture, pp. 162–167.

BRIGGS, H. M. 1949. Modern Breed of Livestock. Macmillan and Co., New York.

BROCK, J. F. 1961. Dietary Proteins in Relation to Man's Health. Federation Proc. 20, No. 1, Part III, Suppl. No. 7, 61–65.

BRONTE-STEWART, R. 1961. Lipids and atherosclerosis. Federation Proc. 20, No. 1, Part III, Suppl. No. 7, 127–134.

BURK, M. C. 1959. Food trends, pounds and percentages. Food. U. S. Dept. Agr. Yearbook of Agriculture, pp. 591–599.

BURLEW, J. S. 1953. Algae Culture—From Laboratory to Pilot Plant. Carnegie Inst. of Washington. Publ. 600. Washington, D. C.

BURNEY, L. E. 1959. The public health service. Food. U. S. Dept. Agr. Yearbook of Agriculture, pp. 452–460.

BUTTNER, J. L. 1910. A Flashless Diet. F. A. Stokes. New York.

CANDAU, M. G. 1961. Programs of the World Health Organization and plans for the future. Federation Proc. 20, No. 1, Part III, Suppl. No. 7, 403–408.

CANNON, P. R. 1945. The importance of proteins in relation to infection. J. Am. Med. Assoc. 128, 360–363.

CHILDE, V. G. 1946. Man Makes Himself. Watts and Company, London, England.

CHRISTIAN, J. J. 1950. The adrenopituitary system of and population cycles in mammals. J. Mammalogy 31, 247–259.

CLARK, J. G. D. 1947. Forest clearance and prehistoric farming. Econ. Hist. Rev. 17, 45–51.

CLARK, J. G. D. 1948. The development of fishing in prehistoric Europe. Antiquaries J. 28, 45–85.

CLARK, H. E., MERTZ, E. T., KWONG, E. H., HOWE, J. M., and DeLONG, D. C. 1957. Amino acid requirements of men and women. J. Nutrition 62, No. 1, 71–82.

COMBS, G. F. 1961. Quality and quantity of final product—poultry. Federation Proc. 20, No. 1, Part III, Suppl. No. 7, 306–312.

COOK, R. C. 1958. Population inflation shrinks the earth. Population Bull. 14, No. 4, 62–63.

COOK, R. C. 1959. World food supply. Population Bull. 15, No. 1, 1–15.

COOK, R. C. 1959. World population review. Population Bull. 15, No. 2, 17–35.

COONS, C. M. 1959. Fats and fatty acids. Food. U. S. Dept. Agr. Yearbook of Agriculture, pp. 74–87.

CUTHBERTSON, D. P. 1961. New activities and goals for the Internation Union of Nutritional Sciences. Federation Proc. 20, No. 1, Part III, Suppl. No. 7, 415–417.

DACK, G. M. 1956. Food Poisoning. Univ. Chicago Press, Chicago, Ill.

DAVENPORT, C. B. 1957. The dietaries of primitive peoples. Am. Anthropol. 47, 60–82.

DAVIS, H. P. 1959. Food: sharing our bounty. Food. U. S. Dept. Agr. Yearbook of Agriculture, pp. 681–690.

DEEVEY, E. S. 1960. The hare and the haruspex. American Scientist 48, 415–431.

DEN HARTOG, C. 1961. Public health indices of nutritional status of man. Federation Proc. 20, No. 1, Part III, Suppl. No. 7, 19–26.

DESROSIER, N. W. 1959. A challenge for the food industry. Food Processing 20, No. 2, 17–19.

DESROSIER, N. W. 1959. The Technology of Food Preservation. The Avi Publishing Co., Inc., Westport, Conn.

DESROSIER, N. W. 1959. Food Irradiation Research in Europe and the United States. OEEC-EPA. 2 Rue Andre Pascal, Paris, France.

DESROSIER, N. W., and ROSENSTOCK, H. M. 1960. Radiation Technology in Food, Agriculture, and Biology. The Avi Publishing Co., Westport, Conn.

DODDS, M. L. 1959. Vitamin C. Food. U. S. Dept. Agr. Yearbook of Agriculture, pp. 150–161.

DUNCAN, G. G. 1953. Diseases of Metabolism. W. B. Saunders Co., Philadelphia, Pa.

FISCHER, K. H., and SWIFT, R. W. 1959. Calories and body weight. Food. U. S. Dept. Agr. Yearbook of Agriculture, pp. 101–111.

FOX, I. K. 1961. Water resources of the world. Federation Proc. 20, No. 1, Part III, Suppl. No. 7, 378–380.

FRANKFORT, H. 1951. The Birth of Civilization in the Near East. Indiana University Press, Bloomington, Ind.

FRAZER, A. C. 1961. Role of lipids in normal metabolism. Federation Proc. 20, No. 1, Part III, Suppl. No. 7, 146–151.

FRIEND, B., and CLARK, F. 1959. Changes in sources of nutrients. U. S. Dept. Agr. Yearbook of Agriculture, pp. 600–609.

FURK, D. M. 1950. Shellfish Poisoning. Fisheries Research Board of Canada Rept. 82.

GARDNER, V. R., et al. 1952. Fundamentals of Fruit Production. McGraw-Hill Book Co., New York.

GAUME, J. G. 1958. Nutrition in space operations. Food Technol. 12, 433–435.

GOLDSMITH, G. A. 1959. Vitamins of the B complex. Food. U. S. Dept. Agr. Yearbook of Agriculture, pp. 139–149.

GOUNELLE, H. 1961. Major human nutrition problems today. Federation Proc. 20, No. 1, Part III, Suppl. No. 7, 389–393.

GRAS, N. S. B. 1946. A History of Agriculture. F. S. Crofts, New York.

GRAY, L. F. 1959. Factors that affect the nutrients in plants. U. S. Dept. Agr. Yearbook of Agriculture, pp. 389–395.

HANRAHAN, J. S., and BUSHNELL, D. 1960. Space Biology. Basic Books, Inc., New York.

HARPER, A. E. 1959. Carbohydrates. U. S. Dept. Agr. Yearbook of Agriculture, pp. 88–100.

HARRAR, J. G. 1961. Socio-economic factors that limit needed food production and consumption. Federation Proc. 20, No. 1, Part III, Suppl. No. 7, 381–384.

HATHAWAY, M. 1959. Trends in heights and weights. U. S. Dept. Agr. Yearbook of Agriculture, pp. 181–185.

HATHAWAY, M. L., and LEVERTON, R. M. 1959. Calcium and phosphorus. U. S. Dept. Agr. Yearbook of Agriculture, pp. 112–119.

HEINZ, H. J. 1961. A five point program for industry's role in improving global nutrition. Federation Proc. 20, No. 1, Part III, Suppl. No. 7, 411–414.

HERTZLER, J. O. 1956. The Crisis in World Population. Lincoln University of Nebraska Press, Lincoln, Neb.

HODGSON, R. E. 1959. Livestock production in transition. Food. U.S. Dept. Agr. Yearbook of Agriculture, pp. 330–339.
HOFFMAN, W. E. 1947. Insects as human food. Proc. Entomol. Soc. 42, 233–237.
HOOVER, S. R. 1959. Quality in animal products. Food. U. S. Dept. Agr. Yearbook of Agriculture, pp. 327–329.
HORWITZ, A. 1961. Food and protection of health. Federation Proc. 20, No. 1, Part III, Suppl. No. 7, 398–403.
HOWE, E. D. 1959. Fresh water from saline sources. In Natural Resources, edited by Huberty, M. R., and Flock, W. L., McGraw-Hill Book Co., New York.
HOWE, P. E. 1950. Foods of animal origin. J. Am. Med. Assoc. 143, 1337–1342.
HUBERTY, M. R., and FLOCK, W. L. 1959. Natural Resources. McGraw-Hill Book Co., New York.
HUNDLEY, J. M. 1959. Food: Statistics and health. Food. U. S. Dept. Agr. Yearbook of Agriculture, pp. 175–180.
HUNTINGTON, E. 1940. Principles of Economic Geography. John Wiley and Sons, New York.
HUNTINGTON, E. 1945. Mainsprings of Civilization. John Wiley and Sons, New York.
JACOBS, M. B. 1951. The Chemistry and Technology of Food Products. Interscience Publ. Inc., New York.
JENNY, H. 1941. Factors in Soil Formation. McGraw-Hill Book Co., New York.
JENNY, H. 1959. Soil as a natural resource. In Natural Resources, edited by Huberty, M. R., and Flock, W. L., McGraw-Hill Book Co., New York.
JENSEN, L. B. 1949. Meat and Meat Foods. Ronald Press Co., New York.
JENSEN, L. B. 1953. Man's Food. Garrard Press. Champaign, Ill.
JONES, C. F. 1941. Economic Geography. Macmillan Co., New York.
JOSLYN, M. A. 1948. Nutrient requirements of yeast. In Yeast in Feeding, Symposium, Proc. R. and D. Associates Food and Container Institute Inc. Milwaukee, Wis.
JOSLYN, M. A., and OLCOTT, H. S. 1959. Food consumption and resources. In Natural Resources, Edited by Huberty, M. R., and Flock, W. L., McGraw-Hill Book Co., New York.
KEYS, A. 1948. Nutrition in relation to the etiology and the courses of degenerative diseases, J. Am. Dietetic Assoc. 24, 281–285.
KEYS, A., BROZEK, J., HENSCHEL, A., MICKELSEN, O., and TAYLOR, H. L. 1950. The Biology of Human Starvation. Univ. Minn. Press, Minneapolis, Minn.
KING, C. G. 1961. Modern trends in the nutritive value of food supplies here and abroad. Natl. Canners Assoc. Information Letter 1813, 48–50.
LARRICK, G. P. 1959. The Pure Food Law. Food. U. S. Dept. Agr. Yearbook of Agriculture, pp. 444–451.
LEACH, J. G. 1940. Insect Transmission of Plant Diseases. McGraw-Hill Book Co., New York.
LEVERTON, R. M. 1959. Recommended Food Allowances. Food. U. S. Dept. Agr. Yearbook of Agriculture, pp. 620–630.
LENNARTSON, R. W. 1959. What food grades mean. Food. U. S. Dept. Agr. Yearbook of Agriculture, pp. 344–352.

Leverton, R. M. 1959. Amino acids. Food. U. S. Dept. Agr. Yearbook of Agriculture, pp. 64–73.

Leverton, R. M. 1959. Proteins. Food. U. S. Dept. Agr. Yearbook of Agriculture, pp. 57–63.

Leverton, R. M. 1959. Recommended Food Allowances. Food. U. S. Dept. Agr. Yearbook of Agriculture, pp. 227–230.

Lennartson, R. W. 1959. What food grades mean. Food. U. S. Dept. Agr. Yearbook of Agriculture, pp. 119–121.

Levine, V. E. 1941. The value of meat as an antiscorbutic. Am. J. Digestive Dis. 8, 454–463.

Libby, W. F. 1952. Radiocarbon dating. Science 114, 291–296.

Little, A. D. 1953. Pilot plant studies in the production of Chlorella. In Algae Culture, edited by Burlew, J. S. Carnegie Inst. of Washington. Publ. 600.

Little, A. D. 1958. Food Acceptance and Flavor Research. Reinhold Publ. Co., New York.

Lowenberg, M. E. 1959. Food needs: Between infancy and adolescence. Food. U. S. Dept. Agr. Yearbook of Agriculture, pp. 296–301.

MacGillivray, J. H. 1953. Vegetable Production. Blakiston Publ. Co., New York.

Macy, I. G. and Kelly, H. J. 1959. Food for Expectant and Nursing Mothers. Food. U. S. Dept. Agr. Yearbook of Agriculture, pp. 273–383.

Martin, H. 1953. Guide to the Chemicals Used in Crop Protection. Canada Dept. Agriculture, London, Ont.

Matchett, J. R. 1959. The development of new foods. Foods. U. S. Dept. Agr. Yearbook of Agriculture, pp. 434–440.

McCollum, E. B. and McCollum, E. V. 1959. Vitamins A, D, E, K. Food. U. S. Dept. Agr. Yearbook of Agriculture, pp. 130–138.

McGinnis, J. 1948. Utilization of yeast in chick and turkey diets. In Yeast in Feeding, Symposium Proc., R. and D. Associates Food and Container Institute Inc. Milwaukee, Wis.

McLean, B. B. 1959. Planning meals for the family. U. S. Dept. Agr. Yearbook of Agriculture, pp. 510–518.

Meyer, J. Phillips, J. N., and Graham, J. R. 1951. On the mass culture of algae. Plant Phys. 24, 539–542.

Meyer, K. F. 1967. Food technology around the world and its contribution, Natl. Canners Assoc. Information Letter 1813, 45–58.

Mickelsen, O. 1959. Water. Food. U. S. Dept. Agr. Yearbook of Agriculture, pp. 168–173.

Mitchell, H. H., and Block, R. J. 1946. Some relationships between amino acid contents of proteins and their nutritive values. J. Biol. Chem. 163,

Miller, A. R. 1959. To assure good, clean meat. Food. U. S. Dept. Agr. Yearbook of Agriculture, pp. 340–343. 599–620.

Mitchell, H. S. 1959. Food: Don't be fooled by fads. Food. U. S. Dept. Agr. Yearbook of Agriculture, pp. 660–671.

Mitchell, H. S. 1948. Evaluation of children in Europe following World War II. Personal communication. Amherst, Mass.

Monty, K. J., and McElroy, W. D. 1959. The trace elements. Food. U. S. Dept. Agr. Yearbook of Agriculture, pp. 122–129.

MORGAN, A. F., and ODLAND, L. M. 1959. The nutriture of people. U. S. Dept. Agr. Yearbook of Agriculture, pp. 186–224.

MOSIER, J. G. 1919. Soils and Crops. Rand McNally and Co., New York.

MURRAY, J., and BLAKE, E. 1959. What do we eat? Food. U. S. Dept. Agr. Yearbook of Agriculture, pp. 609–619.

NAIR, J. H. 1949. Mass taste panels. Food Technol. 3, 131–136.

NATIONAL ACADEMY OF SCIENCE-NATIONAL RESEARCH COUNCIL. 1950. The problem of heat injury to dietary protein. Natl. Research Council Reprint 131. Washington, D. C.

NATIONAL ACADEMY OF SCIENCES-NATIONAL RESEARCH COUNCIL. 1959. Evaluation of protein nutrition. Natl. Research Council Publ. 711. Washington, D. C.

ORR, J. B. 1943. Food and people. Pilot Press, London, England.

ORR, M. L., and WATT, B. K. 1957. Amino acid content of foods. Home Economics Research Rept. 4, U. S. Dept. Agr., Washington, D. C.

OSER, B. L. 1958. The food industry in a changing world. Food Technol. 12, 493–496.

OSER, B. L. 1961. Modern technology as related to safety in foods. Federation Proc. 20, No. 1, Part III, Suppl. No. 7, 224–230.

PASCHAL, G. 1954. Odors and the sense of smell. Airkem, Inc., New York.

PATE, M. 1961. The world's children and tomorrow. Federation Proc. 20, No. 1, Part III, Suppl. No. 7, 409–411.

PENTZER, W. T. 1959. Food marketing, quality and cost. Food. U. S. Dept. Agr. Yearbook of Agriculture, pp. 408–417.

PERYAM, D. 1958. Food preferences and food habits. Personal communication. QM. Food and Container Inst., Chicago, Ill.

PERYAM, D., et al. 1958. Food Preferences and Personality Evaluations. QM. Food and Container Inst., Chicago, Ill.

PETERSON, W. H. 1948. Vitamins and minerals of yeast. In Yeast and Feeding Symposium Proc., R. and D. Associates Food and Container Institute, Inc. Milwaukee, Wis.

PHILLIPS, R. W. 1959. Feeding 6,280 million. Food. U. S. Dept. Agr. Yearbook of Agriculture, pp. 671–680.

PHIPARD, E. F., and PAGE, L. 1959. A guide to eating. Food. U. S. Dept. Agr. Yearbook of Agriculture, pp. 267–271.

PRESCOTT, S. C., and DUNN, C. G. 1940. Industrial Microbiology. McGraw-Hill Book Co., New York.

POLITICAL AND ECONOMIC PLANNING. 1955. World Population and Resources. Essential Books Inc., Fairlawn, N. J.

REITZ, L. P., and BARMORE, M. A. 1959. The quality of cereal grains. Food. U. S. Dept. Agr. Yearbook of Agriculture, pp. 378–388.

RUSSELL, E. J. 1954. World population and World Food supplies. George Allen and Unwin, Ltd., London.

RUTTAN, V. W. 1958. Technological change and resource requirements in American agriculture. J. Agr. and Food Chem. 6, 652–656.

RUTTAN, V. W. 1960. Human resource problems in American agriculture. Address presented to Subcommittee on Agriculture, Committee for Economic Development, Dec., Washington, D. C.

RUTTAN, V. W. 1961. Economic factors important in agriculture. Influence of using less productive land on economics of food production. Personal communication, Lafayette, Ind.

RUTTAN, V. W., and STOUT, T. T. 1957. Regional patterns of technological change in American agriculture. J. Farm Econ. 40, 196–207.

RUTTAN, V. W., and STOUT, T. T. 1960. Regional differences in factor shares in American agriculture. 1925–1957. J. Farm Econ. 42, 52–68.

SAX, K. 1955. Standing Room Only. Beacon Press, Boston, Mass.

SCHLOSSER, G. C., and GILPIN, G. L. 1959. What and how to cook. Food. U. S. Dept. Agr. Yearbook of Agriculture, pp. 519–555.

SCHULTZ, H. W. 1958. Chemicals in foods. J. Am. Dietetic Assoc. 34, 492–495.

SCHUTZ, H. G., and KAMEN, J. H. 1957. Temperament correlates of food preferences and rejections. Address presented at Midwest Psychological Assoc., May 3.

SCRIMSHAW, N. S., and BRESSANI, R. 1961. Vegetable protein mixtures for human consumption. Federation Proc. 20, No. 1, Part III, Suppl. No. 7, 80–89.

SEBRELL, W. H., JR. 1953. Chemistry and the life span. Chem. Engr. News. 27, 3624–3629.

SEBRELL, W. H. 1961. The prospect of meeting protein needs. Federation Proc. 20, No. 1, Part III, Suppl. No. 7, 393–397

SEN, B. R. 1961. Problems of food and nutrition—views and programs of FAO. Federation Proc. 20, No. 1, Part III, Suppl. No. 7, 384–386.

SHAW, B. T. 1961. Prospective world production and distribution of food. Federation Proc. 20, No. 1, Part III, Suppl. No. 7, 373–377.

SHEPHARD, H. H. 1951. The Chemistry and Action of Insecticides McGraw-Hill Book Co., Inc., New York.

SHERMAN, H. C. 1952 Chemistry of Food and Nutrition. Macmillan and Co., New York.

STEARNS, G. 1959. Food needs: Infants and toddlers. Food. U. S. Dept. Agr. Yearbook of Agriculture, pp. 283–285.

STEFANSSON, V. 1937. Food of the ancient and modern Stone Age man. J. Am. Dietetic Assoc. 13, 102–119.

STEFANSSON, V. 1956. The Fat of the Land. Macmillan and Co., New York.

STEFANSSON, V. 1958. The B and B diet. Ladies Home J. 75, No. 11, 4, 46.

STORVICK, C. A., and FINCKE, M. L. 1959. Food needs: Adolescents and young adults. Food. U. S. Dept. Agr. Yearbook of Agriculture, pp. 303–310.

STIEBELING, H. K. 1959. Food in our lives. U. S. Dept. Agr. Yearbook of Agriculture, pp. 1–6.

STIEBELING, H. K., and DREIS, T. A. 1959. Food habits. Food. U. S. Dept. Agr. Yearbook of Agriculture, pp. 631–635.

STRAUS, M. W. 1949. Irrigated areas of the world. United Nations Scientific Conference on the Conservation and Utilization of Resources, Lake Success, N. Y.

SUNDERMAN, F. W., and BOERNER, F. 1949. Normal Values in Clinical Medicine. W. B. Saunders Co., Philadelphia, Pa.

SWANSON, P. 1959. Nutritional needs after 25. Food. U. S. Dept. Agr. Yearbook of Agriculture, pp. 311–325.

SWIFT, R. W. 1959 Food energy. Food. U. S. Dept. Agr. Yearbook of Agriculture, pp. 39–56.

TAMIYA, H., *et al.* 1953. Kinetics of growth of Chlorella, with special reference to its dependence on quanity of available light and on temperature. In Algae Culture, edited by BURLEW, J. S., Carnegie Inst. of Washington. Publ. 600.

TAMURA, E., *et al.* 1958. Nutrition studies on Chlorella. Annual report Nat. Inst. of Nutrition, Tokyo, Japan.

TANNER, F. W. 1953. Food Borne Infections and Intoxications. Twin City Printing Co., Campaign, Ill.

TAYLOR, A., POLLACK, M. A., and WILLIAMS, R. J. 1942. B vitamins in normal human tissues. Univ. Texas Publ. 4237, Austin, Tex.

TEITELBAUM, H. A., and GANTT, W. H. 1956. Effect of starvation on sperm count and sexual reflexes. Science 124, 363–364.

THATCHER, F. S. 1953. Microbiological standards for foods. Food Technol. 12, 117–122.

THIMANN, K. V. 1955. The Life of Bacteria. Macmillan and Co., New York.

TISCHER, R. G. 1958. Feeding men during space flights. Food Technol. 12, 429–430.

TODHUNTER, E. N. 1959. The story of nutrition. Food. U. S. Dept. Agr. Yearbook of Agriculture, pp. 7–23.

TRACHTMAN, L. E. 1959. Mental subnormality. Horizon 6, No. 3, 1–4.

TRESSLER, D. K., and LEMON, J. M. 1951. Marine Products of Commerce. Reinhold Publ. Corp., New York.

UNITED NATIONS. 1946. World Food Survey, Food and Agr. Organization of U. N. Washington, D. C.

UNITED NATIONS. 1952. Second World Food Survey. Food and Agr. Organization of U. N. Rome, Italy.

UNITED NATIONS. 1953. The determinants and consequences of population trends. Population Studies No. 17, United Nations, New York.

UNITED NATIONS. 1954. Statistical Yearbook. United Nations, New York.

UNITED NATIONS. 1954. Projected population in 1980. The past and future population of the world and its continents. World Population Conference, Paper No. 243, United Nations, New York.

UNITED NATIONS. 1957. Agriculture in the World Economy. Food and Agr. Organization of U. N. Rome, Italy.

UNITED NATIONS. 1957. The State of Food and Agriculture. Food and Agr. Organization of U. N. Rome, Italy.

UNITED NATIONS. 1958. Yearbook of Fishery Statistics. Food and Agr. Organization of U. N. Rome, Italy.

UNITED NATIONS. 1958. The Future Growth of World Populations. Population Studies No. 28, United Nations, New York.

UNITED NATIONS. 1958. World Population Situation and Prospects. U. N. Memorandum, Dec. 22, United Nations, New York.

UNITED NATIONS. 1959. The State of Food and Agriculture. Food and Agr. Organization of the U. N. Rome, Italy.

U. S. DEPT. AGR. 1952. Yearbook of Agriculture—Insects. Washington, D. C.

U. S. DEPT. AGR. 1953. Yearbook of Agriculture—Plant Diseases. Washington, D. C.

U. S. DEPT. AGR. 1955. Water—Yearbook of Agriculture, Washington, D. C.

U. S. DEPT. AGR. 1957. Soil—Yearbook of Agriculture. Washington, D. C.

U. S. DEPT. AGR. 1958. Land—Yearbook of Agriculture. Washington, D. C.

U. S. DEPT. AGR. 1959. Food—Yearbook of Agriculture. Washington, D. C.

VAN DER STEUR, J. P. K. 1961. Nutritional aspects of processing and chemical additives on fats and oils. Federation Proc. 20, No. 1, Part III, Suppl. No. 7, 217–223.

VAUGHAN, W. T. 1940. Why we eat and what we eat. Sci. Monthly 50, 148–154.

WATT, B. K., MERRILL, A. L., and ORR, M. L. 1959. A table of food values. Food. U. S. Dept. Agr. Yearbook of Agriculture, pp. 231–266.

WELLS, O. V. 1959. Food Programs: The years ahead. Food. U. S. Dept. Agr. Yearbook of Agriculture, pp. 701–711.

WENT, F. W. 1957. The Experimental Control of Plant Growth. Chronica Botanica Co., Waltham, Mass.

WILLIAMS, R. J. 1951. Nutrition and alcoholism. Univ. Okla. Press, Norman, Okla.

WILLIAMS, R. J. 1953. Free and Unequal. Univ. Texas Press, Austin, Tex.

WILLIAMS, R. J. 1956. Biochemical Individuality: The Basis of the Genetotrophic Concept. John Wiley and Sons, New York.

WILLIAMS, R. J. 1956. Human nutrition and individual variability. Borden's Rev. Nutrition Research 17, No. 2, 11–26.

WILLIAMS, R. R. 1961. Classical nutritional deficiency diseases. Federation Proc. 20, No. 1, Part III, Suppl. No. 7, 323–327.

WINTON, A. L., and WINTON, K B. 1939. The Structure and Composition of Foods. John Wiley and Sons, New York.

ZSCHEILE, F. P. 1950. Role of Genetics in Food Quality Improvement. Nutrition Rev. 8, 65–69.

Index

27355

DATE DUE

DEC 20 '68			
MAR 10 '69			
MAY 2 '72			
NOV 26 '73			
DEC 11 '75			
GAYLORD			PRINTED IN U.S.A.